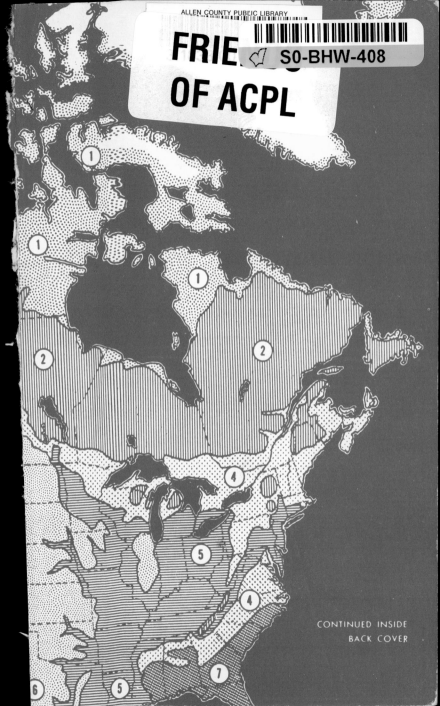

FRIE ✓ **S0-BHW-408**

OF ACPL

CONTINUED INSIDE
BACK COVER

2-10-64

THE MAMMAL GUIDE

THE MAMMAL GUIDE

Mammals of North America north of Mexico

BY RALPH S. PALMER

State Zoölogist, New York State Museum and
State Science Service

Color illustrations, maps, and
drawings by the author

Doubleday & Company, Inc., Garden City, N.Y.

DESIGNED BY DIANA KLEMIN

1249604

Dedicated to the subjects that are described and
pictured in the pages that follow

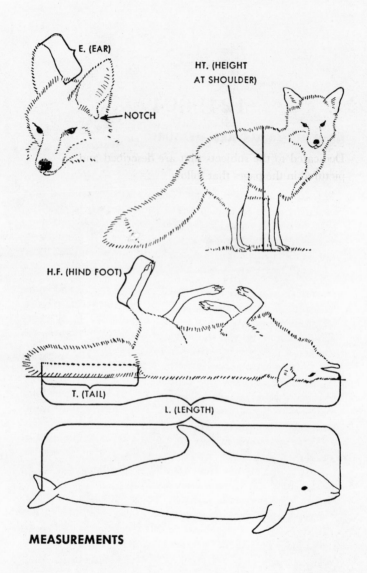

MEASUREMENTS

HOW MAMMALS ARE MEASURED

Measurements used in this Guide, also the standard ones used in more technical works (including those listed in the following pages), are explained here. Note that these measurements are made in a *straight line,* not along curve of body surface. For conversion of measurements from English to metric system, see inside back cover.

LENGTH (customarily abbreviated to L. or l.) : tip of snout to end of fleshy tip of tail, *not* end of hair. Whales, Dolphins, and Porpoises are measured from tip of upper jaw (it may be the shortest) to notch or mid-point between flukes.

TAIL (customarily abbreviated to T. or t.) : base of tail on top to end of fleshy tip, *not* end of hair.

HIND FOOT (customarily abbreviated to H.F. or h.f.) : back of heel to tip of longest toenail. Not used in this Guide.

EAR (sometimes abbreviated to E. or e.) : measured either (1) from crown at base to tip of cartilage, *not* end of hair; or (2) from notch to cartilage tip. Should be written out as 'ear from crown' or 'ear from notch.' In this Guide the latter is used, for Hares and Rabbits only.

HEIGHT AT SHOULDER (written 'ht. at shoulder' or sometimes simply 'ht.') : from ground to top of shoulder when in standing position. Used in this Guide; other ht. is explained where used.

9

ABBREVIATIONS USED IN TEXT

Most abbreviations used are standard and self-explanatory. Examples are: N. or n. for North or northern, mts. for mountains, av. for average, oz. for ounces, and lb. for pound(s).

Abbreviations for standard measurements of mammals are given and defined on page 9.

On track diagrams: L, left; R, right; F, front; and H, hind. These are used in combination; for example: RH for right hind.

wt. Weight in ounces or pounds. For conversion from avoirdupois to metric system, see data inside back cover.

* In a group of species described under one heading, those illustrated in color (or by a drawing in case of Whale tribe and the Manatee) are indicated in text by an asterisk before their name.

ACKNOWLEDGMENTS

In preparing text, illustrations, and maps, I have referred constantly to the published literature on mammals available to me, also to my field notes, sketches, photographs, and a file of clippings of mammal pictures assembled over a period of years. In addition, persons listed below have provided helpful aid in various ways; some even have contributed unpublished data. I am most grateful for this help, which has been kindly given, and take personal responsibility for the manner in which data or suggestions received have been utilized in this volume.

The following persons have supplied data on request or have read manuscript pages submitted to them and have suggested improvements: Allen H. Benton, Harold E. Broadbrooks, C. H. D. Clarke, H. Dean Fisher, Harold B. Hitchcock, Charles P. Lyman, William V. Mayer, Joseph C. Moore, Oliver P. Pearson, Colin C. Sanborn, Victor B. Scheffer, Richard G. Van Gelder, and Ernest P. Walker.

For loan of or access to specimens for study, I am indebted to persons in charge of the U. S. National Museum and Biological Surveys Collections, especially David H. Johnson and Viola S. Schantz; also to Harold E. Anthony, American Museum of Natural History; Harold E. Broadbrooks, University of Arizona; W. J. Hamilton, Jr., Cornell University; Barbara Lawrence, Museum of Comparative Zoölogy at Harvard; Robert T.

Orr, California Academy of Sciences; and Colin C. Sanborn, Chicago Museum of Natural History.

For loan of reference material for use when working on illustrations: Alfred M. Bailey, Joseph C. Moore, Robert T. Orr, and especially to Ernest P. Walker for use of many of his unique photographs.

Francis Harper read almost the entire manuscript; his advice on editorial matters and the many suggestions he supplied from his store of field experience have been of great value. Myrtice Blatchley also read most of the manuscript and offered many helpful suggestions. For other aid and suggestions, thanks are due Richard H. Pough and also to the staff of Doubleday, especially Clara Claasen.

FOREWORD

In the Animal Kingdom, mammals (Class Mammalia) are characterized by possessing more or less hair at some stage in life. Even the whales and their allies have some hair during at least some stage of their existence. Young are born alive and nursed at the mammae or breasts—hence the name mammal. Other characteristics of mammals require a more technical description and are omitted here.

PROCEDURE: Study the color plates in the center of this book first, then use the maps and descriptions. By checking the maps, one can eliminate many species as probably not occurring in a given area; this may narrow the probabilities greatly when identifying a mammal. Then, by studying the descriptions, many species can be identified quite readily. Closely related species generally are treated under one heading which facilitates comparison.

FIELD IDENTIFICATION: This is easy in some groups and difficult or impossible in others. Here are some factors to consider. In some cases *external characters* of two or more species are so much alike that positive species identification is dependent on study of *internal characters,* such as tooth shape or number, proportions of skull bones, or other concealed anatomy. This book deals almost exclusively with external characters. *Age variation:* In some species the young have different color or shape than the adults. *Sex variation:* In some species male and female

15

are not alike in shape or color. *Individual variation:* Individuals of the same age and sex—even litter mates—may vary, especially in color. *Geographical variation:* Populations may differ markedly in different parts of the geographical range of a species. Amount of variation in size and color within a given species may be so great that it cannot readily be distinguished from a related species in one part of the range, yet the two may be distinguished readily elsewhere. When a species shows marked variation over its range, this fact is discussed in the text. *Seasonal variation:* Some mammals have different coats at different seasons, or shed antlers or horn sheath, or even part of the skin or nails. *Wear and fading:* There is much wear and fading of the coat in many mammals, which tends to invalidate clear-cut color descriptions and sometimes to obscure identifying species characters.

Among birds, behavior, voice, and appearance serve to identify them to each other and to humans, even at a distance. By using binoculars we can, perhaps, match the marvelous vision of birds and improve our score at field identification. In general, it is not so with mammal identification. They lead secretive lives, and an individual may be known to its own or another species only at close range—and often with the aid of a very keen nose! In many cases we cannot match these conditions. Especially with many of our smaller mammals and also the whale tribe, even a mammalogist of long experience, on encountering them under field conditions, would hazard only an 'educated guess' as to their specific identity. His guess would indicate the most likely probability, based on his evaluation of all factors observed, and involving his total knowledge of species likely to occur in the area. Total knowledge includes data on appearance, signs, habitat preferences, and general life history; the need for such knowledge is one of the main reasons for including this range of topics in this volume.

Quite often, however, one may obtain a specimen or

have it available for close examination. Under these circumstances, data given in this book should enable a person to identify many species that he could not name otherwise. For example, a Flying Squirrel is readily recognized as such. Suppose, however, that in the area where ranges of the Northern and Southern species overlap, one finds a young Flying Squirrel and is not sure from size or appearance as to which species he is examining. By parting the hair on the belly and noting its color at the base, he can determine the species (dark in the Northern, white in the Southern). He has, in some measure, adapted for his use a principle used by mammals themselves; he has made identification at close range.

MAMMAL NAMES: Common names tend to grow out of the language, but not always with the most satisfactory results. Misapplied names become established, as Buffalo for Bison or Blackcat for Fisher. Common names, contrary to the desires of naturalists, often do not show group relationships. Because we have no 'official' or 'standard' common names for mammals, I have selected those deemed appropriate, with the aim of showing relationship within the smaller groups (genera) where a selection could be made of names that are likely to be understood.

Let us take Meadow Mouse as a case in point. This is a common name for *Microtus pennsylvanicus,* but it does not show relationship with other species of the genus *Microtus.* Mouse alone is too general a term; we might call all *Microtus* species various kinds of Meadow Mice were it not for the fact that some are dwellers in woodland or on plains or tundra. The word Vole applies to all species equally well and is accepted in the Old World, so I have used it in this book, and for *Microtus* species only. Yet it is not entirely satisfactory because (1) for some reason, people confuse the spoken word Vole with Mole, and (2) other Mice than those of the genus *Microtus* also are called Vole—and rightly so—in the Old World. Since we all are well adjusted to saying *Hip-*

popotamus and *Boa constrictor* (these are scientific names), perhaps we will not shy away from encouraging scientific names to come into general use for some of our mammals.

CLASSIFICATION: As with other forms of life, classification of mammals consists of dividing them into groups, each smaller subdivision showing progressively closer relationship. Going from large to small categories in the Class Mammalia, an example of classification is as follows:

ORDER	Carnivora	Flesh-eaters
FAMILY	Canidae	Foxes, Wolves, Dogs
GENUS	Canis	Wolves, Dogs
SPECIES	lupus	Gray Wolf

The plural of 'genus' is 'genera' (examples: a genus, 10 genera); the singular and plural of 'species' are the same (examples: a species, 10 species). Name of the genus is capitalized; the species name is not. The two are written together (example: *Canis lupus*). In this book each genus has been treated as a whole under one heading in most instances and divided to come under several headings only in a few cases; the genus name appears under the common name or names in the heading. Sometimes there is only one species in a genus, in which case genus and species name both are given in the heading. In the text, common names are followed by an abbreviation of the genus name and then the species name written out. Gray Wolf (*C. lupus*) is an example.

Recognizable variations of a species are called subspecies; they are labeled scientifically by another Latin or Latinized name following the species name, making a total of three (example: *Canis lupus labradorius*). In this book subspecies, which are numerous in some species, are not listed, but variation within a species is described. Generally speaking, accurate identification of such variations cannot be made without comparing series of specimens.

Many more mammal 'species' have been named than

actually exist. Much of this came about in a logical way. If a mammal varied over its geographical range, in color, size, or otherwise, in noticeable degree, the different 'varieties' often were given species names. When more specimens were obtained, and from additional localities, so that variation and distribution were better understood, various named 'species' often were found actually to comprise a single one. This process of gaining a better understanding of relationships of our mammals is, of course, a continuing one. Scientific, as well as common, names are far from stable as yet. The reader should bear these facts in mind when he consults various books on mammals, for there is logic behind the apparent discrepancies that he is sure to encounter. In general, scientific names apply more widely and are more stable than common names.

LITERATURE: Your local library undoubtedly has various books on mammals. Natural history museums can refer you to publications on mammals of your area, if such have been published. For those who have a scientific interest, the following are essential:

Hamilton, W. J., Jr. 1939. *American Mammals*. N.Y.: McGraw-Hill. Contains very readable chapters on various topics, including classification, food, reproduction and early life, hibernation, migration, useful mammals, and injurious mammals.

Miller, G. S., Jr., and R. Kellogg. *List of North American Recent Mammals, 1952*. This U. S. National Museum *Bulletin* is scheduled for publication in 1954 by the Government Printing Office, Washington, D.C. Gives scientific names and word descriptions of ranges.

Journal of Mammalogy, a quarterly dating from 1919, which contains a wealth of material, mostly on North American mammals and not by any means always written in technical language. It is published by the American Society of Mammalogists, which welcomes to membership persons having an interest in any phase of the study of mammals.

Anderson, R. M. 1949. *Methods of Collecting and Preserving Vertebrate Animals* (Rev. 2nd ed.). National Museum of Canada, *Bulletin 69.* A well-illustrated and thorough treatise on collecting and preserving specimens.

PROJECTS: The dearth of information about many of our mammals is evident from the brevity of the accounts of them in this book. Many facts of value have been discovered by interested individuals who had no technical training in mammalogy but who observed and carefully recorded what they saw. We are well aware that some mammals are common and successful species in the face of human occupation and use of the land, which is an indication of their secretiveness and general adaptability. Most mammals have, in fact, kept their lives and habits unknown to us in such large measure that a great deal remains to be discovered about even the commonest species of any North American locality. One need not feel that he must go far afield or seek out rare species in order to make good or unique observations and studies of mammals.

CONSERVATION: No mammal species is all 'good' or all 'bad.' The Eastern Gray Squirrel has aesthetic value in parks and is an important game species in much of its range. When, however, it gnaws insulation from telephone cables or eats food put out at bird-feeding stations, it is 'bad' in the eyes of some people. The economic status of a species varies for many reasons, and in different parts of its range, or with the changing seasons, or at different population levels, or with changing human land-use practices, and so on. Some species have been overexploited for human use, such as some furbearers, game species, Seals, and Whales. Bounties have been applied to some mammals, almost universally with none of, or only a small fraction of, the desired results. Some mammals have been introduced or transplanted—and not by any means usually with beneficial results or with long-time values considered. Such practices, as well as poison campaigns against predators and rodents, are to be strongly condemned unless preceded by a careful study by competent scientists of all factors involved; then those practices that are at all feasible should be carried out in a manner allowing the most good for all life. Even with increasing land utilization by humans, extermination never should be the attained or desired goal.

There is great need for further research and study on which to base sound practices for maintaining an optimum population of our native mammals in the face of the increasing human population and expanding human demands on the land and on all forms of life. Truly, some of the destruction of the past was inevitable, as in the case of vast herds of Bison, whose very existence was incompatible with increasing human occupation of the land. But the reduction of the Bison to near extinction was unnecessary. Our national, state, and local parks and refuges often have been established mainly for other purposes than maintaining our native mammal fauna, but have included it incidentally. They are not adequate for the conservation of some species or populations needing this type of protection. On the other hand, especially in some populations of game mammals, there are more individuals than the environment can support on a sustained yield basis. When the facts become more generally understood, we shall increase our harvest of these surpluses. In the last analysis, proper maintenance of our mammal fauna depends on group action by enlightened individuals who value mammal life and who will aid in its preservation and maintenance, so that we and future generations may utilize, study, and enjoy it.

LOCATER MAP

CONTENTS

24 **Contents**

26 **Contents**

28 **Contents**

30 Contents

THE MAMMAL GUIDE

MARSUPIALS   Order Marsupialia

OPOSSUMS   Family Didelphiidae

Opossum
(Possum)
Didelphis marsupialis
Plate 35

About House Cat size; short legs; white face; pointed nose; naked black ears with pinkish tips; nearly naked, long, prehensile (grasping) tail, black for basal ⅔ or less; usually grizzled gray color. Brownish or blackish ones are common in some places. Only 1 in 9 or 10 is black in N.; in Fla. more black ones occur; in s. Tex. the ratio of blacks to grays is 5 to 1. Both phases occur in the same litter. Has appearance of grin as it exposes its teeth when frightened or when it 'plays Possum' (feigns death). Females have fur-lined abdominal pouch. L. 24–34 in., t. 10–13, ht. at shoulder 5½–7, wt. 4–14 lb. No marked seasonal or age variation in color.

Possums usually are seen in beam of auto lights when foraging for carrion, garbage, or other food, or when hunted. Five toes with claws show in front track; hind foot has blunt-ended nailless 'big toe' which can be

33

moved at right angle to other 4—a unique feature among our mammals. Tail drags and leaves a mark between footprints; it is used as an added 'hand' for grasping objects when climbing.

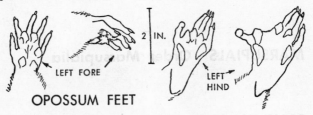

LEFT FORE   2 IN.   LEFT HIND

OPOSSUM FEET

HABITAT: All types of lowland to upland terrain, preferably near water. Common on farmland. Introduced in Calif., Ore., and Wash.

REPRODUCTION: Females breed as yearlings before fully grown. A hollow tree or log, or cavity in ground, under buildings, or debris, serves as a den. Female gathers dry vegetation in her mouth, transfers several collections to her tail, which is held curled in a loop, then carries load to the den for lining. Male lines his den similarly. Gestation: 12½ days. Breeding season: about Jan.–Sept. (2 litters) in S. and Apr.–May (1 litter) in N. Litter size: 8–18, about 7 surviving the period of pouch life. Young at birth are like tiny sightless embryos; 18 weigh ⅟₁₅ oz. and 20 fit easily in a teaspoon. With strong foreclaws they crawl into pouch, and any not attaching to the 13 or fewer nipples perish. At 2 months have fine hair coat and eyes open; stay attached to nipples 65–70 days, then move about freely and eat solid food, but suckle for another month before going their separate ways. In latter period they often travel clinging to the mother's fur, sometimes with tails wrapped around hers as she holds it arched forward over her back. Enlarged nipples require time to shrink; litters are spaced about 3½ months apart. Most Possums survive less than 2 years, although captives have lived over 7; females occasionally live past breeding age.

HABITS: Mainly active after dark. Solitary except at mating. Appears slow and stupid compared to most mammals. Death-feigning may have survival value, for the Possum appears to be unpalatable to many mammals and a 'dead' one is passed up. Many, however, are killed by predators and in accidents, but reproductive capacity is high.

An excellent climber. The opposable 'big toes' are useful in grasping limbs, or the Possum can also lower itself by using the muscular grasping tail. Usually silent, but the courting male makes a clicking sound with tongue or teeth; rarely one may give a sort of gurgling growl, wheezy bark, or moan. Possums become very fat in fall and are inactive in dens during cold spells in winter; these periods may last for days in N., although one finds individuals active in coldest weather, tunneling through snow. Often they suffer loss of ears and part of tail from freezing, loss of the latter being a handicap in climbing. Has increased its range northward in past few decades, but cold weather limits this extension.

Possums eat almost anything: carrion, insects and many other invertebrates, Mice, reptiles, amphibians, mushrooms, many fruits and berries, cultivated garden crops, especially corn and grains. Individual home range is about 15–40 acres but, with overlapping ranges, 1 Possum to 4 acres is not unusual. Most of the wandering and home-seeking occurs in autumn and early winter.

ECONOMIC STATUS: The coarse fur makes durable coats and trimmings. In S., combined value of flesh for food and pelt for fur makes hunting more profitable. Meat is good, especially roasted and with fat removed. Possums are a nuisance when foraging in gardens and about buildings, but are easily captured. Alleged damage to poultry is a considerable overstatement of known facts. Often plentiful, the Possum may take considerable hunting and trapping pressure off other economically important mammals.

MOLES AND SHREWS   Order Insectivora

MOLES   Family Talpidae

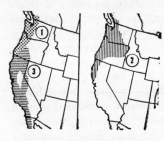

Western Moles
(Broad-footed Moles)
Scapanus
Plate 4

Stocky body; tail slightly haired; conical snout with nostrils opening upward; eyes and ears not evident externally; front feet broader than long and with large claws; soft silky fur.

MOLE (*Scapanus*) **species: 1.—*Townsend's** (*S. townsendii*): largest, has beautiful nearly black pelage. L. 8–9 in., t. 2+, wt. 4–6 oz. **2.—Pacific** (*S. orarius*): smaller, and with smaller front feet; grayish-brown in summer and blackish in winter. L. 6¼–6¾ in., t. 1⅖. **3.—California** (*S. latimanus*): colored like the preceding and slightly larger. Adults and young of these Moles are alike in color; seasonal variation consists of darker winter pelage. Where 2 species occur together, it is best to have specimens identified by a mammalogist.

Commonest signs are numerous mounds ('molehills'), about a pace apart, made of small clods of earth which are pushed up volcano-fashion through a vertical tunnel beneath the center of the pile. (Pocket Gophers push up finely broken soil through an inclined tunnel toward the side underneath.) Moles also push up ridges by tunneling just below or among grass roots in the turf. They themselves are seldom seen on the surface.

HABITAT: Fine-textured soils for digging, combined with adequate food. To over 9,000 ft. elevation. Townsend's: open valleys, meadows, thickets, and coniferous forest. Pacific Mole: drier meadows and thickets. California Mole: medium to rather dry soil.

REPRODUCTION: Few facts are known. Nest chambers are in deep tunnels and lined with dry grass or leaves. Townsend's probably breeds in Feb.; the 2–4 young in the annual litter usually are born in Mar. The Pacific Mole usually has 4 young, born in Mar. or Apr. Young of these Moles approach adult size and are independent of the mother by June.

HABITS: These tunneling animals tend to be solitary, or slightly colonial, except in the breeding season. Food consists of a variety of invertebrates, some vegetation, and perhaps occasionally the flesh of other small mammals. Captives drink water freely. In dry periods they dig and seek food at deeper levels. They are more active at night and in early morning, probably because there is more movement of worms and other food at these times. Their elaborate tunnel systems are much traveled by Mice and Shrews. One Townsend's Mole in 77 days constructed 302 mounds in a ¼-acre field.

ECONOMIC STATUS: Fur of Townsend's Mole has been marketed. Mole ridges and mounds disfigure lawns, meadows, and gardens and are a nuisance to mowing machines. Plants are uprooted or have the roots cut. Bulbs and seeds are eaten, but part of this damage may be done by various Mice that travel in Mole tunnels. The food habits of these Moles generally, however, do not conflict with man's interests, while their tunneling aerates the soil.

Hairy-tailed Mole
(Brewer's Mole)
Parascalops breweri
Plate 4

Stocky body; conical snout; no external ears; eyes nearly hidden; large front feet; blackish fur. The only e. Mole with a short hairy tail. L. 5¾–7 in., t. 1–1½, wt. 1½–3 oz. Males are slightly larger than females. No marked sex, age, or seasonal color variation. Signs of its presence are surface ridges, over shallow subsurface tunnels, and mounds ('molehills'), about 6 in. in diameter, of dirt pushed up through a vertical passage from the tunnel system. Occasionally it travels on the ground surface. Often caught by cats and other mammals and left uneaten.

HABITAT: Usually in well-drained soil, where there is more or less woody growth, occurring less often in fields and damp gullies. Sea level to about 3,000 ft. elevation (in Appalachians).

REPRODUCTION: Females breed the spring following their birth. The nest is a 6-in. ball of dry vegetation about a foot below ground surface. Mating occurs in Mar.–Apr. Gestation requires between 4 and 6 weeks. The annual litter of 4–5 young is born Apr.–May. At birth they are naked, except for a few vibrissae ('whiskers'), and weigh about ⅓ oz. They are reared by the female and probably are weaned and independent in about 4 weeks. Old age is attained in 4 years, but most of them have much shorter lives.

HABITS: This Mole is active in its tunnel system at any hour. In some areas it makes few mounds. Tunnels, wider than high—about 1½ x 1 in.—are dug near ground surface in summer and much deeper in fall and winter. Different individuals sometimes build an interlocking network of passages, and other Moles, also Mice and Shrews, travel these routes. Some tunnel systems are used for a number of years. A high-pitched squeak is the only known vocal sound. Food: earthworms, various insects and larvae, and other small invertebrates. Like other insectivores, its appetite is enormous, and an unfed captive shows signs of starvation in a few hours. Individuals probably do not have a home range much more than 100 ft. in diameter, and 2 Moles per acre is a fairly high population density.

ECONOMIC STATUS: Tunnels and mounds on golf greens, lawns, and at field edges are a nuisance. I consider it much easier to trap than the Star-nosed Mole.

Eastern Mole
(Common Mole)
Scalopus aquaticus
Plate 4

Stocky body; conical snout, naked at end, with nostrils opening upward; eyes covered with skin; no external ears; large front feet, broader than long; tail relatively short and nearly naked. Color grayish in N.; in s. and w. parts of its range it is paler and browner in color; in Tex. it approaches purplish-red or coppery. L. 5½–8 in., t. 4⁄5–1⅖, wt. 1½–2 oz. Males are slightly larger than females. Relatively little sex, seasonal, or age variation in color, except young are rather plain gray. Indications of its presence are ridges, where the Mole, by its shallow subsurface tunneling, has pushed up the ground surface. It makes mounds ('molehills') rarely, if at all. Ordinarily it spends little time on the ground surface, yet dead ones left by predators are found quite often.

HABITAT: Well-drained loose soil in fields, meadows, pastures, and open woodland. More numerous in S.

REPRODUCTION: Females probably breed the spring following birth. The nest, of dry vegetation, usually is about a foot below ground surface or under a boulder, stump, or roots of a bush. There are several entrances. Breeding occurs in Mar. or earlier, and the gestation period is unknown. The annual litter contains 2–5 young. Naked at birth, they are covered with gray fur in 10 days and retain this coat for several weeks. They probably are independent when about a month old.

HABITS: As with other Moles, it is active in its tunnels at all hours and seasons. Although rather solitary, occasionally 2 or 3 occupy an elaborate tunnel system together. Tunnels, near the surface, are easily made, the dirt being packed aside or pushed upward. These tunnels are used all year in most of this Mole's range. In N., deeper winter tunnels are in more compact earth; loosened dirt is kicked backward, then the Mole turns around and pushes it to the surface. The cores of earth found after the snow has melted show where winter excavating has resulted in surface accumulation. It sleeps with head curled under body and forefeet directed backward; like other Moles, also Shrews, its sleep is very profound and it is very active when awake. Probably an average of half its wt. in food is eaten daily. Food: earthworms, also insects and other invertebrates, and some vegetable matter. Two or 3 Moles per acre is a high population. Predatory birds and mammals, perhaps also snakes, capture this Mole. It has a strong odor, like other Moles and Shrews, and often is left uneaten.

ECONOMIC STATUS: Lawns, golf greens, and meadows are disfigured by its ridges. Tunneling, however, aids in soil aeration, and many ground invertebrates are eaten. Some damage is done to field crops.

Shrew-mole
Neurotrichus gibbsii
Plate 4

Smallest Mole. Tapering snout, with nostrils opening on sides; no external ears; narrow front feet; eyes nearly concealed; sparsely haired, fairly long, thick tail. Three middle claws on all feet are markedly elongated. Individuals range from dark gray to sooty blue-black in color. L. 4–5 in., t. 1¼–1¾, wt. ⅖ oz. No marked sex, seasonal, or age variation in color. Not likely to be confused with other Moles because of its smallness, or with Shrews because of its flattened feet and large tail diameter. Indications of its presence are small tunnels in leaf mold, but one might not be sure what mammal made or even occupied these without trapping; also, various Mice and Shrews travel in them.

HABITAT: Dark humid places with soft earth, such as wooded ravines, swamps, marshy wooded areas with underbrush, or along streams. Occurs infrequently on dry hillsides. Sea level to 8,000 ft. elevation.

REPRODUCTION: A nest found in Wash. was made of a handful of leaves placed in a small rotted stump. There may be several litters annually, since breeding occurs in all months except Dec. and Jan. Gestation period is greater than 15 days, but unknown. Litter size: 1–4. Newborn young are naked, have a body length of 1 in., tail ⅕, and weigh ¹⁄₄₀ oz.

HABITS: The Shrew-mole spends part of its time in its rather simple tunnel system in leaf mold or soft earth; it also travels and forages in surface runways (more extensive than its tunnels) and on the ground elsewhere. Low bushes are climbed. It swims rapidly. It is active at any hour and is somewhat gregarious. On the ground it moves cautiously, rapping its nose lightly against the ground surface, and scuttles to shelter under a leaf or log when frightened. The only recorded vocal sound is a faint musical twittering, audible for a few feet. Food: earthworms, isopods, insects, other assorted animal matter, and a small amount of plant material.

Star-nosed Mole
Condylura cristata
Plate 4

Stout body; glossy black or dark brown fur; snout with rosette or 'star' of 22 fleshy rays (no other mammal has this); eyes small but apparent; ears hardly evident externally; broad front feet; fairly long, sparsely haired, scaly tail. L. 7½–8¼ in., t. 2½–3¼, wt. 1½–3 oz. Young are dull black. In both sexes the tail increases greatly in diameter (to size of a lead pencil) during winter and early spring. Commonest indications of its presence are mounds ('molehills') about a foot in diameter in mucky soil, also tunnels on the ground surface under snow. In early spring the glands give off a pungent odor like wild parsnip which can be detected about this Mole's workings. It travels on the ground surface quite often. It swims and dives well.

HABITAT: Damp meadows, areas of cattails, streams, swamps, moist woods, and bogs.

REPRODUCTION: Females probably begin to breed when about 10 months old. The spherical nest, about 8 in. in diameter and of dry vegetation, usually is below ground surface, although sometimes in a rotted stump, pile of leaves, or hummock in a marsh. Probably male and female consort during winter, but part after breeding. Gestation period is unknown. The annual litter is born early Apr.–June and contains 3–7 (usually 6) young. At

birth they are pinkish and hairless; the nose 'star' is conspicuous. Fur appears in 10 days; they have a good coat
at 3 weeks, weigh about 1 oz., and leave the nest to go
their independent ways.

HABITS: This Mole is active at all hours and seasons. It has
many irregular tunnels, wider than high and about large
enough for inserting two fingers; some lead directly into
water. There is no surface ridge to reveal subsurface
tunneling. It swims well under water, using all 4 feet
and sculling with the tail, and travels under ice in winter.
Not only does it tunnel in snow, but also occasionally
runs about on the surface. Many occur about Muskrat
houses. Rather gregarious, several may use adjoining
tunnel systems. It travels and forages on the ground
quite often, scurrying to shelter or quickly digging down
out of sight if frightened. Voice: a high-pitched squeak,
seldom heard. Food: earthworms, crustaceans, aquatic
insects, and a host of other invertebrates, also small fish
occasionally. Considerable food is obtained on the bottom
of streams and ponds. When the Mole is searching for
food the fleshy rays (also called tentacles) on the snout
are in constant motion—except for the 2 median upper
ones, which are held rigidly forward. The rays are drawn
together while the Mole eats. The forepaws are used in
holding food in position during feeding. When the Mole
drinks, its snout and all rays are immersed, sometimes
for as long as 5 or 6 seconds. A captive individual was
observed to come out of the ground, go into a dish of
water, and at once begin grooming; in a few minutes it
had washed thoroughly. Probably 2 Moles per acre is a
fair population, but five times that many is not unusual
in swampland. I have trapped several species of Mice and
Shrews in its tunnels.

ECONOMIC STATUS: Damp lawns and wet portions of golf
courses are disfigured by its mounds. It gets into Muskrat
traps frequently. This unusual mammal generally does
not otherwise conflict with man's interests.

SHREWS   Family Soricidae

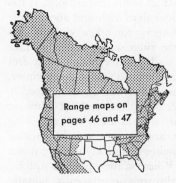

Range maps on pages 46 and 47

Smaller Long-tailed Shrews
Sorex (part)
Plate 5

Except for Pigmy Shrew, included here are our smallest
mammals. Pointed tapering
snout; ears barely visible;
tiny delicate feet; 32 black-
tipped teeth; tiny eyes (light-
sensitive only?); tail more
than 1¼ in. (longer than in
Pigmy Shrew). Some, such as the Common Shrew, are
grayish-brown, shading to paler below; the Smoky is
brown in summer and gray in winter; the Arctic has a
dark dorsal stripe, lighter sides, and still lighter belly;
some species are grayish the year round. Except for
Water Shrews (treated separately), collectively they fall
in this size range: l. 3–5⅔ in., t. 1¼–2½, wt. ½₂–½ oz.
Young usually are grayer or darker than adults.

Maps and descriptions are aids in identifying these
Shrews, but ranges are imperfectly known and specimens
often require careful study by a mammalogist. Some
species are rare and others occur very locally within
their general range. Latest monograph: Jackson, *U. S.
Dept. Agric., N. Am. Fauna* 51 (1928).

Indications of presence are small round holes in leaf
mold and ground litter, especially about logs or rocks, or
tunnels in snow. Occasionally one sees a Shrew dart
rapidly over the ground. Because of their pungent odor,
most mammals seldom eat them. Tapering pointed snout
and tiny eyes distinguish them from rodents, but compare these with other Shrews.

HABITAT: Forest floor, grassy or brushy places, fresh- and salt-water marshes, swamps, rocky places, tundra, mts. to above tree line.

SHREW (*Sorex*) **species: *Common** or **Masked** (*S. cinereus*): grayish-brown; paler underparts; in Subarctic areas adults have a poorly defined dark dorsal stripe and grayish sides; l. 3⅛–4¼ in., t. 1¼–1¾, wt. 1/12–⅕ oz. Compare with Arctic and Tundra Shrews below. Marshes to deep forests. **Mount Lyell** (*S. lyelli*): drab brown; l. 3¾, t. 1½. Crest of cent. Sierras above 6,900 ft. **Malheur** (*S. preblei*): brownish-gray; l. 3½, t. 1½. Very small. E. Wash. ***Smoky** (*S. fumeus*): in summer, dull brown, paler below, tail brown above and yellowish below, feet pale; in winter, gray, tail pale below, pale feet; l. 4¼–5, t. 1¾–2, wt. ⅕–⅖ oz. Dry forest. ***Arctic** or **Saddle-backed** (*S. arcticus*): tricolored; wide blackish-brown dorsal stripe, sides brownish, underparts grayish; pattern brighter in winter; young plain (no dorsal stripe); l. 4¼–4⅔, t. 1½–1⅔. Compare with Common Shrew above. Wet or dry terrain with short or tall plant cover. **Tundra** (*S. tundrensis*): not as distinctly tricolored as preceding, but otherwise very similar and probably the same species. Alaskan island Shrews, also with dark dorsal stripe: *S. jacksoni* of St. Lawrence I.; *S. hydronomus* of Unalaska I. in Aleutians; *S. pribilofensis* of St. Paul I. in Pribilofs. **Merriam's** (*S. merriami*): pale drab gray; underparts and feet nearly white; l. 3¾–4, t. 1½. Arid terrain. **Southeastern** (*S. longirostris*): dark brown, with paler underparts; l. 3–4, t. 1–1½. Atlantic Plain and Piedmont Region. **Long-tailed** (*S. dispar*): dark grayish, only slightly paler below; tail nearly uniformly colored; l. 4¾–5¼, t. 2⅕–2½. Rocky and damp terrain. **Gaspé** (*S. gaspensis*): slightly smaller than the preceding, but probably the same species. **Trowbridge** (*S. trowbridgii*): drab gray-brown in summer, darker and grayer in winter; tail bicolored—nearly

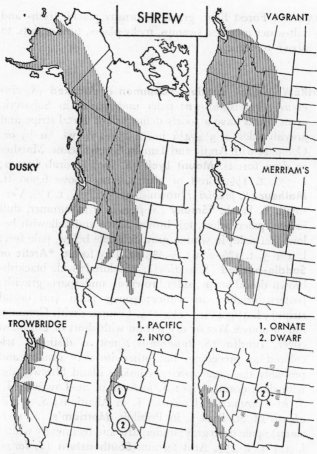

whitish below; l. 3½–5¼, t. 2–2½. **Vagrant** (*S. vagrans*): reddish-brown in summer, brownish-black in winter; l. 3¾–4⅗, t. 1½–1⅘. **Dusky** (*S. obscurus*): dull brown above, shading to whitish below, with bicolored tail; l. 4–5½, t. 1⅗–2½. Often hard to distinguish from some other Shrews within its range. **Pacific** (*S. pacificus*): usually medium brown and nearly uniform; l. 5⅓–6, t. 2–2¾. A large species. **Ornate** (*S.*

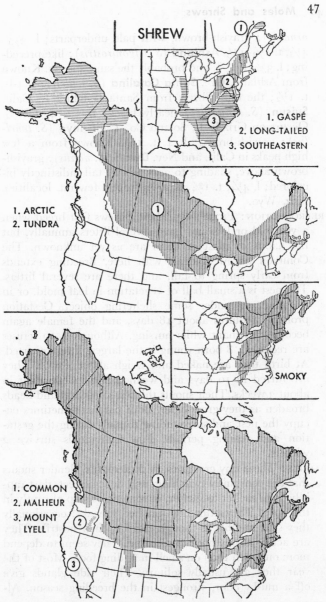

SHREW

1. GASPÉ
2. LONG-TAILED
3. SOUTHEASTERN

1. ARCTIC
2. TUNDRA

SMOKY

1. COMMON
2. MALHEUR
3. MOUNT
   LYELL

ornatus) : grayish-brown, with pale underparts; l. 3⅗–4⅓, t. 1½–1⅘. **Ashland** (*S. trigonirostris*) : like preceding; l. 3⅚, t. 1⅓; and probably the same species. Known from Ashland, Ore. **Santa Catalina** (*S. willeti*) : l. 4+, t. 1½; the only Shrew from Santa Catalina I., Calif. **Suisun** (*S. sinuosus*) : nearly black; l. 3⅔–4, t. 1½. Occurs on Grizzly I., Solano Co., Calif. **Inyo** (*S. tenellus*) : grayish-brown; l. 4, t. 1⅗. Known from a few high peaks in Calif. and Nev. **Dwarf** (*S. nanus*) : grayish-brown above, shading to gray below; tail indistinctly bicolored; l. 4¼, t. 1¾. Known from a few mt. localities, Ariz.–Wyo.

REPRODUCTION: Probably all these Shrews first breed when a year old or less and have several litters annually, but the habits of most of them are as yet unknown. The Common Shrew is dealt with here. Breeding extends from early spring to fall, and there are several litters. The nest is a small ball of vegetation in leaf mold, or in a stump, or under some sheltering object. Gestation probably requires about 18 days, and the female again becomes pregnant while nursing. Although 4–10 fetuses are recorded, 8 born young is the largest litter reported. At birth they are naked and weigh about 1/200 oz. They are furred in 10 days and weaned and independent in about 3 weeks. Their snouts thicken somewhat and heads broaden as they grow older. Both parents sometimes occupy the nest and surrounding tunnels during the gestation and rearing periods. Few individuals survive 2 winters.

HABITS: These tiny creatures, with sleek fur, slender snouts that are constantly twitching, and delicate feet, dart rapidly from shelter to shelter, or sometimes stop abruptly in the open. They utter high-pitched squeaks; occasionally they sniff audibly as though clearing their nostrils. They are active at any hour and season. They seem to depend more on touch than on smell in finding food. Most of the year they are usually solitary. Their side glands give off a musky odor, strongest in the breeding season. Although they make their own runways and also dart over the surface of the ground, or burrow in snow, much of their traveling is in subsurface runways of Mice, Moles, and the Big Short-tailed Shrew. They climb up stumps readily, also cabin walls. One species (*S. cinereus*) is reported to breathe 850 times per minute and heart to beat 800 times per minute; for comparison a Ruby-throated Hummingbird's heartbeat is 550–650 times per minute.

These Shrews eat insects, worms, mollusks, and the dead bodies of larger creatures. Various dormant insects and other invertebrates in the leaf mold are their winter mainstay. When animal food is scarce, they subsist for a while on berries, nuts, and the soft parts of plants. Shrews have deep slumber, then in their waking hours they are extremely active, using energy rapidly. Their own wt. in food daily may be required just to sustain life, and several times that amount commonly is eaten. These Shrews are surprisingly numerous some years and scarce others, the high point coming about every third or fourth year. They are eaten by Owls, Hawks, other birds, and various predatory mammals. House Cats kill but rarely eat them. People far more often find Shrews dead than see them alive.

ECONOMIC STATUS: Because of their diet, all of the smaller Shrews probably are more beneficial than harmful, from man's viewpoint. Most of the tiny round holes that trappers find in frozen unskinned fur animals are made by Shrews, not Mice. In a peak year of Shrew numbers considerable fur is damaged; they even eat holes in drying pelts, and the trapper sometimes finds his supply of frozen meat riddled with holes. Shrews are caught easily in Mouse traps baited with oatmeal, oatmeal and bacon fat, or peanut butter. A dead Shrew decomposes very rapidly unless kept cool; it may not be salvageable as a specimen if the sun shines directly on it even for a few minutes. He who would trap these mammals for study would do best to set traps in shaded places and tend them in the cooler hours.

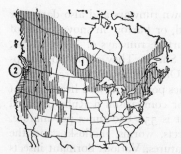

Water Shrews
Sorex (part)
Plate 5

Largest of Long-tailed Shrew group and, in general, like smaller Long-tailed Shrews, except hind feet with fringe of stiff hairs along outer margin.

1.—*Northern (*S. palustris*): glossy blackish-gray or blackish with gray or grayish-brown underparts, except black all over in NE. L. 5½–6 in., t. 2½–2¾, wt. ⅖–⅘ oz. *S. alaskanus* from Point Gustavus, Glavin Bay, Alaska, probably is the same species. **2.—Pacific** (*S. bendirii*): dark brown; l. 6–7, t. 2½–3+. No other Long-tailed Shrews are as large as these Shrews; Moles have big forefeet. Few people have seen a Water Shrew alive.

HABITAT: In and about rocky streams and rills, lake and pond margins, beaver meadows and ponds, mt. pools.

REPRODUCTION: Probably 2 or 3 litters annually; trapped females have had 5–7 fetuses. Maximum age is reported as 18 months.

HABITS: Water Shrews actually are plentiful in some mt. areas. The hair fringe on the hind feet is an adaptation for swimming. Following data are for the Northern species, which is better known. It swims and dives expertly; when submerged, a coating of small air bubbles gives it great buoyancy, so that it bobs to the surface easily. It has been observed almost literally running on the water, evidently supported in part by surface tension. It dives to the bottom in shallow water and 'stands' on its nose, probing for food among rocks and sand, and shakes itself dry on coming ashore. It may be slightly gregarious. Food: aquatic insects and other small invertebrates, occasionally fish eggs and small fish, and perhaps some plant material. Not all of this is obtained from the water.

ECONOMIC STATUS: Few facts are known. Fish probably capture these Shrews and the Shrews eat some fish eggs.

Pigmy Shrew
Microsorex hoyi
Plate 5

Smallest in wt. of our mammals; like the smaller *Sorex* (p. 44) in appearance, but with slightly shorter and more slender tail and smaller feet. L. 3¼–3¾ in., t. 1–1⅛, wt. of a dime (sexually mature at about 2.3 grams; 28.4 gms. = 1 oz.). Grayish-brown or gray above and paler below. Even mammalogists cannot always tell it for certain from small Common Shrews (*Sorex cinereus*) without noting that in upper jaw the third single-cuspid tooth from the front is tiny, wedged between the second and fourth, and barely visible from the side; this tooth is not reduced in *Sorex*.

The Pigmy Shrew generally is rather rare, and many mammalogists never have captured it. Its insect-like holes in leaf mold are not quite large enough to admit a pencil. It can travel in tunnels of large beetles; often it goes on the ground surface or in tunnels and runways of other Shrews and various Mice.

HABITAT: Usually drier woodland, grassy clearings, thickets, and under ferns, but also moist sphagnum areas.

REPRODUCTION: Few facts are known. It breeds in spring and summer, evidently having more than 1 litter per year, usually of 5–6 young, but with a record of 8 fetuses. Maximum age is probably under 2 years.

HABITS: This Shrew usually travels and forages among dead plant material. It is active at all hours and seasons. Although it has proved to be common in some Ont. localities, usually it is scarce and captured only after most

Mice and other Shrews have been trapped out of the area where it occurs. A high-pitched thin squeak occasionally is uttered. Its odorous side glands are proportionately larger than in *Sorex* species; they probably serve as a means of communication between individuals. Food: insects (it can kill those up to grasshopper size easily), other invertebrates, and carcasses of dead animals. A captive sat up like a Squirrel, eating food held in its forepaws.

Little Short-tailed Shrew
(Least Shrew)
Cryptotis parva
Plate 5

Shortest, but not least in wt., of our mammals; a brownish or grayish, chunky, bob-tailed Shrew—like a small edition of the Big Short-tailed Shrew (*Blarina*)—but with tail shorter and more slender and 30 black-tipped teeth. Tiny beady eyes probably are light-sensitive only. L. 2⅘–3¼ in., t. ⅖–⅗, wt. of 2 dimes—⅐–⅕ oz. Young are dark slaty-gray. Other Shrews of same body size have longer tails, including young or small individuals of the Big Short-tailed Shrew. Indications of its presence are oval entrances (wider than high) to its small tunnels, made in loose soil, and surface runways under a canopy of dead grass or weeds. Much of its traveling is done in runways of other small mammals.

HABITAT: Prefers dry unmowed fields and dried-out marshy areas; occurs also in damp woods, marshes, and in Fla. hammocks.

REPRODUCTION: Females probably begin breeding when 3–4 months old. The spherical nest, smaller than a baseball and of shredded vegetation, is built under a stump, log, rock, or in a ground cavity. Several adults have been found in one nest. Breeding occurs all year in S. and Mar.–Nov. in N. A female gave birth to litters 24 days apart. Litter size: 3–6. Young at birth weigh about 1/50 oz. In 3 days they are an inch long and signs of slaty dorsal fur are evident. By the seventh day they are well furred above, and a day later the silvery belly fur is noticeable. In 21–24 days they are 2/3 as large as the mother, weaned, and ready to go their independent ways. Adult size is attained in a month. The female alone rears the young, killing insects for them as the nursing period wanes. A female born in captivity lived 2 years and had ceased breeding before the end of this period. Most of these data were supplied by Dr. E. P. Walker, who has studied this species at the National Zoölogical Park in Washington.

HABITS: This Shrew is somewhat gregarious and colonial, several sometimes occupying a nest together. Two appeared to co-operate in tunneling, one doing most of the digging and the other pushing away the loosened soil or packing it aside. It has a habit of forcing its way along just beneath the ground surface, pushing up a tiny ridge as it goes. Runways of the Cotton Rat, Rice Rat, Meadow Vole, and other small mammals are much utilized for travel. When awake it is very active, moving about with a rapid 'shivering' of its snout; it sleeps very soundly. Some captives have had no noticeable odor, but in the wild a pungent odor sometimes is detectable. One observer noted a faint Flicker-like call audible for 20 in.; captives give bird-like chirpings and a rapid twitter. Food: insects, mollusks, earthworms and other small invertebrates, small lizards, and dead animals. Its bite seems to paralyze earthworms; when the prey is quiet the Shrew proceeds to eat it. Insects sometimes are killed and piled in a tunnel for future use. An individual's home range probably is only a fraction of an acre in size. Barn Owls capture these Shrews.

ECONOMIC STATUS: Occasionally it nests in beehives and eats bees and their larvae.

Big Short-tailed Shrew
(Mole-shrew)
Blarina brevicauda
Plate 5

A large stocky Shrew; short tail; 32 black-tipped teeth; very small external ears; tiny eyes that are light-sensitive only. In NE. silvery-gray in color, paler below; in W. and S. more sooty. L. 3¾–5+ in., t. ¾–1+, wt. ⅖–1 oz. Males have larger scent glands and thicker throat skin than females. Old adults of both sexes have thicker snouts than young. Young are darker than adults. In parts of S., weaned young are about the size of large examples of the Little Short-tailed Shrew (*Cryptotis*), but the latter has a markedly smaller tail and 2 less teeth.

Signs of its presence are tunnels, 1 x ¾ in., wider than high. One finds these 'flattened' runways by breaking into leaf mold around stumps, logs, rocks, or by lifting decaying fallen bark or logs. Snow tunnels also are made. The musky odor of this Shrew is much in evidence in spring. Mammals kill, but seldom eat, this Shrew.

1 IN.   TRACKS OVERLAP   TAIL MARK

BIG SHORT-TAILED SHREW, FORAGING

HABITAT: All types of woodland up to low timber on mts.; brush-grown land, mossy and boggy areas, and marshes. Prime requisites are more or less vegetation and a litter of plant material on the ground.

REPRODUCTION: Some early-born ones breed late the same

summer; later-born ones breed the following spring. The spherical nest of dry grass or leaves, about 5 in. in diameter, usually is beneath a log, stump, or in a cavity in leaf mold. Gestation requires 18–20 days. Breeding occurs from spring to early fall, and the female may be pregnant while nursing a litter. Several litters of 3–9, usually 5–7, young are produced annually. Perhaps the male stays with the female during at least part of the rearing period. Young are naked at birth, but soon grow a dark gray coat and, in about 4 weeks, are over half the size of the mother, weaned, and independent. Very few survive 2 winters.

HABITS: This mammal is active the year round and at all hours; it travels on the ground surface mainly at night. The network of runways is built by pushing through plant debris, moss, or snow—seldom through earth. Much traveling and foraging are done in surface and subsurface runways of Moles and rodents. Although not markedly gregarious, individuals use each other's runways. Voice: a high-pitched rapid twitter. A poisonous extract from the submaxillary glands is present in the saliva and aids in overcoming Mice and other sizable prey. A case is recorded where the bite of this Shrew caused a man's arm to swell; discomfort lasted over a week. Insects, spiders, centipedes, salamanders, young and adult Mice, and carcasses of animals are eaten. Snails and slugs evidently are immobilized by the Shrew's poison, then sometimes stored underground for later use. Nuts and berries are known food items. Population peaks occur at about 4-year intervals. When numbers are low, an individual's home range (several overlap) may have up to a 25-yd. radius, or less than ½ acre; when it is high, 25 Shrews per acre is not unusual.

ECONOMIC STATUS: This Shrew eats many Mice. It aids in soil formation by tunneling in forest litter. It is a host for ticks. Sometimes a mammalogist must trap most of these Shrews out of an area before he can get a satisfactory catch of other small mammals.

Desert Shrew
(Eared Shrew)
Notiosorex crawfordi
Plate 5

Medium silvery-gray, washed with brown; big ears for a Shrew—they show very noticeably; tail notably shorter than in Long-tailed Shrews (*Sorex*) of similar body size. Adults have decidedly brownish faces and a faint, narrow, mid-dorsal, chestnut-colored stripe. L. 3⅖ in., t. 1.

HABITAT: Arid desert areas, as well as where considerable vegetation grows. Sea level to 6,500 ft. elevation. It has been taken among rocks, in tangles of sagebrush and other vegetation, from Woodrat nests, and a beehive. Reported in se. Okla. and nw. Ark. since above map drawn.

REPRODUCTION: A litter of 3 young is reported.

HABITS: It is known to eat insects and centipedes. Only a few dozen specimens of this Shrew have been captured.

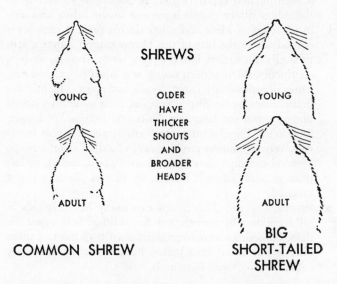

SHREWS

YOUNG

OLDER
HAVE
THICKER
SNOUTS
AND
BROADER
HEADS

YOUNG

ADULT

ADULT

COMMON SHREW

BIG
SHORT-TAILED
SHREW

BATS   Order Chiroptera

Bat anatomy diagrams are on the following page.

AMERICAN LEAF-NOSED BATS   Family Phyllostomidae

Peters' Leaf-chinned Bat
Mormoops megalophylla
Plate 2

A medium-sized reddish-brown Bat with slender body and conspicuous dermal outgrowths on the chin—a chinleaf which is deeply divided. L. 3⅗ in., t. 1, wt. about ⅖ oz. Our only Bat with this chin structure. A cave species whose habits are little known.

California Leaf-nosed Bat
Macrotus californicus
Plate 2

Above medium size; pale brownish-gray; large thin ears and long noseleaf. L. 4 in., t.

57

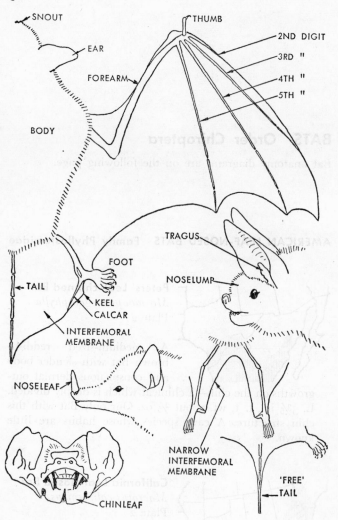

SNOUT

EAR

FOREARM

BODY

THUMB

2ND DIGIT

3RD "

4TH "

5TH "

TRAGUS

NOSELUMP

FOOT

TAIL

KEEL

CALCAR

INTERFEMORAL
MEMBRANE

NOSELEAF

NARROW
INTERFEMORAL
MEMBRANE

'FREE'
TAIL

CHINLEAF

BAT ANATOMY

1⅓, wt. ⅗–⅘ oz. Our other Bats with very large ears do not have a noseleaf.

HABITAT: Arid country, spending the day in caves and mines.

REPRODUCTION AND HABITS: The single young is born in June. This common desert Bat flies alone, coming out well after dark. Food: insects, including locusts, moths, cicadas, and beetles. From about a score to 200 or more individuals form a colony in a mine or cave, each hanging separately. This Bat has very long legs. When alighting, it makes a half-turn roll and hangs up directly by the feet instead of first by its thumbs and then shifting to head-down position. It is very alert when roosting and takes wing before being approached closely. Perhaps it is only locally migratory.

Long-tongued Bat
(Hog-nosed Bat)
Chœronycteris mexicana
Plate 3

Above medium size, with Fox-like head and ears; well-developed erect noseleaf; tail vertebrae extend through less than half the width of the interfemoral membrane. No lower front teeth. Brown above, with head and underparts lighter; a sooty phase occurs in females at least. L. 3¼ in., t. (vertebrae) about ⅖, wt. ½–¾ oz. Its much wider interfemoral membrane distinguishes it from the Long-nosed Bat.

HABITAT: Arid country, roosting in caves, mines, and rock crevices.

REPRODUCTION AND HABITS: The single young is born in early summer. Probably this Bat feeds in part, at least, on the nectar of flowers. Rapid movement of the long tongue is made easier by the absence of small front teeth (incisors) from the lower jaw. The Long-tongued and

Long-nosed Bat both make a faint rumbling sound with the wings when in flight.

Long-nosed Bat
Leptonycteris nivalis
Plate 3

Much like the preceding, except more slender snout, taller ears, and interfemoral membrane only about ⅛ in. wide at the mid-point (no visible tail vertebrae). Lower front teeth present. Color above varies from dark sooty to yellowish-brown. L. 3 in., wt. ⅔–1 oz. This Bat has been captured in caves in s. Ariz., once from a colony of over 200. Like the Long-tongued Bat, it is adapted for flower-feeding.

Common Fruit-eating Bat
Artibeus jamaicensis
Plate 3

A rather large robust Bat, with stout head, fierce facial expression, well-developed noseleaf, and interfemoral membrane less than ½ in. wide at mid-point (no visible tail). Brownish-black above, with lighter underparts. L. 2⅘ in., wt. ⅘–1 oz. Once captured at Key West, Fla. Although usually a cave dweller, this Bat often spends the day in tree foliage.

In the winter of 1870, C. J. Maynard observed Bats in Key West, Fla.; one, which was found on a tree leaf and killed by a boy, was sketched and reported as *Artibeus* by Maynard, *Bull. Essex Inst.,* vol. 4, no. 10, p. 144 (1872), also in H. Allen's Monograph of the Bats of N. Am., *U. S. Nat. Mus. Bull.* 43, p. 52 (1893).

TYPICAL INSECT-EATING BATS   Family Vespertilionidae

Range maps on
pages 62 and 63

Myotis Bats
(Little Brown Bats)
Myotis
Plate 1

Small Bats. The tragus is erect and tapering; interfemoral membrane not furred above; all have 38 teeth. Colors range from blackish-brown to reddish-brown or, in some desert forms, to very pale buff; never a striking color pattern. Two phases—darker and lighter or duller and brighter—are known for several species. All 13 species fall within this range: l. 3½–4½ in., wt. ¼–⅓ oz. in summer and half as much more when fat at onset of hibernation. Young are darker and duller than adults. One or more species may be found almost anywhere n. to the limit of trees. By using brief descriptions and range maps, one can identify some species with fair certainty, but others are difficult even for a museum expert. Latest monograph: Miller and Allen, *U. S. Nat. Mus. Bull.* 144 (1928).

In comparison, the Pipistrelles and Evening Bat have a blunt-ended tragus, and the Big Brown Bat also is larger than any Myotis species. Small Bats seen in flight or roosting in a building, cave, or tree cranny most likely belong to this common and widespread group.

HABITAT: Varies with the species—woodlands, along watercourses, deserts, etc. Several species (also other Bats) may hibernate in the same cave, each selecting an area having temperature and humidity suiting its peculiarities.

Myotis species: *Little Brown (M. lucifugus): over much

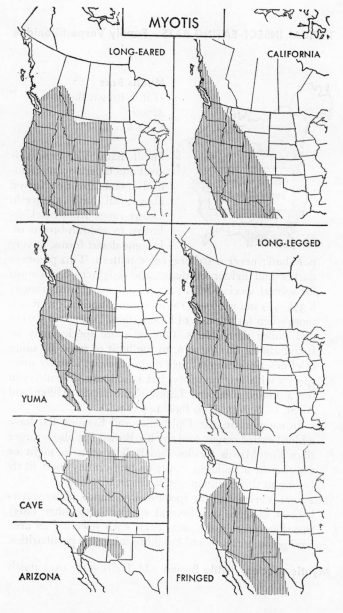

MYOTIS

LONG-EARED

CALIFORNIA

LONG-LEGGED

YUMA

CAVE

ARIZONA

FRINGED

MYOTIS

LITTLE BROWN

KEEN'S

GRAY

1. LEAST
2. SOUTHEASTERN

INDIANA

of its range color above is dark brown, but varying from blackish-brown in NW. to pale buff in SW.; dorsal hairs have glossy tips that give a sheen; ear laid forward reaches nostril. Widely distributed and often common. **Yuma** (*M. yumanensis*): dull brownish; interfemoral membrane, above and below, with hair extending to slightly beyond a line joining the knees. **Southeastern** (*M. austroriparius*): dull yellowish-brown; fur has thick woolly appearance, with no strong color contrast between tip and base. Not common. **Gray** (*M. grisescens*): dorsal fur rather velvety in both smoky-brown and russet phases, with hair nearly the same color throughout its length. **Cave** (*M. velifer*): dull brown or drab above, with bases of hairs dark; wing membrane arises from base of toes; ear laid forward reaches nostril or slightly beyond. **Arizona** (*M. occultus*): fur above bright ochraceous-tawny with burnished tips; a dull olive phase looks much like the Little Brown Myotis. **Keen's** (*M. keenii*): dark brown, quite like the Little Brown Myotis, but hairs less glossy; ear laid forward extends $\frac{1}{16}$–$\frac{1}{8}$ in. beyond nose. **Long-eared** (*M. evotis*): pale brown; ear laid forward extends $\frac{1}{5}$–$\frac{1}{4}$ in. beyond nose. Not common. **Fringed** (*M. thysanodes*): buffy-brown; only Myotis with conspicuous fringe of stiff hairs along free edge of interfemoral membrane. **Indiana** (*M. sodalis*): very like Little Brown Myotis, but has keeled calcar and smaller feet. **Long-legged** (*M. volans*): fur above reddish- or tawny-buff, darker at base; a small Myotis having distinctive, bluntly rounded ears that barely reach the nostril when laid forward; calcar keeled; fur below extends out to elbow and knee. **California** (*M. californicus*): lusterless fur, varying from rich brown in NW. to pale buff in arid SW., always much darker at base; a small Myotis; ear laid forward extends slightly beyond nose. Hard to tell from Yuma and Small-footed Myotis. **Least** (*M. subulatus*): size very small; relatively long yellowish-brown fur; black face and ears give a masked appearance. Sometimes hard to tell from California Myotis; compare with the Pipistrelles.

REPRODUCTION: In the Little Brown Myotis, females are sexually mature when a year old. Copulation occurs in fall and often again in spring, the sperm from fall unions surviving in the female till spring, when the ovum is fertilized. Then the single young is born after 50–60 days' gestation. (Some Myotis species have 1 young annually, others 1–2, still others 2.) Born nearly naked and with eyes closed, it clings to the mother, who carries it for several days; then it is left at a roost. It first flies when 3–4 weeks old. A few banded individuals have lived over a decade.

HABITS: Various species of Myotis occasionally fly in full daylight. Each has its own pattern of flight; thus the Little Brown Myotis appears feeble and erratic, while Keen's has a strong and direct flight. Some, perhaps all, can maneuver in a cubic space of 3 ft., this being much less than the Big Brown Bat needs and almost on a par with the little Pipistrelles. Probably all are more or less gregarious, the females roosting in groups ('maternity centers') in summer, when males tend to be scattered and solitary. In winter quarters, some hang in clusters or patches and some in smaller groups or singly. Like other Bats, in flight they avoid obstacles by means of echo-location—that is, by emitting sounds that echo from the obstacle back to the Bat and reveal the distance between it and the Bat. Some of their sounds are above the range of human hearing (ultrasonic), but they have an audible flight call, also a buzz heard only a few feet, and a click heard several feet. Most of these Bats evidently have local seasonal migrations to and from caves and other places of hibernation. Food: insects, caught and eaten in flight.

ECONOMIC STATUS: These Bats leave a musky odor, a greasy spot where they hang, and droppings below, hence are a nuisance in houses. These Bats or others do not carry the *human* bedbug (it is another kind); rabies is reported from two genera. Rarely one may alight on any part of a person, but they do not try to get into women's hair.

Silver-haired Bat
Lasionycteris noctivagans
Plate 1

A medium-sized Bat; ears about as broad as tall; tragus relatively broad and blunt; basal half of interfemoral membrane sparsely furred.

Adults usually are dark blackish-brown above, the hairs being tipped with silvery-white, and with less tipping on the ventral body surface. In W., some individuals are nearly black. L. 4¼ in., wingspread 11–13, wt. ¼–½ oz. Young have nearly black fur with light tips, a pattern with greater contrast than that of most adults. Color distinguishes it from the Hoary Bat or Red Bats.

HABITAT: A migratory tree Bat, found along watercourses in wooded areas and up into coniferous forests in mts.

REPRODUCTION: Breeding occurs in early fall. It probably does not breed in s. two-thirds of U.S., except perhaps in mts. The 1–2 (usually 2) black, wrinkled young are born June–July. When small, they are carried by the mother; in about 3 weeks they are capable of weak flight and follow her awhile.

HABITS: Often abroad before sundown, flying low or up to 40 or more ft. above ground. Its flight has a distinctive fluttery quality, with sidewise darts, twists, and frequent short glides. An individual has a fairly definite hunting route, probably not over 100 yds. in diameter; routes may overlap, with several individuals flying in the same general area. Males probably are solitary in summer, when females are notably gregarious. In daytime this Bat hangs singly, in hollows in trees, under bark fragments, or in dense foliage. Some migrants have strayed to sea;

they have occurred in Bermuda. Resting individuals have been found aboard ships, in buildings, cave entrances, and trees. Food: soft-bodied insects.

Pipistrelles
Pipistrellus
Plate 1

Our smallest Bats. Tragus fairly blunt and with tip bent forward. L. 2⅖–3⅖ in., wingspread about 5¾, 34 teeth. **1.—Western** (*P. hesperus*): varies from pale smoky-gray to deep brown; always paler below. **2.— *Eastern** (*P. subflavus*): varies from yellowish-brown to warm brown, but occasionally grayish or blackish individuals occur. Pipistrelle fur is tricolored: dark at base, then a wide lighter zone, then darker tips. Wt. ⅛–¼ oz., approaching the latter in fall at onset of hibernation. Young are darker than adults. In comparison, the Myotis species have a tapering, pointed tragus.

HABITAT: Low arid country to coniferous forests in mts. and elsewhere; often in shady woods, about cliffs, in canyons, and along watercourses. Hibernates in caves.

REPRODUCTION: The Eastern Pipistrelle breeds in late summer and again in early spring, the 2 periods producing only the annual litter of 1–3 (usually 2) young. They are born in late May in S. and from June to mid-July in N. They cling to the mother for a few days and can fly when less than 3 weeks old. Some banded individuals have lived 6 or more years.

HABITS: Pipistrelles emerge about dusk, fly for a while, rest, then fly again before sunrise. Flight is weak and erratic. They can maneuver in perhaps a smaller space than is required by any of our other Bats, except possibly the Lump-nosed Bats. They are not cave dwellers in summer; at that season the Western Pipistrelle is known to roost under loose rocks. The sexes live apart in the rearing season, when porches, open barns, and probably rocky places serve as maternity roosts. When hibernating in caves they hang singly or in clusters of less than 50, with Little Brown Myotis and other Bats often using the same shelter. They are very dormant then and do not shift about as some other Bats do. Food: insects.

Big Brown Bat
Eptesicus fuscus
Plate 1

A medium-sized Bat. Dull chestnut or sooty-brown above, varying to pale brown in arid SW. and rarely elsewhere; fur relatively long and lax. L. 4–5 in., wingspread about 12, wt. ½–¾ oz. and half as much more when very fat. Young are darker and duller than adults. Size and color distinguish this Bat from others. This species is shown (p. 58) in the upper diagram of Bat anatomy. It commonly enters houses and quite often is seen in flight outdoors or indoors at midday.

HABITAT: Wilderness, settlements, and even large cities; from sea level to fairly high mt. elevations. Hibernates in caves, mines, rock crevices, buildings, behind signboards, and elsewhere. Only Bat in n. U.S. and northward that hibernates regularly in houses.

REPRODUCTION: Mating occurs in fall. The young are born in May in S. and to mid-June or even later in N. Litter size: 1 or 2 (usually 2); 4 fetuses have been reported once. Young at birth are naked, have eyes closed, and weigh about ⅒ oz. They are weaned in 3 weeks and attain adult size in 2 months. Some banded individuals have lived at least 9 years.

HABITS: This Bat attracts attention, especially when it flies in houses, churches, and other buildings during the colder months of the year. Its strong flight is marked by frequent and sudden changes in direction. It needs more room than most Bats of its size for maneuvering, being handicapped in a cubic space of 5 or 6 ft., although it navigates well in narrow passages. It goes into hibernation late (males earlier than females) and comes out early. It prefers dry areas in caves, hence does well in buildings. The number at one site usually is small—several to perhaps 20, but suitable places sometimes attract many more. Audible sounds include a shrill alarm call like the sound of escaping steam, a click, and a body vibration noise given when at rest. Food: beetles and other insects.

ECONOMIC STATUS: Sometimes a nuisance in houses. The bedbug found at its roost or on the Bat is not the one that normally feeds on human blood.

Red Bats
Lasiurus (part)
Plate 1

Medium-sized Bats, with short rounded ears and tragus; upper surface of interfemoral membrane wholly covered with fairly long hair.

BAT (*Lasiurus*) **species: 1.—*Red** (*L. borealis*): male a beautiful reddish-rusty, with whitish hair tips giving a frosted appearance; female rather dull buffy-chestnut, with fewer white-tipped hairs. The Red Bat occasionally is pale—a sort of cream color—with warm chestnut overcast. L. 3¾–4½ in., wingspread 13–14, wt. ½–⅓ oz. Young have shorter and grayer fur. **2.—Seminole** (*L. seminolus*): slightly smaller than the Red; both sexes much darker—a rich mahogany-brown—and with less frosty overcast; interfemoral membrane usually is very

dark chestnut-brown. Fur color of these two Bats is distinctive, but compare with the Silver-haired and the
larger Hoary Bat.

HABITAT: Non-hibernating migratory tree Bats, usually
found in or near woodland. During the day they hang
from vegetation, often within reach from the ground.
The Red Bat has wandered to Bermuda. Authentic reports of this species occurring in caves are based on
finding the remains of over 200 individuals in a cave in
Ind. and a single specimen in a cave in Tenn. In Penna.
a Seminole Bat was found dead in Sept. in Berks Co. and
one was captured in October in Lancaster Co., these being the known occurrences of this species n. of S. Car.

REPRODUCTION: These data are for the Red Bat. Breeding
occurs in Aug. and the young are born from late May to
mid-June. Litter size is 1–4, usually 2–3; the mother has
4 nipples. The mother carries the young in flight, sometimes until their combined wt. exceed hers, then leaves
them at a roost but nurses them for some time longer.
They can fly and catch insects when about a month old.

HABITS: Both of these swift species have narrow wings;
often they fly fairly high and descend earthward more or
less in spirals. They are capable also of rather slow flight.
The Red Bat is known to alight on vegetation to pick off
insects. It can maneuver in a smaller enclosed space than
the Big Brown Bat—an advantage when hunting or
when seeking a roosting place in foliage. The Red migrates northward in Apr.–May and southward in Oct.–
Nov. Thus the population shifts in fall to the s. states,
while the Seminole Bat evidently makes a shorter southward flight. Both species are more or less gregarious,
although individuals of each roost singly (but sometimes
several in the same clump of foliage), and the sexes tend
to stay apart during the time when young are reared.
Food: insects.

Hoary Bat
Lasiurus cinereus
Plate 1

A large Bat; hoary in appearance; short rounded ears with black rims; upper surface of interfemoral membrane wholly furred. Basal color of fur varies from deep reddish- to sooty-brown, next there is a lighter zone, then usually a more or less brownish zone with white tips. L. 5–5½ in., wingspread 15–16, wt. ¾–1½ oz. Young are a pale mouse gray. Compare this species with the smaller Silver-haired Bat.

HABITAT: A migratory tree Bat, usually seen about water-courses or over meadows. It hangs from tree branches.

REPRODUCTION: Breeding occurs in late summer. Litter size: usually 2, although 4 nipples are provided. Young are born from late May to early July, usually in June. It is believed that they are capable of flight when about a month old.

HABITS: This beautiful, large, narrow-winged Bat comes forth in the fading twilight, generally later than the Red Bat, flying in a direct and seemingly purposeful manner. Many naturalists never have seen it alive. Most specimens have been captured quite by accident at their day-time roosts in foliage. When migrating, it sometimes flies in early evening; it is a late-fall migrant. In summer, sometimes several of the same sex occur together, but the sexes tend to remain apart then as with most of our Bats. An individual that was cold in Nov. gave a loud cicada-like buzz. Considering its size, probably it eats fairly large insects, though it is known to take items as small as a mosquito.

Yellow Bats
Dasypterus
Plate 2

Bats of above medium size. Quite like the Red Bat externally but with taller, slightly pointed ears and fur only on basal half of upper surface of interfemoral membrane. **1.—Western** (*D. ega*): yellowish-tan or gray-brown; l. 3¾–4½ in., wing-spread 11–12½. **2.—*Eastern** (*D. intermedius*): even tan color with reddish-tan fur on interfemoral membrane; somewhat larger than the preceding. **3.—Florida** (*D. floridanus*): varies from reddish-brown to grayish-cream, with fur on interfemoral membrane sometimes tending toward chestnut; same size as preceding. The last two actually may be one species. In comparison, the Hoary Bat and Red Bats have upper surface of the interfemoral membrane completely furred.

Yellow Bats fly high, on a seemingly direct and purposeful course. For the Florida species 2–3 young are reported, but all have 4 nipples. They are not cave or house Bats and little is known about them.

Evening Bat
(Twilight Bat)
Nycticeius humeralis
Plate 1

Rather like the larger Myotis Bats, but with short sparse fur, thick, leathery, and more rounded ears, and somewhat curved broad tragus. Adults vary from a rich warm brown to dark chocolate. L. 3⅕–3⅗ in., wt. ⅕–⅓ oz. Young are dull blackish. All Myotis have pointed ears; the Big Brown Bat is larger.

HABITAT: Woodlands; roosts in hollow trees.

REPRODUCTION: Breeding probably occurs in late summer, as the sexes are together then. Two young are born in late May. Evidently the mother does not carry them in flight, for no flying females with young attached have been reported.

HABITS: This Bat has a slow steady flight, often traveling quite high and then coming down near the ground to feed. Evidently it migrates to and from the n. part of its range.

Spotted Bat
Euderma maculata
Plate 3

Blackish, with a white patch at base of each ear, one on each shoulder, and one on the rump; ears nearly 1¼ in. long. L. 4–4⅖ in. A rare Bat, having unique color pattern, recorded only from Mesilla Park, N. Mex.; Yuma, Ariz.; Piru, Mecca, Yosemite Valley, and Kern Co., Calif.; Reno, Nev.; Salt Lake City, Ut.; and Billings, Mont.

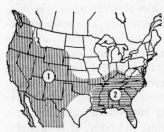

Lump-nosed Bats
(Big-eared Bats)
Corynorhinus
Plate 2

Fairly large Bats; very large thin ears; a club-shaped enlargement on each side of muzzle between nostril and eye; long, woolly, erect fur. **1.—Western** (*C. rafinesquii*): buffy-tan to warm brown above, but darker—a deep sooty color—in Pacific NW. L. 3½–4⅓ in., wingspread 12–13, wt. ⅓–½ oz. **2.—*Eastern** (*C. macrotis*):

of about the same size; cinnamon-brown above; belly hairs have clear white tips. Young are grayer than adults. The two may not be separate species. The combination of noselump and large ears distinguishes these Bats.

HABITAT: Roosts include caves, mine shafts, buildings, and hollow trees; habitat preferences away from roosts are unknown.

REPRODUCTION: Breeding occurs in autumn, but the sperm does not fertilize the egg until spring. In both species a single young is born annually, usually in May–June. Usually it is left hanging at a roost, where it is fed, until strong enough to fly and forage for itself. In the Western species, the fertilized egg requires 56–100 days' gestation (evidently time span varies depending on temperature of female). The newborn Bat is pink, hairless, has eyes closed, ears are not erect, and it weighs $\frac{1}{13}$–$\frac{1}{10}$ oz. In 4 days it has short gray hair, ears become erect in about 7 days, and a few days later the eyes open. It can fly in $2\frac{1}{2}$–3 weeks and at 6 weeks may fly out at night. Nursing continues up to 2 months, although it eats other food before then.

HABITS: These Bats leave their roosts well after dark and have not been observed feeding. Capable of swift silent flight, they are very agile on the wing. They also can sustain themselves by means of very slow wingbeats—a moth-like hovering flight that enables them to maneuver in as small a space as the tiny Pipistrelles. The sexes are together in late summer and fall and at the same roosts in winter, but are separate in spring and early summer. Dormancy in winter is not complete, and they shift about at a roost; associates at these places include Pipistrelles and various Myotis. Lump-nosed Bats hang singly and in small groups, with their big ears coiled backward in a close spiral and folded against the body. It is probable that these Bats feed, at least in part, on soft-bodied insects and that they hover close to foliage or actually alight on it to get such food.

Pallid Bat
Antrozous pallidus
Plate 2

A Bat of above medium size; large thin ears are separated widely at the base; on the blunt muzzle the nostrils are surrounded by a single small horseshoe-shaped ridge; pale, wool-like, cream-colored fur has smoky cast that gives it a soiled appearance; underparts are creamy-white. On the Pacific slope they are larger and darker than farther eastward. L. 4⅖–5 in., wt. about ¾ oz. A combination of color, simple muzzle, and large ears distinguishes this Bat.

HABITAT: A cave Bat. The Pallid Bat prefers warm areas, treeless or forested; it favors rock crevices for a daytime roost.

REPRODUCTION: This Bat has 1–2 young, born in May–June. Adults of both sexes frequently occur together during the season of birth and rearing, which is quite unusual among our Bats.

HABITS: The Pallid Bat, which has large eyes for its size, takes flight in evening a few minutes before there is too little light for good observation by humans. Often it hunts close to the ground or foliage. Small numbers of individuals have been found in winter in a dormant condition. In Calif. it has been observed hunting the flightless Jerusalem cricket by hovering just above the ground, or even alighting, then carrying this bulky insect to a feeding station or night roost (not the regular daytime roost) and there eating it. Under such places have been found hundreds of cricket heads and legs. Natural roosts appear to be crevices in cliffs and occasionally hollow trees, but many spend the day in attics and dark crannies of buildings. They are very agile when scrambling about in such quarters. Small numbers of Free-tailed Bats often occur in Pallid Bat colonies.

FREE-TAILED INSECT-EATING BATS Family Molossidae

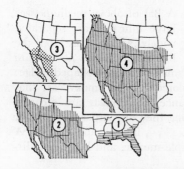

Free-tailed Bats
Tadarida
Plate 2

Mouse-like or 'free' por-
tion of tail (figured, p. 58)
extends well beyond the
interfemoral membrane.
All have deep vertical
grooves or wrinkles in the
upper lip, short dark brown
(sometimes nearly black) fur, and long narrow wings.
The four kinds may comprise one species; two are in this
size range: l. 3½–4 in., t. 1⅛–2½. **1.—Eastern** (*T.
cynocephala*): chocolate-brown to nearly black fur. **2.—
*Mexican** (*T. mexicana*): brownish-black to smoky-
brown. The following are larger. **3.—Pocketed** (*T. fem-
orosacca*): light brown to brownish-black; l. 3⅗–4¼,
t. 1½–1¾. **4.—Big** (*T. molossa*): dark brown fur, whitish at base; l. 4⅖–5⅖, t. 1¾–2⅛. The Mastiff Bats are
similar in appearance but much larger.

HABITAT: Roosts are in caves, crevices, and buildings. The
Mexican Free-tailed is the common house Bat of the SW.
Except for the rather solitary Pocketed Free-tailed, hundreds or thousands may roost together. They usually fly
out in the open away from vegetation.

REPRODUCTION: One young in the annual litter appears to
be the rule in the family Molossidae. Females of the
Eastern Free-tailed breed when less than a year old.
Breeding occurs in late winter and spring, gestation requires 11–12 weeks, and the young is not carried in flight.
The Mexican Free-tailed is said to breed in Mar. in Tex.
and to give birth in June.

HABITS: Having narrow wings, relatively heavy bodies, and

very rapid flight, Free-tailed Bats need more space in which to maneuver than any of our others except the Mastiff Bat. The take-off flight is straightaway; when foraging, changes in course are very abrupt. Except for the Pocketed Freetail, all evidently are colonial species, gatherings ranging from a few individuals to the several million *T. mexicana* that occur in fall at Carlsbad Caverns, N. Mex. At this place their departure from a cave near the close of day has been likened to smoke pouring from a volcano and is visible for 2 mi. The better-known species have local seasonal movements but probably no long migrations; they also are active and feed in winter, although they are torpid for periods. Food consists of flying insects, including beetles and moths; consumption of the latter by the smaller Freetails perhaps is unusual among our Bats. Free-tailed Bats from the tropics occasionally are transported long distances n. in shipments of fruit.

ECONOMIC STATUS: Droppings that accumulate under roosts make a rich fertilizer that has been gathered in marketable quantity in several states. Freetails, like other housedwelling Bats, are a nuisance because of their presence, droppings, and musky odor.

Mastiff Bats
Eumops
Plate 3

Our largest Bats. About half the tail is 'free' (figured, p. 58); ears are thick, very wide, and joined across the forehead; fur short. **1.— *Western** (*E. perotis*): sooty-brown fur, pale cream at base; l. 6½–7 in., t. 2, wingspread 19–21, wt. about 1½–2½ oz. Males, larger than females, have a throat gland which is enlarged Dec.–Mar. and subsides by mid-Apr.; a strong penetrating odor at roosts during season the gland is active. **2.—Eastern** (*E. glaucinus*)*:* nearly black in color, with a chestnut cast; about ¼ smaller than the preceding. Both are recognized readily by their large size and 'free' tails.

HABITAT: The Western roosts in rock crevices and buildings; it prefers warm areas such as orange-growing country. The Eastern has been taken once at Miami, Fla., and may have come via fruit steamer from farther s.

REPRODUCTION: The Western probably breeds at any time in winter. The single young, born May–June, is hairless at birth, has a well-developed snout but undeveloped ears.

HABITS: The Western Mastiff Bat is common within its range. It comes out late in the evening and is believed to fly high at times, but probably hunts rather close to the ground. It is agile on the ground, and some prey may be captured there. About 20 of these Bats in a building are a sizable colony, but up to 70 have been found at one site, where they hang in rows or roost singly. This Bat needs a large free space below its perch in order to take flight successfully; some die because evidently they have sought shelter in places out of which they cannot maneuver. Voice is a loud shrill scream. This Bat does not really hibernate, although it has short periods of inactivity in winter. It appears to be non-migratory, but does have different summer and winter roosts. Nothing seems to be recorded about its food habits; the sharp incisor teeth, which can cut an ugly gash in a person's hand, and large mouth would indicate that sizable prey is taken.

ECONOMIC STATUS: A nuisance in buildings.

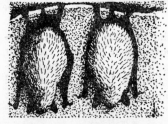

BATS HANG HEAD DOWNWARD
WHEN AT ROOST OR HIBERNATING

FLESH-EATERS   Order Carnivora

BEARS   Family Ursidae

Black Bear
Ursus americanus
Plate 7

Smallest of our Bears; facial profile straight; front claws short and rounded. Most individuals have a glossy black coat, brown snout, and many have a white patch on the chest. The reddish-brown (cinnamon) phase is commonest in the Rockies and elsewhere in W. Two color phases are known to occur in some litters. Along the Brit. Columbia coastal area are chocolate-brown Bears. A white or creamy phase with brown eyes ('Kermode's Bear') occurs on Gribble I. and vicinity, Brit. Columbia. A whitish-blue phase with brown snout ('Blue' or 'Glacier Bear') occurs in s. Alaska and n. Brit. Columbia.

L. 50–65 in., ht. at shoulder 27–36 (smallest in n. coastal Brit. Columbia, s. Alaska, and Yukon Terr.). Females usually are somewhat smaller than males. Few adults weigh as much as 600 lb.

In brown phase, this Bear might be confused with the Grizzly, but latter has a shoulder hump, dished-in face, and long front claws. Commonest Black Bear signs are tracks, Bear trees (bitten and/or clawed by a Bear), or sight of the animal.

HABITAT: From sea level up through the coniferous forest

BLACK BEAR

RH

LF

12 IN.

RH

RF

RH

RF

GRIZZLY BEAR

BIG BROWN BEAR

LH

RF

zone in mts., wherever there is adequate food and cover. Formerly all of forested N. Am.; now scarce in or absent from many settled areas.

REPRODUCTION: These data are from Penna. studies, with additions. Females probably begin breeding when 3 years old. Copulation takes place in June–July; evidently the fertilized ova grow little if any in summer and fall, since embryos are only ¾ in. long by early Dec. The Bear becomes very fat and builds a bed for winter sleep (a semi-dormant condition and not true hibernation). The Bear scoops out a depression in the ground and lines it with leaves and twigs. If under a tree, branches may be pulled down over it. Some sites are under upturned roots, fallen trees, or overhanging ledges. Evidently caves or other completely underground sites are not used commonly.

Often the Bear is wholly exposed to falling snow, which melts on the resting mammal. If disturbed, she departs at once. Here the young are born in late Jan. or Feb. after 200–210 days' gestation.

Cubs at birth have a thin coat of fine black hair, eyes are closed, and they weigh 8 oz. or less each. Eyes open in about 40 days, but vision appears to be poor for several weeks thereafter. Litter size: usually 2; 1 is common, 3 not rare, 4 rare, and 5 very exceptional or else combined litters. They leave the winter bed with the mother in late Mar. or Apr., when about 2 months old and weighing about 5 lb. They continue to nurse for some time. The mother teaches them to feed and to care for themselves. They stay with her through the winter, then separate. A Penna. growth study yielded these wt. data: 10 mo., av. 55 lb. (30–80); 22 mo., 105 (80–130); 34 mo., 155 (125–185); 46 mo., 205 (180–240); 58 mo., 255 (215–295); 70 mo., 305 (255–350). Usually this Bear breeds only every other year. Life span perhaps ordinarily does not exceed 12–15 years; a female lived 24 years in captivity but did not breed the last 3 years of her life.

HABITS: The Black Bear has a well-defined home range in which it travels a good deal. The owner marks its area by biting and/or clawing trees, these signs being recognized by other individuals. I have seen a spruce so marked at least 6 years in succession, probably by the same individual. They climb well as cubs, but poorly—if at all—as adults.

In hot weather they like to lie in damp places; occasionally they are semi-dormant for a few days. They tend to be rather solitary and, when meeting at garbage pits or other feeding places, often are quarrelsome. Very young cubs have a humming, also a moaning, sound; later they have a whine that, in adult life, becomes a loud and somewhat human-sounding cry. There also is a sort of grunt and a woofing sound. Winter sleep occurs even in Fla., a Bear sometimes lying down there without even making a bed. The rule everywhere is that males retire later than females. In Penna. some males are known to remain active throughout mild winters. A semi-dormant Bear inhales about 4–5 times per minute. Little wt. is lost during winter sleep, and only after a Bear has been active for a period in spring does it become lean. It should be noted that, if this Bear could truly hibernate, then its temperature would approach that of the environment, the Bear would be completely helpless, and in this condition the female could not give birth to cubs.

This species is practically omnivorous, but probably consumes relatively little fresh meat in the wild under ordinary circumstances. Food consists of fruits, berries, rodents, carcasses, nuts, fish (stranded or caught by the Bear), insects and their larvae, and occasionally pigs and sheep. It covers extra food and returns later to feed again. Even small cubs eat tender buds and leaves, also green grass. In spring, adults strip bark from the bases of conifers, eat its soft inner layer, and nibble the moist tree trunk. Firs and cedars thus are girdled and killed. A Bear will work at a bee-tree for days to get at the honey. Over spans of a few years the Bear population tends to increase and, if a food shortage occurs then, non-breeding individuals may make local emigrations.

ECONOMIC STATUS: The Black Bear makes a good hunting trophy. Its fur, which becomes prime late, is of little value. I have eaten excellent doughnuts fried in Bear grease and have used it for softening boot leather. The flesh is dark and, if the fat is trimmed off, is not strong in taste when cooked. It should be cooked well to avoid the possibility of contracting trichinosis. Black Bears often are serious pests when they break into camps and destroy food and other property. Killing livestock is a trait not shared by all of them. One should not get close to park Bears when feeding them, nor leave food about camp or auto where they can get at it; this is simply inviting trouble. The Black Bear is one of the few large mammals that is readily baited to a trap by using a carcass of one of its own kind.

Grizzly Bear
Ursus horribilis
Plate 7

A large thickset Bear, with dished-in facial profile and maned hump on shoulders; front claws often twice as long as hind and but little curved. Usual color is deep brown, darkening to brownish-black along spine and on limbs and ears; grizzled (light tipping on hair) on upper parts of body. Many, however, are yellowish; others are grayish or blackish. L. 6–7½ ft., ht. at shoulder 3–3½. Adult males usually weigh about 500 lb. and females 400; wild individuals up to 800 are recorded, also a fat zoo captive at over 1,150. Eight to 10 years are required to reach full size and wt.

Variation during a long growth period, or because of sex differences, or inherent in Grizzly stock over its geographic range, led, in the past, to description of many alleged 'species.' They are treated under one heading here. The Grizzly and Big Brown types of Bear intergrade; some specimens cannot be referred clearly to either. The Old World Brown Bear (*U. arctos*) has been taken once on St. Lawrence I., Alaska. It, plus our Grizzly and Big Brown types, may be a single wide-ranging and very variable species.

Because of its dished-in face, shoulder hump, and long front claws, this Bear should not be confused with other kinds. Perhaps commonest indications of its presence are tracks and Bear trails; hind tracks are up to 12 in. long and show little if any claw prints; the front tracks are about 6 in. wide by 8 long and usually show 5 sizable claw imprints. Footprints are usually separate (not one track over the other). Claw imprints are small or absent in tracks of both the smaller Black Bear and the larger Big Brown Bear. See diagram, p. 80.

HABITAT: Uplands, mts. to above timber line, and tundra; extirpated from extensive plains areas it formerly occupied.

REPRODUCTION: The Grizzly is believed to breed first at 3–5 years of age. Midsummer courtship may last a month or more, mates grazing, playing, and wrestling together. Then they separate and, usually, lead solitary lives. As with the Black Bear, the fertilized ova show little or no growth prior to winter sleep. The female digs or enlarges a sizable winter den, often 12 or 14 ft., into a hillside; she lines it with vegetation and there, about Jan. or Feb., gives birth to 1–4 (usually 1 or 2) cubs. A cub at birth is covered with fine gray hair, is about 8½ in. long, and weighs about 1½ lb.; eyes are closed for 9–10 days. In summer, occasionally a male joins a female with cubs for a while. As yearlings the cubs den with the mother, then separate from her. Perhaps occasionally they remain longer with her. The Grizzly evidently breeds not more often than every other year. Life span perhaps usually is 15–20 years, although much older zoo captives are known.

HABITS: Like other Bears, this one has no regular home—aside from its place of winter sleep—but wanders within its home range. It travels at any time of day or night, but tends to be more or less nocturnal in settled areas. It swims well. Cubs climb trees; adults do not. The Grizzly is not gregarious and, when 2 or more meet at a feeding place, usually they ignore each other entirely or acknowledge another's presence by a snarl. Cubs have a whine and a purring hum; adults cough, sniff, growl, roar, and grunt. Both sexes have winter dens (they may be used more than 1 year) in N., males denning later than females; in the s. part of the Grizzly's range the male does not den. Even in n. Alaska some Grizzlies are abroad in spring by early Apr. Food: grass, berries, fruits, leaves, bark, rodents and other mammals, lizards, snakes, insects and larvae, stale and fresh meat, and salmon (stranded or caught by the Bears) in quantity. Grass is much eaten in spring. Many Ground Squirrels are dug out, especially in fall. Livestock is killed and eaten, though rarely in any numbers. Food may be covered with dirt and the Bear returns to feed again, often after days have passed. Home ranges overlap; each perhaps usually is less than 20 mi. in diameter, and the Bears follow established pathways, stepping in their own (or another Bear's) footprints when going over a given route. The only serious predator on the Grizzly is man.

ECONOMIC STATUS: A Grizzly hide is a good trophy but has little value as fur. The meat is fairly good eating if lean, and the grease has many uses. The Grizzlies that kill cattle and sheep ought perhaps to be either trapped or pursued by hounds and shot. Generally, a Grizzly minds its own business, but it will attack a person in self-defense; unprovoked attacks are rare. Only a few hundred Grizzlies remain in the U.S., mostly in Mont. and Wyo. Fortunately there are large areas in nw. Canada and in Alaska where the Grizzly still lives relatively unmolested by man.

Big Brown Bear
('Kodiak' Bear)
Ursus middendorffi
Plate 6

Largest carnivore. Very heavy build, massive head, and dished-in face; color more uniform and with less grizzling than on most Grizzlies (but individuals range from pale yellowish to brown to nearly black); claws short, stout, curved, and usually dark in color. The Big Brown, of which 8 alleged 'species' have been described, appears to be a coastal and island derivation of the Grizzly, and it varies for the same reasons as the latter (see p. 83). The 2 types intergrade. L. to about 8 ft., ht. at shoulder 4–4½. Males are much larger than females. A medium-large male at 7 years weighs about 1,000 lb., a female of same age about 600–700. Perhaps a mature male in the wild occasionally reaches 1,500 lb., but such individuals must be rare.

Massive size and curved claws (which seldom show in tracks) distinguish this Bear. Hind tracks of a full-grown male are 6–8½ in. wide by 12–14 long, and front tracks about 7–8 in. wide; tracks of mature females are at least ⅓ smaller. This Bear makes trails, often directly up steep slopes, which are visible from a long distance; its tracks are found from sea level to high above snow line.

HABITAT: Alaska Peninsula, coastal strip s. nearly to Brit. Columbia, and various adjacent islands. From sea level to high country; swamps, streams, woods, tundra, and snow fields.

REPRODUCTION: The Brown Bear probably first breeds when 4 or 5 years old. Mating occurs in July, and the pair has a courting period that may last up to several weeks. Then they separate. In captivity a female Brown Bear mated with a Polar Bear and gave birth after a 180-day gestation period—perhaps an abnormally short time. Cubs are born in the winter den in Jan. or early Feb. It is believed that the first litter usually consists of a single cub; then there are 1 or 2 (occasionally 3) in subsequent litters. They weigh about 1½ lb. at birth and have eyes closed. Mother and cubs leave the den in Apr. or May and travel together during the summer, then den together and stay as a unit through the second summer, and perhaps occasionally may den near one another the winter following. The female breeds at intervals of 2, or sometimes 3, years. Perhaps life span ordinarily is about 15–20 years, although a zoo specimen lived for over 25 years.

HABITS: More fantastic tales have been circulated about the strength and prowess of this Bear than can be readily imagined. It is solitary and tends to be diurnal. It lives in a rugged land characterized by quick and drastic weather changes. At times it travels at a fast bounding gallop, often going thus without stopping for a mile or two straight up a steep mt. slope. Like the Grizzly, it has deep and direct trails, and any Bear occurring in an area utilizes trails made by its predecessors. On leaving the winter den, a Bear usually travels about, in, and near the higher snow fields for a few days, then comes down to valley floors and beaches. Many miles are covered in a single day. At this time it is very fat and appears not to be hungry, but after 10 days or 2 weeks without eating it has worked off much fat and begins to develop an appetite. Small at first, and perhaps satisfied with young grass and other vegetation, its appetite soon becomes enormous and the Bear eats quantities of grass, sedges and other vegetation, roots, moss, Mice, Ground Squirrels, and carrion. Then it moves back into the mts. By early autumn the Bear returns again to the lowlands to feed on salmon, varying this diet with grass, berries, and other plant food. Any putrid fish or meat is readily eaten; unused portions are buried for a later meal.

The Big Brown Bear does not stand in a stream and scoop out salmon by the hundredweight. Its fishing method is to pounce on a salmon in shallow water, pinning the fish down with his paws and then, grasping the prey in its jaws, usually carrying it ashore to be eaten. As a rule, not more than 3 or 4 salmon are taken for a meal. Some salmon eaten are exhausted after spawning or already dead. When several Big Brown Bears occur at one place fishing, they give the illusion of being very abundant. It should be remembered, however, that nearly all of the population then is concentrated along the streams of the coastal lowlands. Probably, on good Bear range such as parts of Kodiak I., one Bear per several square miles is a very high population. Man is their only predator.

ECONOMIC STATUS: A noted hunting prize. In general, the

larger the Bear, the less likely it is to have a good pelt; a fairly high population must be maintained, therefore, to produce a few mature Bears in trophy condition. Meat of this Bear is not eaten. Occasionally this bear has killed livestock. So-called unprovoked attacks on humans may not exist; the charging Bear is guarding a food supply or its offspring. The number of potential spawning salmon eaten in a few localities only is enough perhaps to out-weigh any cash value obtainable at these places from utilizing the Bears themselves. Although the Big Brown Bear's actions are unpredictable, many people have ex-aggerated ideas of it as a hazard to human life and a menace otherwise to man's interests.

Polar Bear
Thalarctos maritimus
Plate 6

A large Bear. Whitish or yellowish-white in color; rel-atively long neck; compara-tively small head; Roman-nose facial profile; eyes, nose-pad, and foot-pads are black. L. 7–8 ft., ht. at shoulder 3–4. Fully grown males weigh 800–900 lb., females about 700; maximum reported wt. of a wild male is 1,600 lb. Cubs have whiter pelage than adults. This long-necked Bear should not be confused with the occasional Arctic Grizzly that may occur within its range; also, the Polar Bear is at sea in seasons when the Grizzly is not in winter sleep. Feet are covered with hair, except for relatively small pads. Hind track usually is over 12 in. long, and the claws leave little or no imprint.

HABITAT: Circumpolar sea ice, often far from land, as well as coastal areas and on tundra of islands and mainland; rarely, if at all, very far inland.

REPRODUCTION: The Polar Bear begins breeding when 3–4

years old before full growth is attained. There is a mid-summer period when, usually out on the ice, the male and female court for some time; otherwise, adults generally are apart. In Nov. and Dec. females go inland ashore to dig a den for winter sleep in a drift of hard-packed snow. After 8 months' gestation the cubs (usually 2) are born in late Dec. or in Jan. The family leaves its icy den about late Mar. There are few data on condition of young at birth or on growth, although this Bear breeds readily in captivity. Mother and cubs go seaward to live, often far out on the ice. Usually they separate from her in their first autumn, when about 10 months old. The Polar Bear breeds every other year. Life span perhaps usually is about 15–20 years, although there are records of zoo captives living 25 and 33½ years.

HABITS: The Polar Bear is a noted wanderer and rapid traveler, even on irregular broken pack ice. It swims readily and dives expertly in cold sea water, propelling itself almost entirely with its forelimbs. Sometimes the mother tows her cubs, who cling to her rump or tail. Sense of smell is said to be unusually acute, and this species may have the best eyesight of any of our Bears. It is solitary, except during courtship or chance meetings of several at the carcass of a stranded Whale or some other food source. In early winter, when females go inland to den and have cubs, males and barren females go out on the sea ice to open water. An adult can travel on ice too thin to support a man. This it does by spreading the legs well apart (distributing weight) and keeping on the move. If ice is very thin, the Bear lies flat on its belly and pulls itself along with its claws. If the ice is too thin for support, the Bear swims beneath it, breaking through with its head to breathe. Voice of cubs is a hum and a whine; adults roar. A certain amount of vegetation is eaten ashore, mainly in early fall. Most food consists of Seals, bird eggs, young Walruses, all manner of marine life found frozen in overturned ice, and carrion such as stranded Whales. This Bear is not scarce over much of its present range, and its chief predator is man.

ECONOMIC STATUS: The skin makes a good trophy or sleeping bag. The flesh is fairly edible if the fat is removed, but should be cooked well to avoid any possibility of getting trichinosis. The liver should not be eaten, cooked or otherwise, by man or dogs, since its concentrated vitamin A content usually causes illness. Chief uses of the Polar Bear are as a zoo mammal and as a source of skins from which the Eskimo makes durable pants.

RACCOONS, COATIS, AND ALLIES
Family Procyonidae

Raccoon
(Coon)
Procyon lotor
Plate 9

Rather robust form; black facial mask; long fur (general tone yellowish-gray to grayish-brown in normal pelage), with 4–6 black rings on tail; snout and ears pointed. Largest and darkest Coons are in the Pacific NW.; l. 32–34 in., t. 10½. Eastern ones are large and medium in color; l. 30–33, t. 9½. Palest are in the Colo. River delta and on the Fla. Keys; the latter also are smallest; l. 25–27½, t. 9½. Wt. of adult n. Coons is 12–16 lb., rarely (when very fat) to over 25; those from some of the Keys only 3–6 lb. Coons stand 9–12 in. high at shoulder. Males are larger than females. Southern ones have poorer, thinner fur than n. ones and more rangy build. The Coon should not be confused with any other mammal, even the Coati and Ringtail (Plate 35). Fore tracks overlap the hind in walking and are placed after them (Squirrel-like) in running.

HABITAT: Prefers wooded or swampy areas having water-

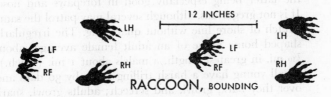

12 INCHES

RACCOON, BOUNDING

courses, den sites, and adequate food. Introduced on Singa and El Capitan I. of se. Alaska.

REPRODUCTION: Many females breed when a year old, some perhaps at 10 months; males are sexually active as yearlings, but may not breed until later. Coons are promiscuous. Those old enough to breed den singly. A hollow tree den is preferred, but cavities under tree roots, in the ground, under ledges, or even caves are utilized. Breeding occurs Feb.–early Mar. in N. and earlier in S. A few (yearling ?) females breed later. Young are born all summer in N.Y. Gestation requires 63 days, and the annual litter contains 2–7 (usually 4) young. Captives studied in N.Y. were found, at birth, to have black skin, yellowish-gray fur, and to weigh 2½ oz. The blackish facial mask was evident in 10 days and the tail rings in 19. Eyes opened in 18–23 days. At 40 days these Coons weighed about 1½ lb. and ate some solid food. At 50 days and 2 lb. wt. they could leave the den of their own accord. In the wild, young are moved by the mother if the den is disturbed or they outgrow it. At 10 weeks of age they travel with her, gathering food, while she teaches and disciplines them. They continue together until late fall and gain wt. into early Nov. Then the young lose the instinct to follow and disperse widely, usually traveling and denning singly. Probably a wild Coon is very old at 7 years, although zoo captives have lived 14.

HABITS: The Coon is mainly nocturnal. It swims well, but

not far or often. It is an excellent climber and a cunning, curious, and clever mammal, with much 'animal intelligence.' Smell is relatively less well developed than touch, the latter being especially good in forepaws and nose. It is not gregarious, although several may patrol the same stretch of shore line without quarreling. The irregularly shaped home range of an adult female averages about 7/10 mi. in greatest length, a male's about 1 mi. (Mich.). Small young have a harsh trilling note; by 30 days and over they bark, growl, and screech; adults growl, snarl, have a throaty cry, an accented whine, a churring noise, and a quavering Owl-like call. None of these sounds has much carrying power.

In S., Coons are active the year round, often sleeping in a tree crotch or on a Squirrel nest; those in N. gain relatively much more fat and stay in dens for periods of winter sleep. The Coon is nearly omnivorous, but especially likes acorns, various nuts, berries and fruits, seeds, corn in the 'milk' stage, and a variety of aquatic life, such as crayfish, crabs, clams, oysters, frogs, and fishes. Mammals (including young Muskrats), birds, reptiles, and amphibians are eaten, also insects. Contrary to popular belief, Coons in the wild do not wash all their food. They may wash food caught in wet sand or mud, to remove sand and grit, and amphibians to be rid of unpleasant secretions of the skin glands. Some Coons live in swamps miles from open water. Examples of high local populations reported are: 8–10 per acre in Miss.; 42 per sq. mi. in Ill.; and 100 taken from 102 acres in Mo. in 4½ days in winter. Perhaps 1 per 10 acres is a fairly good population in most areas.

ECONOMIC STATUS: The Coon is clever and takes to water when closely pursued by hounds. Its fur is much sought when prices are up. The meat is good, and in S., where pelts are poor in quality, some Coons are killed for meat alone. Damage done to gardens and poultry by Coons usually is a negligible and local matter. Squirrel damage to corn sometimes is attributed to Coons. It is expert at opening garbage cans. The population can be increased by putting den-boxes in trees; these should be made of good boards, the den measuring 14 in. sq., 36 tall, and having an entrance 5 x 6 in. on a side and near the top.

Coati
(Coatimundi)
Nasua narica
Plate 35

Somewhat Raccoon-like, but more slender and elongated, and with long tapering tail. Long snout; short coarse fur varying from yellowish- to rusty-brown to grayish to blackish (but a tendency toward brown- and gray-phased individuals) ; contrasting brownish-black and whitish facial pattern; and more or less distinct dark rings on the long tapering tail. Males, very much larger than females, measure: l. 3¼–4¼ ft., t. 20–25 in., ht. at shoulder 9–12 in., wt. 10–25 lb. Young are darker than adults, with tail rings more distinct. It walks with feet flat on the ground; front and hind tracks show 5 toes and are rather like the hind track of the Raccoon.

HABITAT: Rocky areas with more or less open forest. Escaped Coatis have lived for a time well beyond the natural range.

REPRODUCTION: Litter size is said to be 4–6; young are born in spring and early summer in Ariz. A 77-day gestation period is reported from the Canal Zone.

HABITS: The Coati is abroad at any hour, but less active around noon and midnight. Dens are in rocky places. Males tend to be solitary except at mating, but females and young associate in bands. Expert tree climbers, whole bands go aloft; the tail serves as a balancing organ when they travel among branches. On the ground the Coati goes at a good rate, occasionally speeding briefly with a sort of rollicking gallop. The tail is carried at a fairly high angle, waving as though slightly unsteady, and the long snout twitches constantly. The Coati swims well. A surprisingly powerful mammal, it is not easily overcome by a large dog. Vocal sounds include a pig-like grunt, a thin scream, and, if it is captured, a variety of snorts and hisses. It is practically omnivorous, eating all sorts of animal matter, berries, and roots. Lizards are a favorite food. It has increased its range northward in the last few decades and now is common in parts of s. Ariz.

ECONOMIC STATUS: Few facts are known; it should not be deemed an unwelcome mammal just because it eats some bird eggs and nestlings.

RINGTAILS Family Bassariscidae

Ringtail
(Ring-tailed Cat)
Bassariscus astutus
Plate 35

Might be described as a Squirrel-like Raccoon, having short legs (it appears to be sitting when it is standing), Fox-like face, tall ears, and flattened bushy tail about as long as body, with black rings that are incomplete on the underside. General tone brownish-gray, paler below, with whitish snout, and blackish area in front of each eye. L. 25–30 in., t. 13–15, ht. at shoulder 6, wt. 2–2½ lb. Females are somewhat smaller than males. Not readily confused with other mammals, but compare with Raccoon and Coati.

This nocturnal creature is rarely seen. Its rather Bear-like tracks, showing 5 toes with claws, often are numerous in the dust of caves and canyons, as are its dry

coiled pellets of excreta, containing bones, hair, and insect remains.

HABITAT: Cliffs, canyons, ledges, and caves, often near
water. Some live in ruins of ancient and modern Indian
dwellings, in old cabins, and in hollow trees.

REPRODUCTION: Young are born May–June in rocky crevices, caves, or other dark places. Gestation period is unknown. The annual litter contains 1–5 (usually 3–4)
young. At birth their eyes are closed, ears are practically
nonexistent, they have a coat of fine whitish fuzz, and
each weighs about 1 oz. Pigmented skin on the tail in-
dicates where black areas of fur will develop. At first
young are cared for by the female only. At 3 weeks either
parent may bring meat; at 34–35 days they have a coat
of adult pattern and eyes are just open; at 2 months they
go on foraging trips; at 4 months they are weaned; and
at 4½ months they are nearly of adult size. The Ringtail
has lived 8 years in captivity.

HABITS: A wonderfully agile night traveler. Using the flattened tail as a balancer, it leaps from point to point on
cliffs and ledges, or climbs steep surfaces of almost any
sort. It gives the appearance of scooting about. Ten-foot
leaps require no apparent effort. Perhaps it is somewhat
gregarious. An excellent ratter and mouser, it is often
kept as a pet in cabins. Local names: Miner's Cat,
Mountain Cat, American Civet Cat, and Cat Squirrel.
Young have a metallic squeak; in about 2 months they
cease squeaking and begin to bark. Adults have an explosive bark and piercing scream. Food: Woodrats and
other rodents, Bats, birds, insects; also fruits, berries,
green corn, and probably nuts.

ECONOMIC STATUS: The fur is poor and of little beauty or
value. A curious mammal, it often gets into traps set for
other mammals. Many have been killed by eating poison
put out in predatory-mammal- or rodent-control operations. It eats birds and their eggs, also many rodents.
A good pet, but it must be kept caged if poultry is about.

WEASELS, SKUNKS, AND ALLIES Family Mustelidae

Marten
(Sable)
Martes americana
Plate 9

Weasel-like form; small head; conspicuous, broad, rounded ears; short legs. Individuals vary from yellowish-brown to dark brown above; they have a rather grizzled appearance in Alaska; in Labrador they are nearly black. The head is paler; underparts are lighter, tending toward orange-buff, often with a yellowish or whitish chest patch. Males: l. 25–30 in., t. 7½–10, ht. at shoulder about 7½, wt. 1½–4 lb.; females are about ¼ smaller and ⅓ lighter.

It looks somewhat like a very small Red Fox when seen on the ground. The Mink is darker, has a smaller tail, and chest patch, if present, is white. The Fisher is larger, darker, and with proportionately much smaller tail. The partly furred Marten foot leaves a less distinct and much more elongated imprint than a Mink's. Front tracks may be nearly as large as hind. In bounding—up to 3 ft.—hind feet are placed in tracks of front or ahead of them (diagram, p. 99); if hind in front tracks, the imprints on one side are slightly ahead of the other.

HABITAT: Prefers mature coniferous forest at any elevation. Mainly terrestrial in winter; somewhat more arboreal in summer. Terrain traveled includes the forest floor, rocky areas, berry patches, and scrub areas above timber line.

REPRODUCTION: Females probably begin to breed the summer of the year following their birth. Den sites: a hollow tree or log, or rarely a hole in the ground. A lining of dry leaves is provided. The courting period in summer

(July) may last about 15 days. Recorded gestations: 220–265 days; fetal development is delayed for varying periods of time and takes place mainly from midwinter on. Young are born in Mar.–Apr. Litter size: 1–5 (usually 2–3) young. Following are data from captives in Que. Young at birth weigh about 1 oz. and have a thin covering of fine yellowish hair. In 8 days several dark gray dorsal stripes (crosswise on the shoulders and lengthwise on the back) are in evidence; these are most prominent at 16 days and disappear a few days later. At 3 weeks a gray tone vanishes and gradually thereafter a brownish one is assumed. Sexual disparity in size is very noticeable by this time. Eyes are open at 39 days. Weaning occurs in 6–7 weeks, and the female then brings meat to the young. They stay with her for about 3 months, when, having attained adult wt., they become solitary. Two captives in N.Y. lived at least 15 and 17 years.

HABITS: The quick and agile Marten has a very alert expression and a sinuous gracefulness when in motion. Although by no means strictly nocturnal, usually it sleeps part of the day. Like the Weasels, its sleep is very sound and it appears to be an incredible bundle of energy on awakening. Generally it is solitary, except when courting, but occasionally 2 play together as litter mates do. Voice: a variety of high-pitched squeals and screams; a female at courting utters clucking notes. A large gland in the groin of both sexes is rubbed on rocks, stumps, and trees; the scent deposited announces the individual's presence.

The Marten often is inactive for several days during periods of very cold or wet weather. Red Squirrels generally are considered the number-one Marten food, but in some areas and seasons other foods are more important. All kinds of vertebrate life are eaten, including carrion, as well as insects, berries, fruits, and perhaps nuts. Blueberries and mountain-ash fruits are favorites in season. If a rodent or other prey is not consumed at one meal, it is buried and the Marten returns to it later. From day to day a Marten tends to travel in an overlapping series of small areas. It likes to tunnel in snow. Some altitudinal population shift with the changing seasons has been noted in mts. High numbers in the population occur 8–11 years apart; these are not related to peaks in Rabbit or Grouse numbers.

ECONOMIC STATUS: Marten fur (Sable) is noted for its beauty and durability. This mammal has been eliminated entirely from some areas and the population is much reduced in most of the remaining range because of trapping or habitat alteration by lumbering or fire. A curious creature, it gets into traps set for Bobcats and other mammals; this could be remedied by restricting trapping to aquatic mammals in critical areas.

Fisher
(Blackcat)
Martes pennanti
Plate 9

Weasel-like form; nearly as large as a Fox, though much more slender; low rounded ears; tapering bushy tail. General color varies from brown to blackish; white tipping of hairs, most prevalent on head and shoulders, is more fully developed in older males. Males: l. 34–40 in., t. 13–15, ht. at shoulder 10–11, wt. 5–12 or rarely to 18 lb. Females: about ⅓ smaller and weigh only about ½ as much. The Fisher is more slender and shorter-legged than any Fox; also, it has rounded, not pointed, ears. A Mink is much smaller. A Marten has lighter color, bigger ears, and bushier tail. In bounding gait, sets of tracks are about 4 ft. apart; remarks on gait given for Marten apply here also.

HABITAT: Prefers extensive forest at any elevation; it fares well in cutover areas grown to mixed woods in the NE. Mainly terrestrial.

REPRODUCTION: Both sexes are reported to reach sexual

maturity in a year, but not to breed until 2 years old. The nest, of vegetation, is in a hollow tree, log, or cavity among rocks. Mating occurs in Apr. Gestation requires 352 days, or about 50 weeks (varies from 338–358), but, as with some others of the Weasel tribe, most fetal de-

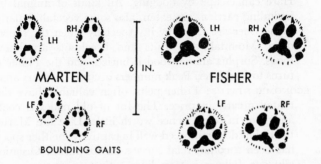

MARTEN   6 IN.   FISHER

BOUNDING GAITS

velopment occurs only in the latter part of this period. Litter size: 1–5, usually 3. Less than a week after giving birth, the mother is bred again. Young at birth are much like newborn Martens. Eyes open in 7 weeks. They can hunt at 3 months. The family breaks up by late fall, but tracks of 2 small Fishers traveling together in winter may indicate that litter mates sometimes associate for a longer time.

HABITS: The Fisher climbs trees much less often than is generally believed; it is abroad a good deal in daylight. Most traveling is done on the ground or on down timber. It swims well, though perhaps not frequently. Adults are solitary for the most part, traveling an irregular route over high and low ground and occasionally taking a fairly straight course for some distance across country. Voice: an explosive scream and a sort of hiss. The Fisher's odor is distinctive, though not as strong or offensive as that of most of the Weasel family. It is inactive during periods of stormy weather. It eats fish occasionally, but whether some of these are caught or all are stranded ones is not known. The Porcupine is a favorite food and, contrary to popular belief, the Fisher does not wholly escape the quills by tearing this mammal open ventrally. Some Fishers die from quills, and most pelts show numerous flattened ones on the flesh side. It can outrun a Varying Hare on a straightaway course, but the Hare can escape by dodging. All kinds of animal life, including carrion, are eaten, also some vegetable matter. Some Deer are killed by it, especially when the snow is deep. Mountain-ash fruits and beechnuts are known foods. Surplus animal food is buried, and the Fisher returns to feed later. Peak numbers occur 8–11 years apart.

ECONOMIC STATUS: Fisher pelts, often valuable, have fluctuated greatly in price. The fur of old males is coarse and poor in color, hence worth little. Like the Marten, the Fisher does not breed well in captivity; neither species has been a commercial success on fur farms. Occasionally one follows a trap line, eating or destroying the catch, but it can be caught readily. Evidently the Porcupine population can be controlled in a large measure by the Fisher. There are not many thousand Fishers in N. Am.

Short-tailed Weasel
(Ermine)
Mustela erminea
Plate 10

A short-legged, slim mammal of large Chipmunk size. End of tail always black. In summer, upperparts brown; underparts whitish or pale sulphur-yellow. Color intensity (darkness) of upperparts increases from E. to W. in s. part of range; light of underparts extends clear to hind toes over most of range, but is reduced to a patch on chin to chest and one in groin from s. Brit. Columbia to Calif. In spring and fall molt periods, which may last several weeks, specimens show transition in pattern from summer to winter coat. A white winter coat is assumed everywhere except from s. Brit. Columbia to Calif. Largest in N. and smallest in area where darkest and without seasonal color change. Males: 1. 8½–14 in., t. 2⅕–4⅕, wt. 2½–5 oz. Females (about ⅘ size of males): 1. 8–12, t. 2–3⅖, wt. 1½–3½ oz.

3 INCHES
SPEEDING

TAIL MARK
HIND TRACKS
OVER FORE

SHORT BOUND SHORT-TAILED WEASEL

In comparison, the diminutive Least Weasel never has more than a few black hairs in end of tail and tail vertebrae are ¼ or less the length of head and body. The larger Long-tailed Weasel, in full summer coat, does not have light of underparts extending down the hind legs, and always length of tail vertebrae equals more than 44% of length of head and body. When making short bounds, the Short-tailed Weasel leaves sets of tracks 13–20 in. apart; when speeding, it often leaps 6 or more ft. The tail leaves a mark. A network of crisscrossing trails is characteristic. This Weasel is curious and, if seen peering from shelter, you may call it into the open by making a squeaking noise.

HABITAT: Field borders, open woodlands, brushy and rocky areas.

REPRODUCTION: The male can breed when a year or less old; some females are bred their first summer, others not until the next year. A ready-made den site is appropriated, such as a cavity under a log or stump, in a rockpile, or a Chipmunk den. Fur and feathers of prey and other debris form the nest. Although mating takes place in early summer, practically all embryonic and fetal development occurs in the last month of the approximately 10-month gestation period. The annual litter of 6–13 (usually 4–7) young is born in spring. At birth wt. is about 1/14 oz.; the young appear to be naked, but close inspection reveals a mane of fine white hair on the neck and scattered hairs along the back. The brown-and-white fur pattern is apparent at 2 weeks, when the mane has reached full development. At 1 month the eyes open and the mane is obscured. Young are weaned in 5 weeks. A 7-week-old male is larger and heavier than his mother. The young play like kittens. Both adults bring meat from the time the young are very small. Litter mates probably disperse in midsummer or later. Perhaps adults sometimes stay paired throughout the year.

HABITS: The Short-tailed Weasel or Ermine, called Stoat in its Old World range, is a persistent hunter and abroad at any hour. It circles and doubles back on its tracks in quest of food. It has a way of disappearing under one's very eyes, especially in winter, when all one sees is the black tail-tip and shadow of the white body. It swims well, climbs trees readily (descending backward), and burrows in snow. Several in an area appear to make almost innumerable tracks. Young squeal and squeak; adults have a barking scream, a sort of hiss, a loud chattering, and, when at play, a purring and a crowing sound. Sometimes a pair hunts together. On approach of this Weasel, a Hare sometimes appears to be immobilized with fear. If driven from a kill, the bold Weasel will attack a dog or even a man. Food: all sorts of mammals (Mice often are a mainstay), birds, cold-blooded vertebrates, and even insects and earthworms. It does not suck blood, as commonly believed; it does kill more than it can eat at once, but such food is usually stored for future use. The population fluctuates markedly, peak numbers occurring every 4–7 years.

ECONOMIC STATUS: White winter (Ermine) fur is of value. Specimens in molt are nearly worthless. When the population is high and fur price low, this mammal is a nuisance on the trap line, eating bait or getting caught in traps set for more valuable furbearers. Occasionally one is destructive in the hen coop, so farmers kill it on sight —and by so doing they remove a destroyer of many rodents.

Least Weasel
Mustela rixosa
Plate 10

Smallest carnivore; slender-bodied; very short-legged; size of medium-sized Chipmunk. Tail never with more than a few black hairs in tip. In summer, upperparts brown; underparts, front feet, and more or less of hind feet white. In winter, all white, except in e. U.S., where some remain brown above and a few are found through the season having brown partly replaced by white. Males: l. 7¼–9 in., t. 1⅕–1⅗, wt. 1⅓–2½ oz. Females (somewhat smaller): l. 6½–9, t. 1–1⅗.

Since tail vertebrae equal ¼ or less the length of head and body and there are never more than a few black hairs in the tail tip, a Least Weasel should not be confused with a small female Short-tailed Weasel. In bounding gait, the fore and hind tracks (about ⅓ smaller than the Short-tailed Weasel's) are nearly in the same spot, and these little pairs of elongated prints are spaced 8–13 in. apart. The tail seldom leaves a mark. The trail is characterized by very abrupt doubling back at frequent intervals, often after only 2–5 bounds. Considered rare over much of its range.

HABITAT: Grassy or brushy areas and open woodland.

REPRODUCTION: This Weasel appropriates and lines a Mouse nest with Mouse fur, or makes one entirely of such fur;

usually the site is below ground, but dens in a clover stack and corn shocks have been reported. Litter size: 3–10, averaging about 5. In the U.S. at least, young may be born any month; perhaps there is more than one litter annually at this latitude. They are reared by the female.

HABITS: In Alaskan localities I have observed tracks of the Least Weasel and handled trapped specimens. It travels on the surface or burrows readily in snow. In the U.S. it has been observed in surface runways of the Meadow Vole, trailing this species by scent. The victim is dragged to a den or other shelter. Some food is stored. Known foods are various Mice, and it is suspected of eating insects. Voice is described as a bark or a shrill shriek. It can emit an offensive musk like other Weasels. Seasonal home range of an individual probably is not over 2 acres.

ECONOMIC STATUS: Arctic garments occasionally are trimmed or decorated with the fur. The Least Weasel would be an efficient mouser to have about camp or other dwelling.

Long-tailed Weasel
Mustela frenata
Plate 10

A short-legged, slim mammal of about Gray Squirrel size. End of tail always black. In summer, upperparts, legs, and feet brown; underparts buffy-or yellowish-white from chin to groin; in Fla. and from Tex. and Ariz. w. and n. into Brit. Columbia, the face is darker than the body, with whitish or pale yellowish areas. In winter, white, often tinged with yellow, in n. part of range; some individuals change to white in a zone extending from s. Vt. to Va., w. to n. Ariz., cent. Calif., and thence n. into Brit. Columbia; s. of this zone none turns white (summer and winter coats are alike). Largest ones are in W. Males: l. 14–23 in., t. 4½–7, wt. 7–14 oz. Females: l. 11½–20, t. 3½–5, wt. 3–9 oz.

In comparison, the Short-tailed Weasel is smaller, with shorter tail, and light portion of summer coat generally extends down the hind legs. The Black-footed Ferret has a facial mask, but its body is uniformly pale and limbs are blackish. The Mink is as dark below as above. Tracks are like the Short-tailed Weasel's, but ½ again as large and hind ones relatively more elongated; gaits are similar. In bounding gait, sets of tracks are 15–22 in. apart. Its trail is more straightaway, with less weaving and turning, than that of the Short-tailed. Often seen in daylight.

HABITAT: Farmland, prairies, woodlands, swamps—in fact, anywhere except away from water in deserts. In U.S., from sea level up to over 10,000 ft.

REPRODUCTION: Mainly N.Y. and Mont. data. Females are first bred in late summer or fall of the year they are born; males can breed by early spring of the year following their birth. The den, in a stump, log, Rabbit hole, or rockpile, contains a loose nest of feathers, bones, and other remains of prey. Breeding occurs in July–Aug., but most embryonic and fetal development is delayed until about the last 4 weeks of a gestation period of 220–337 (average 279) days. The annual litter of 4–9 young usually is born in Apr. Wt. at birth is about ⅛ oz., and there are some fine white hairs on upperparts. At 3 weeks the adult summer pattern is evident and some solid food may be eaten. Eyes open in 37 days, and nursing ends in 5 weeks. The male sometimes brings food to the young. Probably they are able to hunt in 7–8 weeks. They attain adult wt. by fall. Captives have lived at least 5 years.

HABITS: This Weasel is more active after dark. It can climb, but does so less often or readily than the Short-tailed Weasel. It has the strong and offensive Weasel scent, which it gives off when frightened. It is solitary in winter and often also at other seasons. In a 24-hr. period it may travel only several hundred feet, or up to several miles, from its den. Young have a squeaking note, later a purr; adults scream, hiss, and have a throaty, rolling *croo*. Food is mainly small rodents, but also mammals of up to adult Rabbit size, as well as birds, cold-blooded vertebrates, insects, and earthworms. A vertebrate, whether large or small, usually is bitten at the base of the skull, and the attacker holds on firmly until the struggle is nearly over. It does not suck blood. Peaks in population occur about 4–7 years apart but seem not to be as pronounced as in the Short-tailed Weasel.

ECONOMIC STATUS: In areas where the pelt is white in winter, it is more valuable than that of the smaller Short-tailed Weasel. Being fearless and inquisitive, it is easily trapped. Although occasionally it kills poultry, it also destroys many rodents. This Weasel is a good ratter and mouser to have about buildings.

Mink
Mustela vison
Plate 10

Short-legged; uniformly dark brown; larger than a Weasel, with bushier tail and usually a white spot on throat. Males: l. 20–28 in., t. 6–8, wt. 1¼–3 lb. Females: about ¼ smaller. Largest occur in Alaska and darkest in Labrador. No marked seasonal color change. A Mink might be confused with a large Weasel, but the latter has more or less light area on underparts. The Marten has a bushier tail, lighter fur, and yellowish throat patch. Tracks show 4 of the 5 toes on each foot; hind feet are slightly webbed. In bounding gait, hind tracks are placed ahead of front ones.

HABITAT: Mainly along or near watercourses, including marshes, tidal flats, and marine islands. In winter, often in woods when streams and marshes are frozen over.

REPRODUCTION: Both sexes can breed when a year old. The nest is any natural cavity in a stream bank or nearby, or in rocks, debris, or a Muskrat house. Lining, if any, consists of fur and bones. Breeding occurs in Feb.–Mar.,

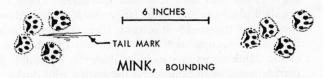

6 INCHES

TAIL MARK

MINK, BOUNDING

and pregnancy lasts 39–76 (usually about 42) days, there being a shorter period in those bred later in the season. A male may mate with several females, but remains with one to help feed the young. Litter size: 3–10 (usually 5–8). Young at birth have a covering of fine light hair. Eyes open and they are weaned in about 5 weeks. They are quite playful and follow the parents until late summer, when the family disbands. A ranch Mink is old at 10 years of age.

HABITS: The elusive Mink is rather nocturnal. It swims and dives gracefully and spends much time in the water. A great deal of traveling is done on land, mainly at night. A persistent hunter and crafty killer, it is fearless in the presence of larger mammals, sometimes including man. It is solitary except when a family group is together in summer. Voice is a piercing scream, hoarse bark, and guttural rolling purr. It screams, spits, hisses, and emits a powerful musk when cornered. A great variety of animal life is captured by the Mink. It pursues and catches even swift fish. Muskrats, birds, frogs, small mammals, and aquatic invertebrates are eaten. It hunts Rabbits and other woodland game in winter. Food is often dragged to a den where several victims may lie stored. A female usually has a home range of 20 acres or less, a male a much larger one. The ranges of several individuals may overlap, and the same den may be used successively by them. The population fluctuates markedly, a phenomenon that has been little studied.

ECONOMIC STATUS: Mink fur is beautiful and durable. La. produces more wild-trapped Mink than any other state, but they are poor in quality compared with n. ones. Preferred breeding stock on Mink ranches is a cross between large Yukon and dark Labrador specimens. There are so-called platinum and other fancy ranch strains. About two-fifths of the marketed pelts are from ranches. Ranching is a difficult operation and no easy way to riches. Diet of the Mink sometimes includes domestic birds, fish at rearing pools, or ducklings and incubating wild ducks.

Black-footed Ferret
Mustela nigripes
Plate 10

Quite like a large Weasel or a Mink in shape. In all seasons, upperparts pale buffy-yellow, with brownish wash on crown and back; a broad blackish mask or band across the eyes; tail colored like body, except terminal third blackish; underparts slightly paler than upperparts; limbs blackish. Males: l. 22–24 in., t. 4½–6, wt. unrecorded (probably 1–1½ lb.); females smaller. Compare with more or less masked examples of the Long-tailed Weasel, which does not have blackish limbs. One of our rarest mammals, this Ferret should be sought (use binoculars) in Prairie Dog towns, where it might be found sitting on its haunches or craning its neck out of a hole. Its Weasel-type tracks may be sought on Prairie Dog mounds.

HABITAT: The Great Plains; also to 10,500 ft. in the Rockies.
REPRODUCTION: Few facts are known, but general pattern may be like the Polecat (*M. putorius*) of the Old World.

A nursing female was captured June 18 in N. Dak. An immature female, light tan in color and with eyes open, was taken alive July 10 in N. Mex.; later she acquired a darker adult coat.

HABITS: This rare mammal, which may wander over a wide area, is more active at night or when the sun is low. It hisses and gives a chattering scold when alarmed. Food: evidently Prairie Dogs, but also other rodents. There is no record of its having been seen eating a Prairie Dog, and once it was seen on the same mound with one; when approached, they went down the hole together. Nothing is known of its habits in the Rockies.

ECONOMIC STATUS: Whether this mammal was common or rare before rodent poisoning was begun appears to be a moot point. At any rate, the poisoning of Prairie Dogs would seem to have eliminated not only its main food but also den holes throughout most of its preferred habitat; also, eating poisoned rodents may have reduced the Ferret population to the present stage of near extinction. It is protected by law in N. Mex.

Wolverine
Gulo luscus
Plate 8

Perhaps best described as appearing intermediate between a Skunk and a Bear —with long fur, arched back, bushy tail, and large feet. Color varies from yellowish-brown to nearly black, with lighter forehead and broad band on each side from shoulder to rump and onto tail; lighter areas vary from nearly white to rufous or brown and in some males are hardly visible. Males: l. 36–44 in., t. 8–9, ht. at shoulder 12–14, wt. 25–40 or more lb. Females: about ¼ smaller. In view of its size, stocky form, and long coat, no other mammal should be confused with it. Of several gaits, a sort of lope perhaps is the commonest. The front track is broader than long. Heel and fifth toe do not always register; the diagram was drawn from tracks in hard-packed snow. Hind and fore tracks may partly overlap or be separate.

WOLVERINE

HABITAT: Treeless areas, brushland, and forest.

REPRODUCTION: There are few data. Breeding is said to occur in Feb.–Apr. after a brief courting period, and adults live apart otherwise. The den is under an over-hanging rock, in a tangle of conifers, or in a hollow log or stump. Litter size: 1–5 (usually 2–3). Gestation period: reported as 60 days, but really not known. Young show the adult color pattern in reverse—the bands along the sides being darker than the rest of the body. They are reared by the mother, and in fall, when they are about ⅔ grown, the family disperses. Cubs are reported occasionally to continue hunting together for a while. A captive lived at least 13 years.

HABITS: The Wolverine is abroad in all seasons and at any hour. Although mainly terrestrial, it can and does climb trees. Its voice, except for a growl and snarl, is unre-corded. It eats any animal that it can secure, even to frogs and snails, and does not disdain carrion. It has been known to drive Bears and Mountain Lions from their kills. A carcass is fed on repeatedly, the intervals between meals being spent at some not-far-distant place. I have seen a well-beaten trail leading from a woodland to a place where a Caribou had been consumed except for some bones and part of the hide. When Moose or Elk are hampered by deep snow, the Wolverine sometimes kills them. Evidently it leaps on Mountain Sheep from a cliff above. A carcass of Sheep size may be dragged a mile or more (although 3 times as heavy as the Wolverine) before a meal is begun. The Porcupine is not immune from attack, but the Wolverine sometimes receives so many quills that it dies. Sometimes it follows a trap line, robbing bait, eating or ruining trapped mammals, and even carrying off and concealing traps or carcasses. It breaks into cabins and food caches, destroying more than it eats by scattering everything about.

ECONOMIC STATUS: The Wolverine is scarce in e. Canada and the U.S., where it needs absolute protection. The few hundred taken annually in Alaska and Canada are used mainly for trimming hoods of winter parkas, because frost that accumulates on the hairs can be brushed off with ease. Many pelts thus used in the Arctic and Subarctic are not handled by fur buyers. The Wolverine has made no friends by robbing trap lines, cabins, and food caches. It requires extensive wilderness areas for survival and has been extirpated from southerly portions of its former range. It still exists in fair numbers in some parts of w. Canada and in Alaska. Some have been killed from eating poison put out for Wolves.

River Otter
Lutra canadensis
Plate 8

A long-bodied mammal, with broad rounded snout, very short legs, webbed feet, and stout tapering tail. The dense fur is brownish or grayish when dry, but appears to be almost black when wet; chin and throat are grayish-white. Males: l. 38–55 in., t. 12–19, ht. at shoulder 9–10, wt. 10–30 lb.; females about 30% smaller.

In comparison, a swimming Beaver or Muskrat has a more squarish snout. On land the Otter has a variety of gaits, including what might be termed a trot and a bounding gallop. Tracks are rounded; 4 blunt toes on all feet register plainly, and the fifth less so. A hind track measures about 2¾ in. long x 2½ wide, and front track about 2 in. each way. In running, hind tracks are staggered ahead of front, with the latter more or less in line with the direction of travel; in bounding, hind tracks are side by side and may cover the front tracks. The heavy tail leaves a mark, often diagonal to the line of travel. Slippery banks are worn into smooth Otter slides where Otters repeatedly slide down into water. When the Otter travels in snow, the trail is a furrow containing the tracks, or an Otter may toboggan downhill with feet held backward.

HABITAT: All types of inland waterways, also marine coves, estuaries, and about islands. It travels overland between watercourses.

REPRODUCTION: Mainly Minn. data. Breeding age is attained in about a year. The male may mate with more than one female but spends most of his time with only one. The den, sometimes with entrances above and under water, may be a cavity in a bank or be a Beaver lodge. Sometimes it is a hollow log ashore, or a heap of vegetation in a marsh, under low bushes or a tree. Dry vegetation serves as a lining. The litter of 1–4 (usually 2–3) is born Feb.–Apr. in N. and earlier in S. Breeding occurs in the water, and the female may again be bred very shortly after giving birth. Evidently a variable time lapse before appreciable embryonic development begins accounts for the variable gestation period of 288–380 days.

A pup at birth has a black silky coat. One weighed 6 oz. when 7–10 days old. Eyes open in 25–35 days. In 85 days or more pups come out of the den and play on land with the mother, who brings food, but they may not be weaned until considerably later. The father is nearby, but the mother keeps him away. When pups are about

100 days old, the mother introduces them to water, sometimes forcibly, and they soon swim well and make short
dives. She may swim with them on her back, then dive
to make them swim. At about this stage the male often
joins the family; he plays with the pups, helps train them,
and is a patient father. Later he leaves the family.
Mother and young are together for perhaps 8 months,
then the latter go their separate ways. A tame female still
was breeding at age 17. One Otter lived at least 19 years.

HABITS: The playful Otter is active at any hour and season.
It is an extremely graceful swimmer and diver and can
stay submerged 4 minutes. Sometimes Otters hunt in
pairs. Mother and young groom each other's fur, and the
latter tumble and play together. Several Otters of any
age may use the same slide together and evidently enjoy
company at this year-round activity. Adults grunt, chatter, have a shrill chirp that sounds like a hiccup, a soft
chuckle, and a variety of other noises; when frightened
or angered, they scream and give forth a strong musk.
Pups commonly give a chuckling sound. Crayfish are a
favorite food. Fish, shellfish, frogs, salamanders, turtles,
earthworms, insects, snakes, Muskrats, Rabbits, waterfowl, and other items are eaten. Some vegetation is eaten,
at least in summer. Except in winter, the Otter eats far
less fish than is commonly realized, and those eaten are
mainly non-game species. It may kill many Muskrats in a
marsh, but usually other food is secured more readily.

Having retiring habits, it often occurs in settled areas
for years without its presence being suspected. Where-
ever it dwells, it has a regular home range and goes from
one place to another in fairly regular sequence, part of
the route often being overland. A mother with pups may
move only a few miles in a season, but males, especially
at breeding time, travel more widely. Home ranges
change as bodies of water freeze or feeding and living
conditions otherwise are altered.

ECONOMIC STATUS: The heavy durable fur is used for collars
and trimmings. An Otter sometimes destroys fish at a

hatchery or rearing pool, or kills Muskrats or perhaps an occasional Beaver, but otherwise it seldom conflicts with man's interests. If captured when not over a few weeks old, it makes an affectionate and gentle pet.

Sea Otter
Enhydra lutris
Plate 8

A long-bodied mammal, with flattened head, broad snout, small ears, small front legs with short webbed toes, large webbed hind feet, and stout short tail. Color varies from reddish-brown through dark brown to nearly black, more or less frosted with white, and with head and neck tending toward grayish or cream color. Males: l. 40–59 in., t. 10–11, wt. 25–75 lb.; females are considerably smaller. Occasionally an adult is whitish clear down the abdomen and including front limbs. Pups are grayer than adults.

This mammal, with its small front feet (not flippers) and a sizable tail, should not be confused with any Seal. The webbed hind feet leave a roundish track, diameter about 6 in., with no toes showing clearly; round front tracks, about half as large, reveal large toe-pads. Droppings, containing fragments of shells of marine invertebrates, may be found on rocks or beaches.

HABITAT: Prefers rocky mainland or island shores having numerous recesses, with kelp beds and reefs nearby. Much time is spent afloat, seldom more than a mile from shore. Old World range includes s. Kamchatka and Kuril and Bonin Is.

REPRODUCTION: Breeding evidently begins at about 3 years of age. Courtship and mating take place in the water, where rutting males fight fiercely among themselves and show no fear of man. The single young usually is born Apr.–May in the water, after a gestation period that must last at least 8 or 9 months, since the newborn pup has a full set of teeth, open eyes, a length of about 17 in., and a wt. of about 3½ lb. The mother, who is solitary when a pup is small, is said to begin feeding the pup bits of soft food after 6 months. She swims on her back while the pup nurses. It may not be weaned for a year or more; that is, until the next pup is born. Females quite often are accompanied by pups of two ages, indicating long attachment to the mother. The young swim well. If the mother is alarmed, however, she takes a small pup under her arm and makes a series of short dives. Full growth is attained in about 4 years. Two individuals lived 8 years or longer.

HABITS: The playful, gregarious, and non-migratory Sea Otter is mainly diurnal, although also active on moonlit nights. The bands (called pods) usually pass the night in kelp beds. A common pose is that of 'standing' in the water, leaning slightly backward, sometimes with paws held to shade the eyes. Vision is fair and sense of smell excellent. They swim on their backs when not in a hurry. During storms they haul out on beaches or rocks and afterward float for hours, evidently sleeping, when the sea is calmer. Favored places where they come ashore are marked by much excrement. There is a good deal of play by pups, but adults quarrel, even during the non-breeding season. Adults squeal, bark, growl, and cough. An alarmed pup has a whistle-like squeal and a harsher, dry-sounding call.

A Sea Otter can stay submerged for 4–5 minutes, but when diving for food usually is down only 15–50 seconds. It tends to have meals 3 times daily, with snacks in between. In Alaskan waters, food consists mainly of sea urchins, mollusks (mostly the blue mussel), and a few crabs and fish. This mammal's bones are heavily pigmented by a purple substance from the urchins. In Calif. waters the abalone is favored, but urchins, crabs, and mollusks other than mussels also are eaten. The manner in which abalones are detached from the sea bottom is not known. When these are brought to the surface, they have a large piece of shell broken from one side. While eating, the Sea Otter floats on its back, using its chest as a lunch counter; old individuals, especially, often break the shells of shellfish by pounding them on a stone brought up from the ocean floor and laid on the chest.

ECONOMIC STATUS: In human eyes, the Sea Otter's pelt is unsurpassed in beauty by any other kind. Beginning soon after 1637, this mammal was slaughtered by thousands. Legal killing in American waters ended in 1911, but recovery in numbers is slow and only a few thousand individuals exist today. There is adequate food for a much larger population. The Sea Otter undoubtedly has the greatest potential value of any mammal in the Aleutian area of Alaska. Probably loss of nursing young during storms and poaching are the chief factors preventing a more rapid population increase. It is unwary of man. The best places to see it are about Amchitka I. in the Aleutians and near Carmel, Calif.

Spotted Skunk
(Civet)
Spilogale putorius
Plate 11

Our smallest Skunk; black, with white spots on the head and several white body stripes that are more or less broken on hind parts into spots or crosswise patches; tail usually with white tip. Males: l. 14–22 in., t. 7½–9, ht. at shoulder 6, wt. 1–3 lb.; females about ¼ smaller. This Skunk, which is largest in the Midwest, also varies geographically in extent and arrangement of white areas. Undoubtedly we have only a single varying species. Its color pattern is unique among our mammals.

Hind tracks (in which claws seldom show) are about 1⅝ in. long, and front 1¼, the general pattern being similar to the Striped Skunk's (diagram, p. 119). In walking gait, tracks are 5–6 in. apart, with hind feet placed in front tracks. In bounding gait, tracks are in pairs—quite Weasel-like, these being spaced 9–14 in. apart, with hind and front tracks in the same spot. In galloping gait, registering is less perfect. The other Skunks are larger and tend to drag the hind feet.

HABITAT: Brushy areas, away from dense stands of mature timber or open fields; desert country with any plant cover. To over 6,000 ft. elevation in Calif.

REPRODUCTION: Mainly Ia. data. The den—any secure, darkened cavity—is lined with dry vegetation. It is not the property of any one Skunk but is used by the population as a whole, with average length of occupancy 3½ months. The gestation period is unknown. Young are born in spring, and there may be a second litter in the s. part of the range. Litter size: 2–6 (usually 4). At birth one weighs about ⅓ oz., is 4 in. long, has eyes and ears closed, and shows the adult color pattern in its fine hair. Eyes open in 32 days, teeth are apparent at 36, solid food is eaten in 42, it is weaned in about 56 days and may reach full size in 104 days. Evidently the female alone rears the young.

HABITS: This nocturnal Skunk is nimble, very playful, full of energy, and less wary of man than its larger relatives. It is active in winter and puts on relatively little fat compared to the Striped Skunk. A good climber, it goes up fence posts, trees, and along beams in outbuildings. Several sometimes play together. It has a curious hand-stand trick of upending and walking on its forefeet, with tail in the air. Sometimes this is play; at other times it is a bluff, or indication of anger, or warning before the powerful scent is discharged. Voice of adults is unrecorded; young cry, have a shrill squeal and a chirping note. Brood chambers and various dens or shelters are used by several individuals in succession. Individual home range, largest in summer, may extend at that season for ½–2 mi. for males, but is much smaller for breeding females. Probably 5–8 individuals per sq. mi. is a high population. This Skunk is omnivorous, but prefers insects—especially crickets. In winter and spring it eats many rodents and, at other seasons, insects, fruit, birds, eggs, carrion, and vegetable matter. If it finds a dead chicken or rabbit to feed on, this is dragged to a den or sheltering cover.

ECONOMIC STATUS: People kill the Spotted Skunk because they regard it as a nuisance, trap it for fur, or run over it with automobiles. Dogs kill many. The pelts bring low prices in the fur market; most are used for jackets and trimmings. This Skunk is a first-rate ratter and mouser. It eats some poultry and eggs, and uproots garden crops when hunting insects. Some farmers encourage its presence. A neat farm provides few den sites and, if no offal is left about, the Skunks tend to stay away. Persons sleeping in the open have gotten rabies from its bite. Not all bites indicate diseased Skunks, since the male, when in mating mood, loses its fear and may bite a person. This mammal has benefited in many ways from agricultural land-use practices.

Striped Skunk
(Common Skunk)
Mephitis mephitis
Plate 11

About House Cat size and well known to everybody; stout body, short legs, bushy tail, and slender head. Black or brownish-black, sometimes entirely so, but generally with more or less white as follows: narrow stripe up mid-line of face; white on nape, continuing as 2 stripes for part or all of body length, or white on nape, continuing as 1 stripe to shoulders or upper back and then dividing into 2 (white areas vary from narrow to wide), or even a single broad white band from nape to tail. The more white on the body, the more there is in the tail. Males: l. 24–30 in., t. 7–9, ht. at shoulder 7–8, wt. 4–10 lb.; females: about ⅕ smaller. The Hooded Skunk (of Ariz. and N. Mex.) has varying amounts of white also, but its tail is as long as head and body, and fur on the nape often forms a sort of ruff. Compare also with the smaller Spotted and larger Hog-nosed Skunk.

5 INCHES

SKUNK, WALKING

Indications of its presence are the well-known odor, small shallow pits where the Skunk has dug for insects, or sight of the Skunk. In walking gait, front track is ahead of hind; in galloping gait, the tracks form a series of diagonal lines, front tracks between hind, with each set of all 4 usually less than 1 ft. apart.

HABITAT: So varied, it cannot readily be described; dens are in dry places.

REPRODUCTION: Striped Skunks first breed when about a year old. The den, which is lined with vegetation, may be a Woodchuck or other hole it finds, a dark place under a building, or the Skunk may dig its own hole. The male probably mates with several females annually. Gestation requires 63 days, and the 4–7 (usually 5) young are born in spring. At birth, wt. is about 1 oz., eyes are closed, and a fine hair covering shows the adult pattern. Young nurse 6–7 weeks and, during the latter part of this period, begin to follow the mother on nightly foraging trips. They disband in late summer or early autumn. Captives are old in 8–10 years.

HABITS: The Striped Skunk is abroad at dusk or after dark.

It swims well, but rarely, and cannot climb trees. A family travels single file, the mother leading. Males tend to be solitary in summer; in winter several females may share a den, often accompanied by a single male who probably keeps out other males. Adults give churring and scolding sounds when disturbed; they also growl, screech, and have a twittering note. A cooing whistle, beginning high and ending in a soft purr, has been heard in autumn. A Skunk gives loud sniffs when approaching a strange object. It stamps its front feet to express hostility. In defensive position it faces its attacker, eying him, with body diagonal to the line of sight, and tail over the back. The scent is discharged as a fine spray from a duct on each side of the anus, in the direction the Skunk is looking. It probably cannot be thrown more than 15 ft. in calm air. The Skunk uses its potent amber-colored fluid sparingly and is armed for several shots; this fluid can be produced at the rate of about ⅓ liquid oz. per week.

Skunks begin to fatten in midsummer and are very fat when winter sleep begins (not true hibernation with much lowered body temperature). Females and young of the year den earlier than adult males, which often are abroad even in s. Canada during warm winter weather. Food: small rodents (many Mice), cold-blooded vertebrates, insects, and grubs (especially beetles), and some vegetable material, including corn. The population tends to increase over a 5- to 7-year period, then declines. Home range of males may be ½-1 mi. in greatest length, and several home ranges commonly overlap. A Skunk per 30 acres is a high population. Practically every Horned Owl in the Skunk's range smells of Skunk—one of its staple foods.

ECONOMIC STATUS: The fur is used mainly for trimmings and jackets. Because of its scent the Skunk is a nuisance, especially when dogs are about. Skunk odor in clothing can be greatly lessened by washing them in a pail of water with a cup of household ammonia added. The Skunk is very persistent, often getting into or upsetting garbage cans. Occasionally it kills poultry or eats eggs, bees, breaks down corn to get the milky ears, or uproots alfalfa or peanuts in its search for insects. It can transmit rabies. It eats many Mice and injurious beetles. De-scented Skunks make fairly good pets.

Hooded Skunk
Mephitis macroura
Plate 11

Shaped like the Striped Skunk, but with tail longer than head and body, and hair of nape often spread into a sort of ruff. Black, with varying amounts of white as follows: usually a thin stripe up mid-line of face; some white on nape, or 1 or 2 white stripes along sides from behind ear to rump, or top of neck all white, continuing as lateral stripes and broad central band down back. If white extends to hind parts, usually the tail-tip is white; if a broad dorsal band, then the upper surface of the tail may have much white throughout its length. Males: l. 26–31 in., t. 13–15; females: about ⅕ smaller.

See comparison under Striped Skunk; also compare with the larger Hog-nosed Skunk. Habitat within our borders is arid country. Habits are said to be much like those of the Common Skunk.

Hog-nosed Skunk
Conepatus leuconotus
Plate 11

Our largest Skunk; snout naked for about 1 in. on top; black, except top of head, the back, and all of tail, white. Males: l. 25–33 in., t. 10½–

14½, ht. at shoulder 8–10 in., wt. 5–10 lb.; females: perhaps ¼ smaller. The solid white tail distinguishes it even from those Hooded Skunks having much white.

HABITAT: Semi-wooded and open areas, to considerable mt. elevations.

REPRODUCTION AND HABITS: Dens are in rocky places or are holes made by other mammals. Gestation of a related S. Am. species is reported as 42 days. Probably a litter of 1–4 young is born annually. This Skunk is nocturnal, shy, and appears to be sluggish. It has the usual Skunk odor and defense method. Sometimes it digs holes nearly a foot deep. Using its strong front claws and rooting with its long bare snout, it often turns the soil over in an area many yards square. It is rather scarce within its range in the U.S.

Badger
Taxidea taxus
Plate 9

A flattened, robust mammal; distinctive black-and-white head pattern; long grizzled fur; short bushy tail. General tone is grayish-yellow, with underparts paler. Males: l. 25–30 in., t. 5–6, ht. at shoulder 9, wt. 12–24 lb.; females: somewhat smaller. Not readily confused with any other mammal. Commonest signs of its presence are the holes it digs, about 1 ft. in diameter, when after rodents. In all gaits, the Badger 'toes in' markedly. In running gait, hind tracks are ahead of fore, with sets of tracks up to 5–6 ft. apart.

HABITAT: Dry open country, to considerable elevations in mts.; escaped captives have lived in the wild in many e. localities.

REPRODUCTION: The nest of dry grass is in a hole dug or

enlarged by the female and is usually 5–30 ft. from the entrance. Breeding occurs in autumn, but there is almost no embryonic development until about mid-Feb.; then the young are born about 6 weeks later. Litter size: 1–5 (usually 2). Young are furred at birth. Eyes open in 4–6 weeks. They are weaned when about ½ grown; then the mother brings them food for an undetermined length of time before they follow her on hunting trips. They disband in late summer. Perhaps the male occasionally helps care for the litter. The Badger has lived 12 years in captivity.

HABITS: Although abroad mainly at night, the Badger may be seen in daytime occasionally at the entrance of its den.

6 INCHES

BADGER, WALKING

NAILS ON HIND TOES SELDOM SHOW

It does not climb, but does sharpen its claws on tree trunks. Making the dirt fly, it can dig itself out of sight very quickly. If pursued, it digs in rapidly and plugs the hole behind itself. In one encounter a dog usually learns not to tackle another Badger. Adults are solitary most of their lives, except in mating and rearing periods. Usually silent, the Badger can growl, chatter, and grunt; also, it hisses by exhaling abruptly. If cornered, sometimes it erects its short tail and emits a strong odor from the glands near the anus.

It becomes very fat in fall and, in n. part of its range, sleeps part of the winter—perhaps with an occasional active period and hunting foray. Farther s. it is active all year. Food: various rodents, which it digs out, also Rabbits, ground-nesting birds, eggs, snakes, lizards, insects, and snails. Carrion is not disdained. Food sometimes is buried, then dug up later and eaten. If a Rabbit, Skunk, or other sizable carcass is secured, the Badger digs a hole, carries in this food, and may remain there below ground with it for several days. It never occupies a hole very long, except the rearing den, so does a tremendous amount of digging. It digs holes to bury its feces.

ECONOMIC STATUS: Badger fur is used to trim garments. Synthetic substitutes have largely replaced Badger hair in high-quality shaving brushes. Badger holes are a menace to horses and riders, but broken legs and bad falls are few now that cattle rarely are run at fast speed. Irrigation ditches sometimes are undermined. One must not overlook the enormous number of rodents that the Badger eats. Many Badgers have died in predatory-mammal-control operations.

FOXES, WOLVES, AND DOGS Family Canidae

Red Fox
(Colored Fox)
Vulpes fulva
Plate 13

Resembles a small Collie Dog in shape; large bushy tail, with white tip; large triangular ears. Usual color varies from bright reddish to pale tawny, with whitish underparts and black limbs; variations include cross or patch, silver, and black. More than one phase may occur in the same litter. Darker ones are more plentiful in N. Adults: l. 36–42 in., t. 13–15, ht. at shoulder 15–16, wt. 6–15 lb. Dog Foxes (males) are larger than vixens (females).

The Red might be confused with other Foxes or perhaps a Collie Dog or Coyote; none of these has a white tail-tip. The Gray Fox has a contrasty facial pattern, cat-like ears, and rather dark underparts. The Red often is seen abroad in daylight. It travels a direct and purpose-ful route, leaving delicate tracks showing small pads, often 4 claws, and much hair on the feet; in winter, hair

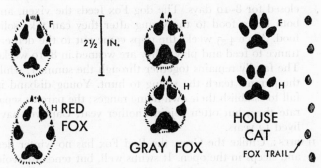

may conceal the pads entirely. Toe-pads of the Gray Fox are much wider. A House Cat's track shows no claws. For dog and Coyote tracks, see p. 134. Hind tracks often register perfectly in front ones. The sharp bark of this Fox is often heard on late-winter nights.

HABITAT: Dry upland, with open areas and patches of cover such as woods; also tundra, treeless mt. areas, lowlands, swamps, marsh edges, extensive forests, and city suburbs. Native on some islands, including Kodiak and Newfd.; introduced on some others.

REPRODUCTION: This Fox begins to breed when about a year old. The den, having no telltale mound, may be in a wooded area or in the open. Sometimes a rodent hole or natural cavity is enlarged, or the den may be dug by the Fox—usually in loose soil. The entrance is about 15 in. high. A hole may be up to 75 ft. long, but generally is much shorter; usually there are several entrances. Shallow holes without side tunnels usually are temporary retreats, not dens. Although pairs are often solitary, sometimes several have dens close together, or 2 litters may even be reared in the same den.

Mating usually occurs in Jan.–Feb. Males, which generally are seasonally monogamous, use their tails as foils when fighting for a female. The 1–10 (usually 4–5) pups in the annual litter, born after 49–55 (usually 52) days' gestation, are well furred and weigh 4 oz. each; eyes are closed for 8–10 days. The dog Fox feeds the vixen, and both bring food to the young after they can take solid food. After 4–5 weeks the pups come out to the den entrance to feed and play. They are weaned in 8–10 weeks. The family remains together through the summer, while the parents teach the young to hunt. Young disband in fall to establish their own home ranges; the parents separate then, but often rejoin another year. Captives have lived 12 years.

HABITS: Unlike the Gray, the Red Fox has no winter den and sleeps in the open. It swims well, but tends to avoid water unless pursued. Its guile when hunted with hounds is proverbial, and its ability to escape from captivity is almost phenomenal. The bark of the dog Fox is a short yelp, ending in a *yurr*, as if gargling; the vixen's voice is more of a yapping scream.

After families break up in fall, the dog Fox wanders a great deal, but the vixen (who establishes the home range for the family) stays within a mile or two of the den. The fall population thus is more evenly distributed. Home range is usually less than a mile in radius. Food, in rough order of preference: Rabbits and Hares, Mice, other mammals, insects, birds, turtles, snakes, carrion, and fruit (especially raspberries). Some food is hidden, and the owner may return to it later, even when not hungry. The population fluctuates markedly, with peaks at about 9- to 10-year intervals; n. of tree line a 4-year fluctuation, evidently caused by changes in rodent numbers, occurs in addition to the longer trends.

ECONOMIC STATUS: Admirers include those who recognize that this Fox provides some check on numbers of Mice, Rabbits, and other crop and orchard pests; Fox hunters and houndsmen; those who pursue the Fox for its pelt;

and those who enjoy seeing a Fox. Foes include persons who have lost chickens, ducks, lambs, and young pigs; also Rabbit and Pheasant hunters who claim that the Fox gets there first too often; and the public at large during rabies epidemics. Thus there are both good and bad sides (from the human viewpoint), the net balance varying with time and place. A bounty on Foxes nearly always has its advocates, as well as those who have very sound reasons for disapproving it.

The Red Fox is not difficult to trap, as most farm hands know. The fur is used for trimming, also for neck-pieces and jackets—especially pelts of silvers and other fancy types. Only the Mink has more ranch-raised color varieties. Ranching of Foxes began in the previous century and reached a boom about 1910–14. Fantastic prices were paid for breeding stock. Rearing for the trade now is done on a sound basis, that of pelt value. The great fluctuations in prices are controlled largely by changes in fashion.

Although Foxes undoubtedly are a permanent reservoir of rabies, outbreaks usually occur only when the population is high. An extensive epidemic may kill nearly all Foxes (of all species) over a wide area. Skunks, Bobcats, rodents, and other mammals are susceptible to it. The bite of a rabid Fox can cause the death of cattle, horses and mules, hogs, goats, and other livestock. There are few human deaths from rabid Fox bites. Dogs must be vaccinated to prevent rabies. Early symptoms in the Fox are loss of fear of man and machines; roaming in daylight, often in farmyards and on highways. Either it goes at a deliberate trot or wanders aimlessly, paying little attention to anything. At this stage it sometimes attacks human beings without provocation and then flees. Later it is more lethargic, does not flee, and may be killed with a club or rock. There is progressive loss of viciousness. In the final stage there is paralysis, usually beginning with the jaw muscles.

A 'negative' control measure consists of letting the disease run its course, thus reducing the number of Foxes and other carriers as rapidly as possible. A 'positive' control measure consists of killing Foxes (and other susceptible wildlife?) in an attempt to reduce the spread of the disease. This sometimes is done to reduce the carriers in an area surrounding a focus of infection, while letting the disease run its course within the area. Spread of the disease among Foxes evidently cannot be halted by this method, for it occurs at widely separated places when the population is high.

Kit Fox
(Swift Fox)
Vulpes velox
Plate 13

Our smallest Fox; slender build; big ears; blackish spot on each side of snout; blackish tail-tip. General color ranges from grayish to pale buffy-yellow—the latter in SW., where it also has very large ears. Adults: l. 24–31 in., t. 9–12, ht. at shoulder 12, wt. 3–6 lb. It might be confused with the young of other Foxes, but its slenderness, big ears, and spirited action distinguish it. At any age the Red Fox has dark limbs and light tail-tip, and the Gray is colored quite uniformly dark. Kit Fox tracks are too small and narrow (1½ x 1⅛ in.) to be confused with those of larger Foxes. Four toes and claws show. The Kit Fox is shy and rarely seen, even where common. Mainly nocturnal.

HABITAT: Plains, foothills, rough terrain, and deserts.

REPRODUCTION: Dens, dug in soft soil, may have as many as 8 entrances. Openings are taller than wide—not a broad oval like the Badger's. Sometimes a Badger hole is appropriated or a Prairie Dog hole is enlarged for use. Gestation period is unknown. Litter size: 4–7. Pups are born in Feb. in S. and later farther N. They are nursed for about 10 weeks, then both parents bring solid food to the den. The family stays together for several months after weaning.

HABITS: This Fox is very quick, graceful, and wonderfully agile. It is unwary and without guile. Evidently it spends more time underground than do other Foxes. If pursued, it dodges and twists rapidly while traveling at high speed, and disappears into a Badger hole or other shelter. Sometimes, when approached in the open in daylight, it flattens itself against the ground to avoid detection. Voice is a sort of undersized Fox bark, more between a bark and a squall, and rather like the *chur-r-r-r* at the end of the Gray Squirrel's 'bark.' Although it is fairly common in a few areas, little has been learned of its habits, home range, or population fluctuations.

ECONOMIC STATUS: The small pale pelt is of little value. The Kit Fox eats many rodents, also poultry and quail occasionally. It has been extirpated from parts of its former range and is rare in much of that remaining, a chief cause being the readiness with which it eats poisoned bait put out for other predators. Probably its numbers will continue to decline.

Gray Fox
(Tree Fox)
Urocyon cinereoargenteus
Plate 13

Appears somewhat more cat-like than dog-like because of its short ears and muzzle and varied color pattern. Line on top and tip of tail blackish. See Plate 13, also comparative remarks under Red Fox. In NE. the Gray is dark and rich in color; in the arid SW. it has a pale washed-out orange cast. Northeastern ones measure: l. 36–44 in., t. 12–14, ht. at shoulder 14–

15. Western Grays are smaller and more slender. Eastern adults weigh 7–13 lb., small ones as little as 4 lb. Pigmy forms on the Santa Barbara Is., Calif., are stockier, darker in color, and of about medium House Cat size; they have been considered a separate species (*littoralis*). Gray Fox males are slightly larger than females. See track diagram on p. 125. The Gray is more nocturnal than the Red, and its yapping bark is coarser, some notes being rather Coyote-like.

HABITAT: Brushy country, woodlands, swamps, and hammocks. Taken once at Lake Athabaska, ne. Alberta, far beyond range shown on map.

REPRODUCTION: Probably some Grays do not breed until their second year. The den usually is in a hollow log or tree, or in a rockpile, generally in woodland. Breeding usually occurs in Feb.–Mar., though less often from Dec. to early May. Gestation is believed to require 63 days, but may be 10 days less. At birth the 1–7 (usually about 4) young in the annual litter have eyes closed, are blackish in color, and weigh about 4 oz. each. They are cared for by both parents and weaned in 8–10 weeks. The male leaves the family first; the female remains with the litter until fall, when they disband. Like the Red, the Gray Fox usually is seasonally monogamous, but occasionally polygamous. Captives have lived over a decade.

HABITS: The Gray Fox lacks the character and craftiness of the Red. Because it is more nocturnal, its presence in an area is often unsuspected. It is a fairly good tree climber, hugging the trunk with forelimbs and forcing itself upward with the hind. It climbs to escape when pursued by hounds and on other occasions also, even hopping about from limb to limb or concealing itself in foliage—hence the name 'Tree Fox.' Grays usually lead rather solitary lives, except during the breeding and rearing season, and evidently do not show the gregarious tendency at whelping time that Reds sometimes do. Individuals usually have several winter dens within an area of several hundred acres; they use these for rest and sleep. The rather harsh voice is rarely heard and recognized. Chief food: Rabbits, Mice, and other small mammals, grasshoppers and assorted insects, birds, reptiles, carrion, and fruit. Other vegetable matter is sometimes eaten.

ECONOMIC STATUS: A Gray Fox pelt makes a handsome coat collar. The Gray has the same positive and negative factors in its relations with man that have been listed for the Red—except that the Gray is not much of a 'sporting' mammal to hunt, as it goes to a den too readily. The discussion of rabies given under the Red Fox applies as well to the Gray.

Arctic Fox
(White Fox, Blue Fox)
Alopex lagopus
Plate 13

A small Fox, with short rounded ears and short face. When fur is short in summer, it has a puppy-like appearance; winter fur is much longer. In 'white' phase, summer fur is tawny and winter coat all white except for black hairs in the tail-tip; in 'blue' phase, summer fur is brownish and that of winter is called 'blue' (actually maltese). Dingy or spotted intermediates between the two phases occur. Blues are rare on the Arctic coast of Alaska, but more common w. and s., also in e. Arctic and Greenland. All are 'blue' on Pribilof I. Adults: l. 29–31 in., t. 10–11, ht. at shoulder 10–12, wt. 6–12 or rarely to 20 lb. Sexes are nearly alike in wt. and size.

The Red Fox and Coyote (both larger) might possibly be confused with the Arctic Fox. Neither of these has the over-all fairly uniform coloration that characterizes all coats of the Arctic Fox, except perhaps intermediates between phases. It is readily observed, being full of curiosity, and its sharp bark is often heard. Tracks measure 1⅝ long x 1¼ in. wide, and soles are so fully haired that the toes, at least in winter, seldom show at all. Red Fox tracks (see p. 125) are larger and stride is longer.

HABITAT: Open terrain having some shade or shelter such as brush, tall grass, or rock outcrops; at times into forested areas. Climbs well on cliffs and, in winter, travels long distances on sea ice. Native on various islands and introduced for ranching on some others. Essentially it is a dweller on marine shores, beaches, sea cliffs, coastal tundra, and sea ice.

REPRODUCTION: This Fox begins to breed at about 10 months of age. The den is usually in a dry slope and has several entrances. Some pups are born above ground and then carried to a den or shelter. The mating season, called the barking period, lasts about 40 days, beginning in Feb., and much loud squalling is heard. Gestation requires 51–52 days, and young are born in late Apr.–June. The annual litter contains 1–14 pups, about 5 ordinarily being raised. At birth a pup has eyes closed, a dark brown fuzzy coat, and a wt. of about 2 oz. Both parents care for the young, which come out of the den entrance when about a month old. A parent sometimes carries them, before they can walk, to other dens or holes near a food supply. The family disbands in fall. Although seasonally monogamous as a rule, and probably even having the same mate in successive years sometimes, polygamy may be fairly common. A captive lived at least 14 years.

HABITS: The Arctic Fox is not shy; it often follows a person and barks at him. When food is plentiful in summer, much time is spent lying in shade. It hunts whenever hungry. Several may den near one another, but it is not markedly gregarious. Its high-pitched yapping bark and yelp are heard all year (squalling at mating time is additional) and have a ventriloquial quality, so that the Fox seems to be much farther away than it actually is. As soon as sea ice forms in fall many of these Foxes go out on it and spend the winter far from land, burrowing in snow for temporary dens and eating dead Seals, Walruses, and Whales, or scavenging food left by Polar Bears. Toward spring it eats young Seals, also small marine life frozen in the ice and exposed when pressure turns the ice over. In general, food consists of rodents, stranded marine life, any flesh that can be scavenged, birds and eggs, and berries in season. About sea-bird colonies it stores birds and eggs for later use. It drinks water when available and eats snow at other times. About every fourth winter, when Mice and Lemmings are scarce, the Foxes disperse and many, presumably young, go some distance s. of the normal range. Few if any survive to return.

SUMMER   WINTER

FOREPAW OF **ARCTIC FOX**

Bears dig out Arctic Fox dens. The more aggressive Red Fox may capture and kill its smaller relative occasionally. Snowy Owls and other large raptorial birds undoubtedly capture some pups.

ECONOMIC STATUS: The 'blue' phase pelt is more valuable than the white. Both are used for trimmings, scarves, jackets, and wraps. The Fox-ranching industry in Alaska has waned with declining fur values. Most ranching was done on islands, where fencing was unnecessary and fish for food was near at hand. Introduced Foxes on some islands have destroyed many nesting waterfowl. If needed in an emergency for human food, Arctic Fox meat should be well cooked to avoid the possibility of contracting trichinosis. The high vitamin A content of the liver often causes toxic effects if eaten by man or dogs. Especially when numerous, this Fox is readily trapped—although maintaining a trap line in its environment is no easy matter.

Coyote
(Brush Wolf)
Canis latrans
Plate 12

Rather like a small Shep-
herd Dog in appearance,
with long fur, and bushy tail
generally darker toward tip.
Tone usually a grizzled buff,
but individuals vary from
grayish to reddish to blackish. Adults: l. 44–54 in., t. 12–
15, ht. at shoulder 23–26, wt. 20–50 lb. Female smaller
than male. The coat is longer and paler in winter. A
Wolf is larger, more rangy in appearance, and generally
carries its tail high, not down near the legs as does the
Coyote, when running. Note comparison with the Red
Wolf on p. 136. Coyote tracks and stride are intermedi-

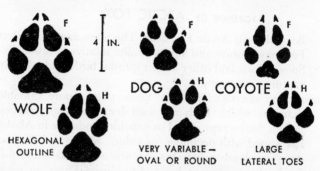

ate in size between those of the Wolf and Fox. General
outline of tracks is more angular (less rounded) than
that of most dogs, and lateral hind toes generally leave
larger prints. The Coyote is often abroad in daylight. Its
weird wild voice is heard especially at dusk and dawn.
HABITAT: The Coyote prefers irregular terrain with open
areas, brush, and woodland; it is at home also on deserts,

plains, in fairly well-wooded areas, and to fairly high mt. elevations. Several e. states have local populations, composed in part at least of Coyote-dog hybrids.

REPRODUCTION: Females begin breeding when 2 years old. The den may be dug by the Coyote, or be a rocky cavern or the enlarged hole of some smaller mammal. Gestation requires 63 days, and the annual litter is born Apr.–June. The 5–10 (usually 6–7) pups are furred at birth and have eyes closed. The male feeds the female and, after weaning, both parents bring food to the pups. Many Coyotes may stay mated for life. In early fall the pups leave the adults to seek home ranges of their own. Coyotes have lived at least 14½ years in captivity.

HABITS: Curiosity is a Coyote trait; it watches from a distance, then often moves out of sight silently and approaches an object from another viewpoint. It has much 'native intelligence' and is faster than most dogs. Members of a pair sometimes hunt co-operatively. It has been known to 'play dead' in order to capture birds. Voice is a tenor bark, often with a howl, wail, or yelp at the end; a rapid series of yips is frequently given. Single Coyotes or several in a group give vocal choruses, especially at dawn and twilight. Coyotes do not travel much in organized bands larger than a family unit. There is winter movement of mt. Coyotes down to lower levels. On its home range, which may cover several hundred acres, the Coyote often passes up prey near the den and hunts far afield. The den is approached by a circuitous route. About ¾ of the food of this nearly omnivorous canine is Rabbits and rodents, the remainder being other animal life (including much carrion) and a variety of vegetable matter—much of which may be eaten when animal food is scarce.

ECONOMIC STATUS: Coyote fur is coarse and used chiefly for trimming garments. Trapping for pelts provides a few people with a livelihood. Because the Coyote kills small livestock, kid Antelopes, poultry, wild birds, and eats eggs, there are areas where local control of numbers may be necessary from man's viewpoint. Unfortunately, use of poison, traps, or payment of bounty are often applied in areas where the interests of man and Coyote do not conflict appreciably or at all. Rabies occurs in the population. Coyotes and Wolves both hybridize with dogs under some circumstances, but apparently they do not cross with each other. Range of the Coyote has expanded n. and e. in recent decades. There is a large and growing folklore about the Coyote, antedated by its symbolic use in Aztec design and its role as a trickster in Indian legends. The Coyote is a part of the Western Range and should be preserved.

Wolves
Canis (part)
Plate 12

1.—*Gray or **Timber** (*C. lupus*) : somewhat like a full-bodied Shepherd Dog in appearance, with long coat and bushy tail. In Greenland and on some Arctic islands, color is pure white; in nw. Canada and in Alaska individuals vary from white to cream to gray to black; elsewhere, color usually is grizzled gray or tawny. Males: l. 55–66 in., t. 13–18, ht. at shoulder 26–38, wt. 60–100, or rarely to 170 lb. in nw. Am. Females: l. to 56 in., t. 11–14, wt. ¼ less than males. **2.—*Red** (*C. niger*) : smaller (seldom over 80 lb.) than the Gray and more trim in form; individuals vary from grayish-brown to reddish-tawny to nearly black. Lighter ones are very Coyote-like, but the nose-pad, over 1 in. wide, will usually distinguish them. Different colors occur in the same litter of either of the Wolves.

A running Wolf usually carries its tail high, not low in Coyote fashion. One may spend years in Wolf country and rarely see it, although tracks may be common and the Wolf howl be heard. The track, especially of the hind foot, generally is angular in outline like a Coyote's, rather than oval like that of most dogs (diagram, p. 134). The front print may be larger than hind. Dog tracks vary greatly and, especially in N., some are indistinguishable from those of Wolf-dog hybrids or Wolves. A Wolf usually travels at a smooth rangy trot; rarely does it walk more than a few steps.

HABITAT: Tundra, plains, and forested areas, from sea level to high elevations. Ill-adapted to civilization; extirpated from much of its continental range and from various islands, including Newfd.

REPRODUCTION: Gray Wolf. The female begins breeding when between 2 and 3 years old; mating for life may be common. The den, a natural cavity, or dug by one or more Wolves, is often occupied during more than one whelping season. Gestation period is 63 days, and the annual litter of 4–11 (usually 4–6) pups is born Apr.–June. They are furred at birth and have eyes closed. The male feeds the nursing female, and later both parents bring food to the young. The male sometimes swallows food and carries it for miles, then disgorges it at the den. After a den life of about 3 weeks the young accompany the parents afield. The family is a closely knit unit and remains together through the first winter; yearlings also have been found at the den with their parents and the next litter. Captive Wolves have lived as long as 10–18 years. The Red Wolf probably differs little from the Gray in reproductive pattern.

HABITS: Wolves travel singly, or in pairs or packs, and are abroad at any hour. Packs are composed of one or more family units, with added stragglers; members co-operate in hunting and killing prey. The following applies to the Gray Wolf. During most of the year in N., Wolves follow Caribou herds or roam over a considerable area, but there are definite home ranges, and pairs return to these to den and rear the litter. In forested areas Wolves may hunt over a route up to several hundred miles in length, going over the circuit quite regularly. Five vocal sounds are recorded: a high plaintive sound used at the den, a throaty howl uttered by lone Wolves and also in the breeding season, a guttural howl (occasionally with a few barks at the end) when hunting to maintain organization of the pack, several short deep barking sounds given when prey is started, and a snarl used at the kill.

Availability governs what a Wolf eats; the diet includes Muskoxen, Caribou, unguarded Reindeer, Mountain Sheep, and Moose in n. areas, and Elk, Deer, and livestock farther s. Even where large mammals are available, Wolves may feed almost exclusively on small creatures such as Hares, Ground Squirrels, Mice, and so on, even to insects—if such food is obtained easily. Some vegetation and fruits are eaten. Stories of game slaughter by Wolves need confirmation; sometimes they do kill in excess of immediate needs, but generally they return to feed on a carcass. The Wolf population fluctuates, with peak numbers occurring at about 15- to 20-year intervals.

ECONOMIC STATUS: Most Wolf fur is used for trimming winter garments such as parkas in N., the long hair making an effective insulation and windbreak about the face. When the Western Range, depleted of Bison, was stocked with cattle, the major phase of the battle between man and the Wolf began. Use of poison, traps, and guns has eliminated the Wolf from very large areas, including some where it might well be a useful aid in culling diseased weaklings from or restricting overabundance of game. No carnivore eliminates its own food supply. Mange, rabies, and other troubles beset the Wolf. Trichinosis is not rare. Because smaller carnivores such as Foxes and Skunks are reservoirs of rabies, elimination of the Wolf and Coyote does not end transmission of rabies to dogs and livestock. As a representative of our native fauna and as an agent capable of influencing game popu-

lations for the better in some measure, the Wolf deserves
a permanent place in its present range.

THE CATS Family Felidae

Jaguar
Felis onca
Plate 14

A very large stocky Cat; usually yellowish-brown and with
black rosettes, some of which
have central dark spots; tail with blackish blotches and
tip; belly whitish, with blackish spots. Adults: l. 62–74
in., t. 20–26, ht. at shoulder 27–30, wt. 125–250 lb., or
rarely heavier. Females are about ⅕ smaller than males.
Young are brownish and spotted (no rosettes). In comparison, the Ocelot and Margay are smaller, more slender, and spots do not form rosettes; the Mountain Lion
is large but plain-colored. Jaguar tracks are 4–5 in. wide
—wider than long—and front tracks are larger than
hind; pad and 4 toes show. Mountain Lion tracks are as
long or longer than wide.

HABITAT: In the U.S. mainly in arid country of the Mexican border region.

REPRODUCTION: The female dens in a natural shelter such
as a cave. Gestation is said to require 93–110 days, and
the young are usually born in spring, although birth may
occur at any season in the tropics. Litters are evidently
spaced at about 2-year intervals. The 2–4 (usually 2)
kits are furred at birth and have eyes closed. Probably the
mother assumes all family responsibilities; young may
stay with her 2 years before departing.

HABITS: The Jaguar hunts mostly on the ground. Although
a silent trailer generally, sometimes it gives deep throaty

grunts. It has no fear of water and swims well. Voice: grunts, snarls, and growls. It hunts the Peccary, often its main food, and also kills Deer, livestock, various birds, turtles and other reptiles, and even fish. There are very few Jaguars n. of the Mexican border, and these individuals probably wander widely. The folk tale that the Mountain Lion and Jaguar fight to the death when they meet has no known basis in fact.

ECONOMIC STATUS: Too scarce to be of much importance n. of the Mexican border. Unlike the Mountain Lion, a cornered Jaguar is a dangerous animal. It does not engage in unprovoked attacks on man, but is known to trail people because of its normal Cat curiosity.

Ocelot and **Margay**
Felis (part)
Plate 14

1.—*Ocelot (*F. pardalis*): about twice House Cat size; short hair; ground color varying from pale gray to deep warm brown; spots are elongated on back and flanks; tail-tip light; belly whitish, with dark spots. Adults: l. 40–50 in., t. 13–15, ht. at shoulder 16–18, wt. 25–35 lb. Females are about ⅕ smaller than males. Young are darker than adults. **2.— Margay** (*F. wiedi*): a diminutive long-tailed Ocelot in shape and pattern; ground color buffy; 4 dark brownish stripes on neck and one on back; some of the irregularly shaped brownish side spots have buffy centers. Adults: l. 32–39, t. 14–16. In U.S. the Margay is known only from Eagle Pass, Maverick Co., Tex. Our other Cats are not of these sizes and patterns.

HABITAT: Dense ground cover or rough terrain, or a combination of these.

REPRODUCTION: Ocelot. Young are born in a rocky den or hollow log, or possibly under a bush, and perhaps at any season. A litter usually contains 2 kits, which show the adult pattern. Probably both parents take care of the young, since mates live together. There are no data on the Margay.

HABITS: The Ocelot hunts at any hour, although mostly at night and on the ground. It can climb readily and swims well. When hunting, mates signal to each other with House Cat-like meows and louder noises. It can make its way through scrub and mesquite with relative ease. If trailed by a dog, it has a Fox-like trait of doubling on its own trail and doing other confusing tricks. Sometimes it sleeps on a tree limb. Food: Rabbits, rodents, snakes (of which it is fond), various birds, and a variety of small animal life. It captures poultry and even young pigs and lambs. It uses its toilet sites repeatedly, accumulating little piles of droppings.

ECONOMIC STATUS: Among our native Cats, perhaps only the Ocelot can stand long zoo confinement with several of its own kind. Some individuals have gentle dispositions and are readily tamed. It can be trapped if it forms the habit of raiding a farmyard.

Mountain Lion
(Cougar, Panther, Puma)
Felis concolor
Plate 15

A very large, long-tailed Cat with plain coat, reddish or brownish in summer and grayish-brown in winter; underparts whitish; 'mustache' mark, back of ears, and tail-tip blackish. Males: l. 6–7½ ft., t. 26–36 in., ht. at shoulder 26–30, wt. 140–260 lb. Females: about ⅖ smaller, l. to 7 ft., wt. to 135 lb. Kittens are buffy, spotted, and have ringed tails.

Commonest signs are tracks. In walking, the hind foot

is placed partly on the print of the front; the retractile claws do not show. In snow, the swinging tail often leaves a mark beside the line of travel. Route is direct, like a Wolf's, not irregular or circling like that of a Lynx

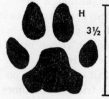 

H 3½ IN.

MOUNTAIN LION

TRACKS MAY OVERLAP, BUT SELDOM REGISTER

F

or Bobcat. In House Cat fashion it scratches boulders, tree trunks, and stumps. Droppings are buried; several of these 'scratch hills' often occur close together.

HABITAT: Formerly in all types of Deer habitat; now restricted mainly to mts., hilly woodland, and s. swamps. From sea level to 11,000 ft. elevation. Occurrence cent. Me. into N.S. established since map on p. 141 drawn.

REPRODUCTION: The female begins breeding when 2–3 years old, and mates are together for a short time only. The den is a natural cavern or in dense woody growth. Gestation requires 90–93 days and, while there is no fixed breeding season, most kits are born in spring. Litters of 1–4, usually 2, young may be spaced as far apart as 2–3 years. A kit at birth is about 8–12 in. long, weighs ½–1 lb., and is well furred; eyes open in 10–14 days. It is weaned in about 3 months; in 6 months it weighs 30–45 lb. and has shed the spotted coat. Young, believed to be up to 2 years old, have been found with the mother, who assumes the entire burden of rearing them except in rare instances. If zoo records are an indication of natural life span, the Mountain Lion lives 10–12 or rarely 18 years.

HABITS: This graceful Cat is active at any hour. Home range covers many square miles, and it may travel far in a night. A creature of habit, it covers familiar routes. Occasionally one follows a person, evidently out of curiosity. Several sometimes play together with objects as House Cats do. Voice is as varied as the House Cat's; the so-called scream is often quite prolonged. The Mountain Lion hunts by stalking and leaping, not by a long chase, and can kill prey much heavier than itself. After a cautious stalk, it springs from the ground, throws its wt. against the victim, and maintains a firm grip. After feeding, it usually covers its prey with debris, then returns in 2–4 days to feed again. Prey may be dragged to a secluded spot or den; also, more than one Mountain Lion may feed at a kill. In semi-desert areas it goes a long time without drinking. Food: all kinds of hoofed mammals (wild and domestic) and a variety of smaller wildlife, but, in general, Deer are a mainstay. It trees readily when chased by hounds.

ECONOMIC STATUS: The hide makes a good trophy. Kittens are good pets but become untrustworthy later. The Mountain Lion does well in zoos. Because it kills livestock, it is hunted extensively. On the rare occasions when one has attacked a person, perhaps the Mountain Lion was injured and starving, had rabies, or was too old to hunt agile prey. Its range now is much reduced, even though it has occupied added terrain in Canada in recent decades. There is reason to believe that it exists in small numbers in some areas where it has long been thought to be absent, which complicates mapping its range. Let us hope that this great Cat may continue to dwell in many localities.

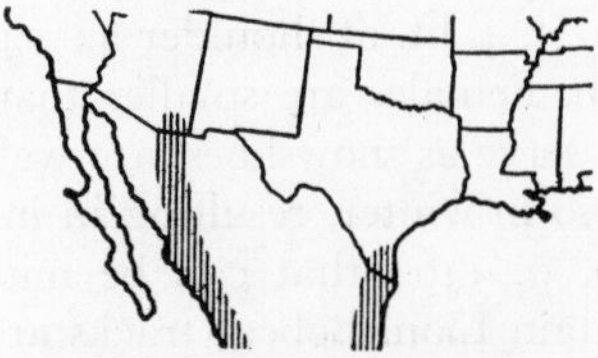

Jaguarundi
(Eyra—in red phase)
Felis eyra
Plate 14

A uniformly colored slender Cat of about twice House Cat size. Two color phases occur: (1) brownish-red with white lips and throat, and (2) a solid gray coat that is darker in winter. Adults: l. 35–50 in., t. 17–21, ht. at shoulder 10–12, wt. 10–20 lb. We have no other long-tailed unspotted Cat of its size.

HABITAT: Prefers thick brush. Rare in U.S., but occurs throughout most of Cent. and S. Am.

REPRODUCTION: Young have been seen in summer and winter, perhaps indicating that breeding occurs at any season.

HABITS: This agile Cat is active at all hours and is not gregarious. It apparently has much-used trails. Food: small mammals, birds, and probably a variety of terrestrial and aquatic animal life. Destruction of thickets of the Rio Grande delta has reduced its habitat in the U.S., but it appears to be common in suitable places farther s. The two color phases, which can occur in the same litter, formerly were considered separate species.

Lynx
(Canada Lynx)
Lynx canadensis
Plate 15

A bob-tailed Cat about a yard long, with seemingly oversized feet; ear tufts usually prominent; over-all color usually gray-buff, lightly shaded and spotted. End of tail completely black—not just on top as in the Bobcat. L. 30–40 in., t. 4, ht. at shoulder 22–24, wt. 12–25, or rarely to 40 lb. Females are smaller than males. The large feet, which serve as snowshoes, are well haired in summer and fully so in winter, resulting in indistinct footprints (diagram, p. 146) that can be mistaken for those of the Mountain Lion. Bobcat tracks are smaller and with more complicated heel-pad. The Lynx places its hind feet overlapping or in front tracks. Commonest gaits are a walk and a sort of gallop, but the Lynx soon tires at the latter.

HABITAT: Forests, thickets, and swamps occupied by its preferred prey, the Snowshoe Hare. Lynxes wander far out on the tundra in some years when woodland food is scarce.

REPRODUCTION: The female is said to breed the year following her birth. The den is usually under a windfall or in some natural cavity. Mating generally occurs in early Mar. and gestation may require 2 months or longer. The annual litter contains 1–4, often 3, kits. They are furred at birth, eyes open in about 10 days, and their coat is more heavily streaked and blotched during early life. They begin following the mother when about 2 months old. She alone rears the litter, which disbands in fall or even as late as the following spring.

HABITS: The Lynx climbs and swims well but hunts on the ground, by sight and smell. Generally it hunts alone, or a family group spreads out in a lateral direction, but several Lynxes hunting or traveling together have been reported. It goes more or less in wide circles or over very irregular routes. Voice, seldom recorded, probably includes a range of Cat noises. The Lynx is so tied to the Snowshoe Hare (its main prey) that the great decline in Hare numbers every 7–10 years is followed, within a year, by starvation among Lynxes. The survivors, in their poor physical condition, do not reproduce well until Hares again are in adequate supply.

ECONOMIC STATUS: The soft, delicately shaded pelt is used for trimmings, neckpieces, short coats, and jackets. The Lynx robs trap lines occasionally but seldom conflicts otherwise with man's interests. Its meat is edible but should be cooked well to avoid any possibility of getting trichinosis. Overtrapping and changes in habitat brought about by man have caused the Lynx to disappear from s. portions of its former range.

Bobcat
(Wildcat, Bay Lynx)
Lynx rufus
Plate 15

A bob-tailed Cat about a yard in length; general tone varies from pale brown (palest in arid SW.) to reddish-brown, streaked with blackish, and usually with dark spots on the whitish belly. Tail usually has several black markings, but the tip is black above and *light below*—not all-black tip as in the Lynx. Ear tufts are small. L. 30–40 in., t. 4–6½, ht. at shoulder 20–23. Females are smaller than males. Yearlings weigh about 8–12 lb. and adults 12–25, or rarely to 40; wt. is usually much overestimated. In any season, the smaller feet of the Bobcat are much less haired than the Lynx's.

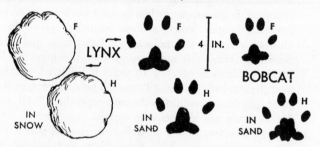

HABITAT: Forests, thickets, swamps, rocky terrain, deserts, and mts.

REPRODUCTION: The female begins breeding when about a year old. The den is in a log, rocky ledge, or thicket. Breeding occurs mainly in late winter, and the annual litter of 2–4, often 3, kits is born after a gestation period of probably more than 63 days. At birth kits have a mottled coat and weigh about 12 oz. each. Eyes open in 9–10 days, before the ears are erect. Kits are weaned in 2 months. They stay with the mother until late summer or even into winter, then depart to hunt by themselves. A captive lived over 15 years.

HABITS: The Bobcat is most active after dark. It swims well, climbs trees readily, and often rests on a limb. Chief prey is Hares and Rabbits, which it stalks by sight and smell. It springs at its prey from the ground and, if it misses, gives up the chase after a few bounds. A hunting trail is very crooked, for the Cat indulges its curiosity by investigating thickets, fallen logs, stumps, and unusual objects. Voice: many rather House Cat-like noises. In addition to the Rabbit tribe, food consists of various other mammals, birds, and even aquatic animal life. Adult Deer are taken, mainly in winter, and fawns are killed with ease. Usually a kill is at least partly covered with debris, and the Bobcat returns to feed again. Young and adults toy with smaller prey. A Bobcat often covers 20–25 mi. in a night over an irregular hunting route. Unlike the Lynx, which is tied so closely to the fluctuating Snowshoe Hare population that it also fluctuates markedly, the Bobcat is less selective in diet, hence probably less subject to any such regular or pronounced fluctuations.

ECONOMIC STATUS: Bobcat fur is used for trimmings and jackets. The meat is edible but should be well cooked. A Bobcat makes an interesting pet. Hunting this Cat with hounds is a popular sport in some areas. It kills small livestock on occasion. The Bobcat manages to survive, often unnoticed, near human population centers.

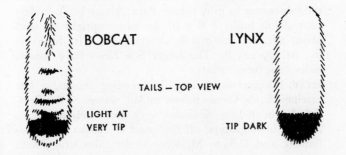

BOBCAT   LYNX

TAILS — TOP VIEW

LIGHT AT
VERY TIP   TIP DARK

SEALS AND SEA LIONS   Order Pinnipedia

EARED SEALS   Family Otariidae

Northern Fur Seal
(Alaska Fur Seal)
Callorhinus ursinus
Plate 17

A medium-sized Seal, with short pointed nose, concave facial profile, and small ears. Hind limbs are turned forward on land. Adult bulls: dark gray to brown above, usually gray on shoulders and foreneck, and with reddish-brown flippers and underparts. Cows: grayish-brown above and reddish-brown or gray below. Pups: glossy black in first coat. Adult bulls: l. 6–7 ft., ht. when upright on land about 4 ft., wt. 400–700 lb. Cows: l. 4½–5 ft., ht. to 30 in., wt. 75–125 lb. The larger Sea Lions have coarse, hairy (not furry) coats.

HABITAT: Ocean waters and, in breeding season, a few marine islands. Comes ashore in Am. waters on the Pribilof Is. in Bering Sea and very rarely elsewhere in Alaska; in migration, off the coast of Alaska, Brit. Columbia, and U.S. to Mexican border; also straggles to

Asia and, in Alaskan waters, occasionally to Pt. Barrow.
From Old World colonies (e. Siberia, Kuril Is.) they go
as far s. as Japan and Korea in winter.

REPRODUCTION: Bulls gather harems. A 7-year-old bull may
gather several cows if he stays away from older bulls; a
bull at about 15 years of age has an average of 40 cows.
Mature bulls come ashore during late Apr.–May and
occupy choice sites near the water's edge to await the
cows; later arrivals include idle bulls and young bachelors
that keep in groups by themselves. Cows arrive early
June to mid-July. They give birth to a single pup within
a few days and are bred a few days later, hence are pregnant practically their entire adult lifetime.

A pup at birth has bluish eyes, glossy black fur, and
weighs about 11 lb. It is nursed in the harem, the mother
going to sea—often a long way—several times a week to
feed herself. Pups learn to swim in 6–8 weeks. At 12–14
weeks they have brown eyes, gray coat, and go swimming
alone. At 4 months they weigh about 35 lb. and are
forced off a milk diet because their mothers separate
from them to begin the southward migration. Energy of
harem bulls is exhausted in fighting to defend their cows
and in keeping cows from straying and mating with other
bulls, so that by the time the younger cows that breed
for the first time at 3–4 years of age come ashore, they
are served by younger bulls. Cows have had pups until
21 years of age; individuals up to about 25 years old are
known, but probably they are well past their prime.

HABITS: This Seal spends most of its life in the water, coming ashore only for the breeding season. On land it travels
rather well for a Seal but must rest frequently. At sea,
where it is an extremely rapid and skillful swimmer and
diver, it usually travels in small groups. Dives to a depth
of about 240 ft. are known. Voice varies—a roar, bark,
bleat, and a 'cough.' Migrations are remarkable, the Seals
in fall going through the passes in the Aleutians and on
s., then back in spring through these passes to the same
remote islands, and individuals usually to the same spot

on the beach. Food: squids, pollack, herring, crustaceans, sealfish, salmon, rockfish, lamprey, greenling, and cod. Much feeding is done at night. Stones sometimes are swallowed. A Seal eats about $\frac{1}{15}$ its own wt. per day. Harem bulls do not eat during the breeding season but subsist on their blubber. As a consequence, they become so thin that they barely have the strength to travel the few rods to sea at the season's end. About half the pups die before Aug. 10 of the year following birth, as a result of storms, hookworm, crowding, and starvation.

ECONOMIC STATUS: Each year about 80% of the population of 3- and 4-year-old bachelors is killed for pelts; the carcasses of most of these are processed into oil and meal. These bachelors stay in groups, away from the breeding population, and are easily driven inland a short distance to be killed. The salted pelts are shipped to St. Louis and there processed for about 90 days. This includes removal of guard hair and straightening and dyeing of the curly underfur. The finished product is famous for its beauty. This Seal has been accused of damaging commercial fisheries, but the return in pelts, meal, and oil from Seals outweighs in value any proven loss. Before exploitation the herd may have numbered about 1,500,000 animals; it was reduced to about 132,000 in 1910, and by 1940 had been brought back to its former numbers through careful supervision under international agreement with Canada and (until 1941) Japan and Russia. The Pribilofs are a special government reservation where one cannot land except under stress of weather or by special permission from the Secretary of the Interior. Because some fishermen believe that the Fur Seal destroys large numbers of salmon, biologists have studied its food habits extensively. Over 4,900 Seal stomachs have been examined—many from areas where salmon were plentiful. Salmon flesh occurred in $1\frac{1}{2}$ per cent of the stomachs; probably these fish comprise under 1 per cent of the annual diet, for the Seals feed mainly far at sea.

Guadalupe Fur Seal
(Townsend's Fur Seal)
Arctocephalus townsendi
Plate 17

Like the Northern Fur Seal, but with more flattened head and longer, more pointed snout; color of bull also quite similar, except grayish (not reddish) underparts. Bull: l. 6 ft., wt. (est.) 300 lb.; cow much smaller, but no data. Since, except perhaps for cripples, the Northern Fur Seal is in Bering Sea in summer, any Fur Seal seen at that season in s. Calif. or adjacent Mexican waters should be examined carefully. It may be that *townsendi* is really only a marginal population of the Southern Fur Seal that occurs from Cape Horn to the Equator.

HABITAT: Marine waters; caves and shores of outer islands.

REPRODUCTION AND HABITS: It is believed that a single pup is born June–July. The only records of this Seal anywhere since 1928 are for a bull (the same one?) seen three times in 1949 and once in 1951 on San Nicolas, outermost of the islands off the s. coast of Calif. Voice: a deep roaring growl when threatening, a deep hoarse growl ending in a querulous note, and a barking cough. Evidently it barks rarely. Bulls, at least, appear heavy-chested and thick-necked in comparison to female and young California Sea Lions; they also act quite differently, being much given to rolling in the water and to roughing up their fur.

ECONOMIC STATUS: Sealers reduced the large population to near extinction prior to 1890. This Seal is nominally protected by the Mexican Government, but undoubtedly it is vulnerable to poaching—if any still exist about Mexican or U.S. islands. Descriptive and historical matter were recorded by C. H. Townsend, *Zoölogica,* vol. 9, no. 12 (1931).

Northern Sea Lion
(Steller's Sea Lion)
Eumetopias jubata
Plate 17

In general like the California Sea Lion (see p. 153), but the coarse short hair when dry varies from light to dark brown, the head is less pointed, the bull has no pronounced head crest, and this Seal is very much larger. Bull: l. 10–12½ ft., ht. ashore to 5 ft., wt. 1,500–2,000 lb. Cow: l. 8–9 ft., ht. 4, wt. 400–600 lb. See the California Sea Lion for further comparative description.

HABITAT: Marine waters and island shores, rarely in enclosed bays.

REPRODUCTION: Quite like the California Sea Lion in general pattern. There are about 10–15 cows per bull in the colonies. The single pup is born less than a week after the cow comes ashore. Shortly thereafter, in June, she is bred again. A pup at birth is dark brown, weighs 35–50 lb., and is 38–40 in. long. In a month or more it takes to water; by fall its coat has lightened and the blue eyes turn brown. It may be attended by the cow for nearly a year.

HABITS: This gregarious Seal is common over much of its range the year round, although widely dispersed in winter. Voice: a deep bass growl and long steady roar; it never barks. In Calif. waters, cows, pups, and immatures remain the year round, but breeding bulls are found only about June 1–Aug. 1. Yearlings of both sexes avoid the colonies. Food: squids, as well as herring and other small schooling fishes. Bulls eat no food in the breeding season.

ECONOMIC STATUS: Alaskan natives use the hide to cover boats. They also eat the flesh. Although reports of damage are often exaggerated, this Seal does follow fishing boats regularly and takes halibut and sablefish off fishing gear. Usually it is wary enough to stay beyond range of accurate gunfire from a heaving boat. Total population estimated (1952) at 60,000.

California Sea Lion
(Black Sea Lion)
Zalophus californianus
Plate 17

A very large Seal, with small external ears, pointed head, hind limbs bent forward when ashore, and general color varying from yellowish-brown to dull black. Usually appears black when wet. Bulls are much bigger than cows, much thicker through the shoulders, have a prominent crest from between eyes to lower back of head, and a small mane. Average bull: l. 8 ft., ht. when erect ashore 4 ft., wt. 500–620 lb. Cow: l. 6 ft., wt. to 300 lb. High forehead of the bull is diagnostic. In general, similar to the much larger Northern Sea Lion, in which the bull lacks the high forehead, and both sexes have less pointed head. The California species has a honking bark; the Northern roars. Their ranges overlap in Calif. and Ore.

HABITAT: Marine waters, islands, and coastline. There are vague reports of occurrence in s. Brit. Columbia.

REPRODUCTION: Cows probably begin breeding at 3 and bulls at 5 or more years. Cows and young bulls raft together off rookeries as the breeding season approaches. Mature bulls arrive in early June, singly or a few together; they take stations on beach or rocks, and then the cows come ashore. There are no closely organized harems. Cows have a single pup, then are bred again soon, mainly June 10–July 15. Pups are brownish-black. They are able, but unwilling, to swim and prefer, when unattended by cows, to huddle in groups. Their blue eyes darken and coat color lightens at time of the fall molt. Cows, if molested, sometimes carry their pups to water. Pups swim in tide pools, then later go to sea with their mothers. They stay together for perhaps the greater part of a year. Captives have lived 23 years.

HABITS: This is the trained Seal of circuses and zoos. It is very playful, even in the wild, and gregarious at all seasons. Adults have a honking bark or howl, never a roar. Some individuals wander up to several hundred miles between breeding seasons, but adult bulls are more or less sedentary. Food, usually obtained after dark, consists of squids and various fishes. Rocks are swallowed for reasons unknown. An adult eats about 12–15 lb. of food per day. Bulls do not eat in the breeding season.

ECONOMIC STATUS: Sometimes this Seal damages fish nets, but otherwise it does no great harm. The Calif. Dept. of Fisheries has allowed killing of nuisance individuals in the vicinity of important fishing centers. It is valuable as a zoo and circus mammal.

WALRUS Family Odobenidae

Walrus
Odobenus rosmarus
Plate 16

A very large, stout marine mammal, with small head, square muzzle with short coarse bristles, 2 protruding tusks, and thick wrinkled hide having short grayish-brown hair that almost completely disappears from old bulls; hind limbs bend forward when on ice or ashore. Bull: l. 10–12 ft., ht. to 5, wt. to well over 2,000 lb.; cow about ⅓ smaller. Cow's tusks are more curved in the middle and more slender.

HABITAT: Shallow marine waters and ice; in some areas, on ice over deep water remote from land; seldom comes ashore. In Arctic, rare from Melville Peninsula w. to n. coast of Alaska.

REPRODUCTION: Cows mature in 4–5 years and bulls in about 5. Cows are bred not more often than in alternate years. In e. Arctic the pup is born mid-Apr. to late May; in Bering Sea in May–June. Gestation requires over 11 months. A newborn calf is about 4 ft. long, gray, and with no external evidence of teeth or tusks. Calves, cows, and bulls travel together, the cows especially showing strong attachment for calves and defending them against danger. A small calf travels on its mother's neck, clinging as she swims and dives. Nursing is said to continue 1½–2 years, by which time the calf has 3- or 4-in. tusks and can dig its own food.

HABITS: Walruses usually go in herds of from several to over a hundred and are probably the noisiest marine mammals of the Arctic. The bellow of a Walrus sounds quite like the voice of a St. Bernard Dog—and even young Walruses make this noise. Adults also utter an Elephant-like trumpeting sound. There are seasonal movements, with the ice, that are better defined in Pacific waters. To feed, a Walrus sinks to the ocean bottom in up to 300 ft. of water and more or less stands on its head, working backward as it uses its tusks to grub mollusks and other marine life from the ocean floor. Pads on the muzzle work the food into the mouth. Mollusk shells seldom are swallowed. The occasional solitary 'rogue' Walrus is said to eat Seals. The stomach of a Walrus, however, holds only about a gallon of food.

ECONOMIC STATUS: In some areas the Walrus is to the Eskimo what the Bison was to the plains Indians. Practically every part is utilized. Since Walrus killing with rifles is relatively easy, numbers of this mammal are declining in parts of its range. In some areas, however, as in and about n. Hudson Bay, evidently the population is holding up well.

HAIR SEALS Family Phocidae

Harbor Seal
(Common Seal)
Phoca vitulina
Plate 18

A small Seal with rather
dog-like face. Basal color
varies from cream to yel-
lowish-gray to dark brown;
the spots or blotches, which
tend to merge along the back, are from a few shades
darker than basal color to nearly black. Adults: l. 4½–
5¼ ft., wt. 125–300 lb. The common small barking Seal
of Atlantic and Pacific coastal waters. Compare with the
Ringed Seal.

HABITAT: Coastal waters, lower reaches of rivers, and in a
few n. inland lakes e. and w. of Hudson Bay. Occurs
occasionally on n. coast of Alaska.

REPRODUCTION: Females do not breed until at least 2 and
males 3 years of age. Breeding occurs in fall, and gestation requires about 9¼ months. The pup (rarely 2 ?)
is born in spring or early summer on an islet or in some
secluded place. The silky white coat is often shed before
birth and passed out when the pup is born, or else it is
shed within 2 days after birth; the pup then is silvery-
white below and grayish above. At birth the eyes are
open, it weighs 17–25 lb., and is 30–34 in. long. Teeth
begin to appear within 2 days. It takes to water any time
after it is a day old, but must come ashore to nurse. It
begins to catch fish in 3–5 weeks and is weaned in about
6 weeks, when the mother takes it to a place where fish
are plentiful and leaves it, usually with other pups. Some
weeks later the pups disperse and mingle with groups of
adults. Growth continues at least 3 years. It has lived

19 years in captivity but probably few—if any—approach this age under natural conditions.

HABITS: Seasonal movements are local. Late-summer groups contain Seals of all ages, but soon the mature ones go to secluded islands and ledges. There they breed in the water. They then rejoin the groups, except for battered males that recuperate in seclusion. Winter is spent usually away from the mainland, except perhaps in N., and in summer the Seals are scattered. They haul out on ledges to sleep. Voice: a bark and a grunt. When hunting, the Seal usually swims within sight of the bottom, looking about and putting on a burst of speed if food is sighted. Food: any available fish, also squids and some crustaceans. About 10 lb. of food per day is eaten.

ECONOMIC STATUS: This Seal eats some commercially valuable fish; also, it damages nets and weirs by getting entangled or biting holes in them. Its hide, meat, and oil are little sought, except by n. natives and, to some extent, in and about Newfd. This Seal and the Gray are hosts of the adult stage of a roundworm (*Porrocaecum*) that, in immature stage, occurs in cod and some other fish. The worms, though harmless, must be hand-picked from fillets to make the fish salable.

Ribbon Seal
Phoca fasciata
Plate 18

Male: dark brown, with band of yellowish-white around the neck, one around base of each forelimb, and one around rump. Female: uniform pale grayish-yellow or grayish-brown, with whitish band across lower back. Young are said to resemble the female. Male: l. to over 6 ft.; female to 5½.

HABITAT: Marine waters, shores, islands, and sea ice.

REPRODUCTION AND HABITS: Gestation is believed to require about 9¼ months. This Seal is found singly or in small groups, usually on sea ice. The skin is used by Eskimos to make highly prized clothes bags.

Ringed Seal
(Jar Seal)
Phoca hispida
Plate 18

A small Seal; very variable in color. Adults: upperparts grayish-brown, often with ring-like mottlings; belly white or yellowish; area about eyes blackish. First digit of fore-finger longer than any of the others. L. 4½–5¼ ft. Males are slightly larger than females. Immatures have grayish or yellowish-gray upperparts, often mottled with ring-like marks of white or yellowish-brown; underparts are light; this is stage known as 'silver jar' in e. Arctic. Adults often look much like the Harbor Seal, but pattern generally is softer and less well defined.

HABITAT: Marine waters and ice near coasts, preferably in quiet waters of bays and inlets. Commonest and most widely found Seal of the Arctic, occurring as far n. as open water exists—recorded to over 82° N. Lat. Occurs in fresh water, as in Nettilling Lake on Baffin I., and elsewhere.

REPRODUCTION: Gestation is said to require about 276 days. The single white or yellowish-white pup is born Feb.–Apr. in a cavity in snow which the mother digs with her stout claws. A tunnel extends a few feet to a breathing hole in the ice. Often there is no visible sign above the snow surface of mother and pup below. The pup's woolly coat is shed in about a month.

HABITS: This Seal is not gregarious or markedly migratory. When slush ice forms in Alaskan waters in fall, however, it often gathers in numbers near the beaches to feed on spawning tomcods. In winter it follows narrow areas of open water and sleeps on the ice. If the ice closes in solidly, the Seal scratches a blowhole and comes there to breathe between dives. In search of open water, it has been known to travel many miles over ice or even land. Its main food is swimming invertebrates, not fish.

ECONOMIC STATUS: Almost every part of this Seal is utilized in the economy of the Eskimo.

Harp Seal
(Saddleback Seal)
Phoca grœnlandica
Plate 19

Male, 3–4 years old or older: yellowish to tawny-gray above, whitish below; head brownish-black; a blackish or brownish saddle-shaped band begins on hind neck and curves downward and backward along each side. Female, carrying her first pup and presumably going on 4 years old: tends toward tawny on back and dull white or straw color below; muzzle and flippers brownish-black; black face and saddle markings begin to appear after this but may not become definite until she is 6 years old. Male: l. 5½–6½ ft., wt. 250–400 lb. Female: to 6 ft., wt. 150–300 lb. 'Bedlamers' (age 2–3 years): dark gray or tawny, more or less spotted on upper sides and back; head and flippers darker than body. 'Graybacks' or 'rustys' (under 1 year): pale gray, with poorly defined spots on back; lighter below. These pelage names are used by sealers in sorting their catch.

HABITAT: Waters and ice of n. seas. Stragglers have occurred s. to N.J.

REPRODUCTION: Breeding probably begins at 3 years for the female and 4 for the male. The pup (twins rarely) is born on the ice, Feb. 25–Mar. 15. Most are born in three areas: Gulf of St. Lawrence, off e. Newfd., and e. of Greenland. A newborn pup weighs 12–15 lb., has woolly white coat, dark eyes and muzzle, and cannot swim. In 2 weeks it weighs 60–80 lb. Males arrive off the breeding places during the nursing period and swim, in large numbers, in view of the brooding mothers. The female deserts her pup when it is about 2 weeks old and joins a male in the water. The unfed pup on the floe sheds its white coat, assumes the gray-backed coat, and is called a 'beater'; at 3–4 weeks it ventures into the water to feed. It eats mainly shrimp-like crustaceans at first, but gradually becomes adept at fishing. Then it leaves the breeding area.

HABITS: This Seal is gregarious and migratory, moving southward in winter ahead of the closing ice and northward after the pups leave the floes. Aside from rearing, there is another gathering on ice, in Apr.–early May, when adults and bedlamers stay on ice without eating for several weeks while they shed one coat and acquire another. At other times they remain in the water near the coasts. Adults have a barking growl but generally are silent; the mother utters a soft low note to her pup; pups whimper and wail. Adults eat fish, especially capelin, and crustaceans.

ECONOMIC STATUS: Pelts of newborn pups are made into women's coats; hides of adults are converted into fine leather. The oil is used for creams, lotions, and margarine. This Seal is pursued far from land on pack ice, hence any hunting regulation requires international cooperation. Harps can stand a rather heavy harvest, but it is being overdone. Those under a year old usually make up ⅘ of the seal catch on ice by vessels. This industry in the W. Atlantic is at least 200 years old but has been studied only very recently. In that portion of the Harp's range known as the "Front" (e. of Newfd. and Labrador) about 430,000 pups have been born annually in recent years; the number is about 215,000 in the Gulf of St. Lawrence. Of the 430,000, in 1951 sealers took 241,000, as well as 113,000 older Seals. The annual pup harvest in the Gulf has been averaging about 60,000.

Bearded Seal
(Squareflipper)
Erignathus barbatus
Plate 19

A large Seal, with small rounded head; upperparts grayish to dull yellowish-brown, shading to silvery or yellowish undersurface; darker spotting obscure or absent; dense bristles on each side of muzzle give a bushy, bearded appearance; third finger on forelimbs longest. Old males: l. to 12 ft., wt. to 1,000 lb. (10 ft. and 500 lb. is more usual); females are smaller. This Seal often looks glossy black when wet.

HABITAT: Cold waters and ice floes, usually near land. Rarely s. to Newfd.

REPRODUCTION: Gestation is said to require 11 months. The pup, born Apr.–May, and up to nearly 5 ft. long, has a slightly curly gray coat, sometimes with a tawny tinge. The mother has 4 nipples (other seals have 2) and is said to tend the pup for a long period.

HABITS: This rather sluggish Seal is not gregarious, noi really common anywhere, nor highly migratory, although fair numbers occur off Newfd. in winter. The mother, if separated from her pup, is said to utter a high-pitched whistling call that ends in a deep sigh. A dull whistling sound is made when diving. A bottom feeder like the Walrus, it scrapes with its claws for mollusks and other invertebrates; fishes and other swimming creatures are less commonly eaten. Also like the Walrus, it often has hundreds of parasitic roundworms in its stomach and quantities of tapeworms in its intestines.

ECONOMIC STATUS: Eskimos use the tough hide for boot soles, boat covers, harpoon lines, and other items that get rough usage. The meat is eaten. Sometimes the liver is toxic to man or dogs because of its high vitamin A content. This Seal has been reported as a vector of trichinosis.

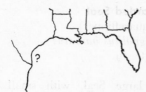

West Indian Seal
(Caribbean Seal, Monk Seal)
Monachus tropicalis

Nearly uniform brown above, tinged with gray; underparts pale; l. to 7½ ft. Nearly extinct, it formerly occurred on shores and islands of the Gulf of Mexico and Caribbean Sea, n. to Key West, Fla., and throughout the Bahamas. No other Seal occupied this area. A sluggish and unwary gregarious Seal, it was slaughtered for hides and oil. One was killed Mar. 15, 1922, near Key West, and there were reports of possible occurrence during the 1940s on the Tex. coast. It was known to occur in Jamaican waters in 1952.

Gray Seal
(Horsehead)
Halichœrus grypus
Plate 18

A large stocky Seal, with long squarish snout; upperparts may be light or dark gray, or even nearly black, usually with obscure spots or blotches; underparts lighter. Male: l. 6–9 ft., wt. 275–800 lb. Female: l. 5½–6½ ft., wt. 250 to over 700 lb. Yearlings are yellowish-gray with grayish blotches on sides. Heavy head and deliberate manner usually distinguish this from the Harbor Seal; both haul out at the same places but tend to keep in separate groups. White-coated pups have been confused with those of the Harp Seal. Compare adults with the Hooded Seal.

HABITAT: Prefers turbulent waters near cliffs or about rocks and reefs; also in estuaries and, at Sable I., Nova Scotia, on sand bars. Has straggled s. to N.J.

REPRODUCTION: The white pup (twins rarely ?) is born

Jan.–Feb. on a ledge, sand bar, or even ice. This pattern fits the Baltic area also, but not the Brit. Isles, where pups are born in autumn and the cow is bred again in about 2 weeks. Nursing lasts at least 2 weeks. This Seal has lived 18 years.

HABITS: A gregarious and rather sluggish Seal, whose seasonal movements are local. In winter this and the Harbor Seal move into the Bras d'Or Lakes of Cape Breton I. Numbers occur in the Miramichi estuary of New Bruns., Magdalen Is., Northumberland Strait, Anticosti, Miquelon, Cape Breton, and Sable I. Voice: a gloomy sound, between a moo and a howl. Deep growls are given. Pups cry like human babies; they hiss if scared. Alarm is communicated by slapping the water with a flipper—a noise that can be heard a half mile in calm weather. Food: fish, usually the slower kinds.

ECONOMIC STATUS: Like the Harbor Seal (see p. 157), this wary Seal is a vector of codworm; otherwise it is of little known significance.

Hooded Seal
(Bladdernose)
Cystophora cristata
Plate 19

Male: very variable; usually dark gray or bluish above, lighter on sides and belly; some have many whitish spots on sides, others dark spots or blotches; face and muzzle blackish; inflatable pouch ('hood') on top of snout. Female: smaller and paler, usually with less distinct markings; hood small. Male: l. 7–8½ ft., or rarely to 10½, wt. to perhaps 850 lb. Female: to 8 ft., wt. to 400 lb. Coat changes described for the Harp (p. 159) apply here also, but they come gradually, and the only clear-cut groups are 'graybacks' (small young) and all others (from small to large). Sometimes confused with the Gray and the Harbor Seal.

HABITAT: Sea ice and cold waters; straggles up fjords and rivers. On e. coast has straggled s. to Fla. Distribution and movements are not fully known. It is reported not to migrate as far n. as does the Harp Seal.

REPRODUCTION: Breeding begins at about 4 years. The pup, wt. 25–30 lb., is born late Feb.–early Mar. The white coat is shed before birth; then its stiff coat is dark bluish above, light gray or white below, with blackish flippers. It can take to water immediately. Typically, a bull, cow, and pup are found together on the ice, and adults refuse to leave a pup when danger threatens. The pup is deserted after 2–3 weeks, and mating takes place. Bulls then are noisy and fight a great deal. Young soon leave the ice; they stay in groups more or less by themselves until attaining breeding age. Except at nursing and mating time, adult males and females tend to stay in separate groups.

HABITS: Gregarious and migratory, this Seal travels with the Harp but tends to keep somewhat apart. It summers in N. toward Greenland and comes s. in fall and winter. Lacking stout claws to keep ice holes open, it resorts to heavy broken ice or the edge of the pack. The male is noted for being able to leap several feet clear of water and for his quarrelsome nature. The male, when sufficiently aroused, inflates his hood; even the fiery red mucous membrane within it is extruded through the nostrils as paired bladders, 6–7 in. long by 5–6 in. in diameter. A severed hood held about 6 quarts of water. Voice: a variable barking growl. Food is mainly fishes.

ECONOMIC STATUS: Because the Hooded Seal is readily captured when it hauls out on solid ice near open water, it has been reduced to near commercial extinction. In the 1940's, Hoods made up about 1% of the annual sealing catch. Sealing practice has been, whenever opportunity afforded, to kill the family—male, female, and pup—leaving none for breeding stock.

Elephant Seal
(Sea Elephant)
Mirounga angustirostris
Plate 16

A giant Seal; hind limbs drag behind on land; sparse hair and peel-
ing skin all over body, especially on
throat and neck. Bull has overhanging inflatable snout.
Adults are yellowish- or grayish-brown, immatures gray.
Bull: l. 15–16 ft., wt. to about 5,000 lb., ht. about 5 ft.
when erect on land. Cow: to perhaps 11 ft. and ⅓ wt.
of bull. Might be confused with a Sea Lion, but the latter
has ears which are noticeable under most circumstances.
Evidently solitary at sea.

HABITAT: Marine waters, island shores and caves. Occasionally n. to Queen Charlotte Strait and one s. Alaska
record.

REPRODUCTION: Breeding occurs Dec. through Mar. Cows
haul out on a beach away from where dominant bulls
are stationed and give birth to a dusky black pup about
4 ft. long. They are bred again in about 2 weeks. Mating
normally is on land, an anomalous condition for a Hair
Seal. A cow nursing a pup often is accompanied by a
yearling, indicating long association with the mother.

HABITS: This gregarious Seal can dive several hundred feet.
It hauls out on island shores at all seasons, laboriously
moving its massive body on land. Excited or fighting bulls
inflate their snouts, which otherwise hang relaxed over
the muzzle; a cow or young bull, when excited, extends
its nose into a pointed tip, revealing that this is inflatable.
This Seal sheds its hair and its epidermis in tatters, young
beginning in Apr. and adults in June–July. The shedding
Seal gets some protection from the sun for its tender new
skin by tossing sand on its back with its flippers or going
to a shore cave. Snorts, sneezes, coughs, grunts, sighs,
yawns, and other sounds are uttered. Pups whimper.
Yearlings have a high-pitched, bird-like scream. Cows

and young bulls give a harsh 'vomiting' sound. The characteristic snoring snort of this Seal is most resonant when uttered by mature bulls. Food: fish and squids, caught mainly at night.

ECONOMIC STATUS: Because blubber of a bull may contain up to 200 gals. of oil, this mammal was killed by the thousands beginning about 1855. It was nearly exterminated by 1892. The Mexican Government, from 1911 on, protected it and probably saved it from extinction. There has been partial recovery of the population and reoccupation of some of the former range.

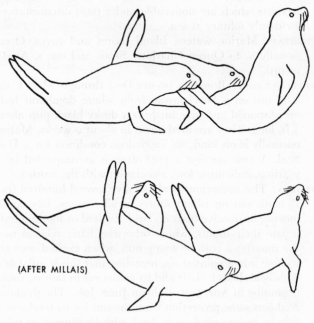

(AFTER MILLAIS)

HAIR SEAL – LOCOMOTION ON LAND

GNAWING MAMMALS   Order Rodentia

For Hares and Rabbits (Lagomorpha), see pages 275–288.

MARMOTS, SQUIRRELS, AND CHIPMUNKS
Family Sciuridae

Woodchuck
(Chuck, 'Ground Hog')
Marmota monax
Plate 27

A large stocky rodent, with flattened head and medium-length furred tail. Varies from yellowish- to dark reddish-brown, with grizzled appearance because of lighter hair tips; underparts paler; feet black or nearly so. L. 18–26 in., t. 5–6, wt. 4–10 or even to 14 lb. Young have less rich coloring. The larger Hoary Marmot of the W. tends toward gray, with black-and-white face and nape. The Woodchuck often sits erect (ht. 11–14 in.) on the mound at its burrow or elsewhere. In running gait, hind tracks are ahead of front.

HABITAT: Dry soil in open woodlands, thickets, rocky slopes, and in and about fields and clearings.

REPRODUCTION: Woodchucks breed when about a year old. The burrow system usually has several entrances and a grass nest in a side tunnel. Males wander in Mar.–Apr.

WOODCHUCK, WALKING

LH — LF

6 INCHES

RH — RF

LH — LF

and probably mate with several females. The annual litter of 3–5 young is born after 31–32 days' gestation; they are hairless, have eyes closed, and weigh 1–1½ oz. each. Eyes open in 26–28 days; the coat is well developed in a month. The mother carries some food into the burrow, but the young, when a month old and still nursing, come out to feed. After 2–3 more weeks, they leave the mother or are forced out. Captives have lived 4–5 years.

HABITS: Most activity is in early morning and in evening. The Chuck is rather solitary. Voice: a piercing whistle, a muffled bark heard rarely, and a squeal when fighting. It becomes very fat in fall; some are relatively inactive by mid-Aug., but others are abroad long after frosts begin. The Chuck's hibernation is not such profound dormancy as some mammals have. In Old World folklore the Badger comes out in spring to look for its shadow; this erroneous Candlemas Day notion was transferred to our Chuck. Males, especially, are often abroad before snow is gone. Food: alfalfa, clover, many other plants (some cultivated), and occasionally snails and insects. Home range usually is less than 100 yds. in greatest length, although rutting males wander widely.

ECONOMIC STATUS: Woodchuck burrows are havens for Cottontails and Skunks and are enlarged for use by Foxes. The Chuck is hunted for sport to a degree that a closed season is provided in Penna. It is a pest in gardens. The several I have had were likable and interesting pets.

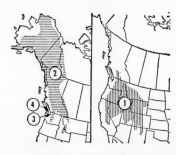

Marmots
(Rock Chucks)
Marmota (part)
Plate 27

Large stocky rodents, with flattened heads and medium-length furred tails. **1.— *Yellow-bellied** (*M. flaviventris*): usually warm orange-brown with grizzled appearance; face blackish, with a more or less whitish band between eyes (often obscure in Colo. and N. Mex.); sides of neck buffy; yellowish to brownish belly; buffy to dark brown feet. L. 19–28 in., t. 6–7½, wt. 4–12 or even to 17 lb. **2.—*Hoary** (*M. caligata*): general tone cool gray, with black-and-white facial pattern; those in n. part of range are nearly black, but have some grayish on nose, cheeks, and belly. L. 25–31 in., t. 7½–10, wt. 5–14 or even to 20 lb. **3.— Olympic** (*M. olympus*): brownish-drab; occurs only on upper slopes of Olympic Mts. **4.—Vancouver** (*M. vancouverensis*): dark brown; restricted to Vancouver I. Compare with the Woodchuck (also a Marmot); tracks are like the Woodchuck's, but larger.

HABITAT: Usually at rock outcrops or slides having nearby vegetation. The Yellow-bellied occurs from low valleys to over 10,000 ft. elevation; the Hoary from medium to high elevations, but also lower down farther n.

REPRODUCTION AND HABITS: The Yellow-bellied breeds about the end of Mar., and young, said to number up to 8, are born in May. The Hoary has up to 5 young. The Marmots are abroad in daytime, often going some distance to feed on vegetation. If several feed in an area, one may act as sentinel, giving a piercing whistle if suspecting danger. The Yellow-bellied, in low hot valleys, has a period of summer inactivity (aestivation) as well as winter hibernation.

ECONOMIC STATUS: Only the Yellow-bellied occurs where

any crops are grown, hence it is a nuisance sometimes. All are aesthetic assets in parks and recreation areas.

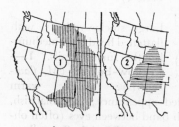

Prairie Dogs
Cynomys
Plate 21

Rather large stout-bodied rodents, with short legs, tail about ⅙–¼ as long as head and body, and internal cheek pouches. **1.—*Black-tailed** (*C ludovicianus*): varies from pale to rich brown, lighter below; tail over ⅕ head and body length, and with black terminal portion. L. 12–16½ in., t. 3–4, wt. 1½–3 lb. Females smaller than males; young paler than adults. **2.—*White-tailed** (*C. leucurus*): more slender and smaller (up to 14½ in.) ; a dark area over eye and on cheek; tail less than ⅕ head and body length, with basal half or more colored above like back, lighter below, and terminal portion white or, if not, like belly but paler (may be pale buffy). Some having worn tails show no light hairs. Included here with *leucurus* are *parvidens* and *gunnisoni* of current books; the 3 perhaps should be called *gunnisoni* collectively. The widely scattered mounds, with or without their stoutish builders on them, are conspicuous.

HABITAT: The Black-tailed prefers short-grass prairies; the White-tailed, grassy upland and mt. areas.

REPRODUCTION: Black-tailed. Some females breed as yearlings. The grass-lined nest usually is in a side branch of the tunnel. Breeding occurs Feb.–Apr., and gestation lasts between 27 and 33 days (not accurately known). Older ones have 2–10 (usually about 5) young, but first litters may contain only 2–3. Newborn young are hairless, have eyes closed, and weigh about ½ oz. They are well furred in 26 days; eyes open in 33–37 days, and they then 'bark.' In about 6 weeks they come out for green food. Weaning probably occurs a week later. Soon thereafter the mother digs a new burrow or moves to a vacant one. After several weeks the young leave the burrow where they were born and singly occupy empty burrows in the colony. A captive female lived 8½ years, a male over 10. The White-tailed breeds later, gestation requires between 28 and 32 days, and litter size is 2–10 (usually 4–6).

HABITS: Prairie Dogs are active by day and both have rather similar habits, although the White-tailed is less colonial. Following applies to the Black-tailed. The crater-shaped mound around the burrow entrance is up to 2 ft. high x 4 in diameter. On sloping terrain the mound may be mainly at one side. Much time is spent keeping it in repair. The 6- to 8-in. tunnel soon narrows to 4–5 in., goes down steeply 3–16 ft., then turns horizontally or slightly upward. Usually a listening room is 3–6 ft. below the surface. The horizontal portion has a nest chamber, usually in a side branch; another branch often serves as a toilet. Voice: yipping notes (its 'bark'), a churring sound, and sharp 'chips'; a flicking of the tail accompanies these utterances.

Prairie Dogs become very fat in fall; probably some have fairly profound winter sleep, although others—even in n. part of the range—come out in mild winter weather. Food: mainly plants of the grass and goosefoot families, but also others, and some insects. Home range usually is under 40 yds. in diameter. All vegetation over 6 in. high is cut for many yards around the burrow, which clears the view for possible predators. That the Prairie Dog, rattlesnake, and Burrowing Owl live together in harmony is a myth, since rattler and Owl eat young 'dogs' and 'dogs' eat Owl eggs and young.

ECONOMIC STATUS: The calculated food intake of 32 Prairie Dogs equals that of a sheep; 256 'dogs,' that of a cow. Within their towns, many of which formerly included hundreds of square miles, the 'dogs' practically denude the landscape of vegetation. Probably millions of them have been killed in rodent-control operations. These rodents now are rare in parts of their range.

Range maps
on pages
174 and 175

Ground Squirrels
('Gophers,' Picket Pins)
Citellus
Plates 20–22

Study plates 20–22 and compare Ground Squirrels with Chipmunks. Note that no Ground Squirrel has a striped face, yet some species often are called Chipmunks because they are rather similar otherwise in appearance, also in actions.

GENERAL REMARKS: These mammals occur in large numbers in much of w. N. Am., from deserts to Arctic tundra, and to fairly high mt. elevations. Their Chipmunk-like tracks often are abundant on dry roads and desert sands. They are colonial, active by day, and polygamous or promiscuous. Some have 1, others 2 litters annually. Young are born hairless and with eyes closed; the female rears them. Usually they stay in the burrow a month or longer, then forage outside for some weeks before dispersing. In some species a profound summer sleep (called aestivation), with lowered heartbeat and breathing rate, continues into winter (hibernation), ¾ of their lives perhaps being thus spent. Some have only hibernation and a few are active in winter, but probably all have the inherent ability to hibernate.

Food is mainly plant materials, but many species also eat quantities of insects. Individual home ranges often encompass an area less than 50 ft. in radius from the burrow system, except for some of the larger species. A host of mammals, birds, and reptiles prey on them. Extensive burrowing activity, for the one to several burrows an individual uses annually, aids in aerating and mixing the soil. There is no mound at the burrow entrance. Those species occurring on cultivated land and livestock range do great damage to crops and grasses. Some eat eggs and young of birds. They have internal cheek pouches, and most species store much food below ground. Many of their fleas transmit sylvatic plague; their ticks are vectors of spotted or tick fever and relapsing fever; tularemia, more commonly associated with Rabbits, is known from them. These diseases, often fatal to man, also have many other mammal vectors.

Latest monograph: A. H. Howell, *U. S. Dept. Agric., N. Am. Fauna* 56 (1938). Related species groups are in separate paragraphs below.

GROUND SQUIRREL (*Citellus*) **species: *Townsend's** (*C. townsendii*): relatively short-tailed; usually plain gray, shaded with pinkish-buff or cinnamon; whitish on flanks and underparts; gray and buff color phases occur in some areas. L. 8–10½ in., t. 1¼–3, wt. 6–9 oz. Inhabits mainly sagebrush valleys and juniper-covered ridges. Gestation: probably 24 days. Annual litter: 7–10 young. Climbs bushes. Voice: a prolonged chipping whistle. Below ground July–Feb. Included here is *C. idahoensis*, which is similar but somewhat dappled, and occurs on n. side of Snake River Valley, from Payette to Glens Ferry, Ida.

***Washington** (*C. washingtoni*): medium-sized, with short tail; grayish tone, dappled with whitish spots; underparts whitish; tail-tip blackish. L. 9–10, t. 1⅖–3⅖, wt. 7–10 oz. Dry slopes with grass or sagebrush. The annual litter of 5–11 young is born Feb.–Mar.; young eat green vegetation by Apr. This mammal is below ground from late June to late Jan. or later. Voice: a soft lisping whistle. A serious pest to agriculture at times.

Idaho (*C. brunneus*): like the preceding, but washed

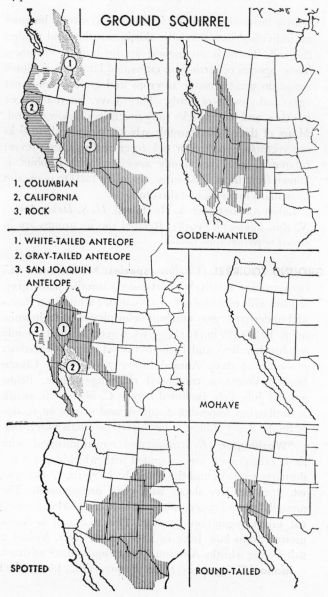

GROUND SQUIRREL

1. COLUMBIAN
2. CALIFORNIA
3. ROCK

GOLDEN-MANTLED

1. WHITE-TAILED ANTELOPE
2. GRAY-TAILED ANTELOPE
3. SAN JOAQUIN
   ANTELOPE

MOHAVE

SPOTTED

ROUND-TAILED

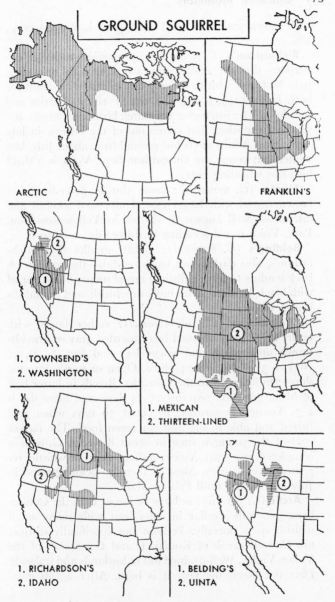

GROUND SQUIRREL

ARCTIC

FRANKLIN'S

1. TOWNSEND'S
2. WASHINGTON

1. MEXICAN
2. THIRTEEN-LINED

1. RICHARDSON'S
2. IDAHO

1. BELDING'S
2. UINTA

with brown and with small light spots. L. 9–10, t. 2¼–2½.

Richardson's (*C. richardsonii*) : medium to large; upperparts drab or smoke gray, overlaid with brownish; pale buffy or whitish below; tail edged with white or buff. L. 11–12¼, t. 2½–3½, wt. 11–18 oz. Prairies and meadows. The litter of 2–11 young, born after about 28–32 days' gestation, first comes out of the burrow in late Apr.–May. Adults are below ground from about July–late winter, but young are abroad into Sept. Voice is a shrill bird-like whistling note.

*Uinta (*C. armatus*) : same size as preceding, but browner, and with larger ears. Unforested foothill and mt. areas; well known to visitors in Yellowstone Nat. Park. Voice is a descending bird-like *tsip e-e-e-e-e*.

Belding's (*C. beldingi*) : slightly smaller than Richardson's, also darker and more reddish—the reddish on back tending to form a distinct broad stripe; tail is tipped with black, bordered with buffy or whitish, and is reddish-brown below.

*Columbian (*C. columbianus*) : rather large, with bushy tail; tawny or hazel face; mottled gray or grayish-brown upperparts, and tawny legs and feet. L. 13¾–16½, t. 3½–4½, wt. 14–18 oz. Open or partly forested slopes; to 8,000 ft. in the Cascades. Breeds in latter half of Mar., gestation requires 23–24 days, and litter size is 2–7. Young are weaned in about 30 days when well furred and able to dig and eat green food. The darker coat of the young is shed in about 8 weeks. Growth is completed in 2 years. Voice: a sharp chirp or whistle, repeated several times. Most of them go below ground in July and remain until Feb. or Mar.

Arctic (*C. parryii*) : as large or larger than the Columbian, generally similar in color, but with many small whitish spots dorsally. Perhaps not specifically distinct are *C. kodiacensis* of Kodiak I. and *C. osgoodi* of the Yukon Valley. Well-drained soil in lowlands and uplands. Does not breed the year it is born. After 25–26 days' gestation, the annual litter of 5–10 young is born in May. They weigh about ⅓ oz. at birth, attain ½ adult wt. in 4 months, and live in the parental burrow their first summer. Voice: a *sik-sik* note is common; other sounds range from a harsh scolding chatter to bird-like chirps, and they are very noisy. Much food is stored below ground.

*Thirteen-lined (*C. tridecemlineatus*): 13 narrow whitish or buffy stripes on a dark brown base, the top 5 being more or less broken into spots; belly and limbs pale tawny to whitish. L. 7–12, t. 2⅕–5, wt. 5½–9 oz. Grassy prairies, also rocky areas and brushy timber margins. The only striped Ground Squirrel within its wide range. Introduced in 1920's and established on Fishers I., N.Y. It breeds in Apr. The 5–13 young are born after 28 days' gestation. In 26–28 days they are well furred, show the striped pattern, and have eyes open; soon after this they are weaned. Voice: a drawn-out *chur-r-r-r* in high key. The period below ground lasts from fall until Mar. or Apr. Much food is stored, but evidently not much of this is eaten. Not generally a serious pest to agriculture.

Mexican (*C. mexicanus*): ¼ larger than the preceding, with rather long tail, 9 linear rows of squarish light buffy spots (sometimes rather obscure), and a brownish patch on the nose. L. 11–12½, t. 4½–5. Voice is a high-pitched, slightly descending trill—*ts-r-r-r-e-e-e-e-e*—lasting a second or a little longer.

*Spotted (*C. spilosoma*): small to medium size, with slender tail; grayish- to pinkish-brown above, more or less spotted with squarish white or buffy spots; underparts buffy or whitish. L. 8½–10, t. 2¼–3½, wt. 3–4 oz. The common Ground Squirrel of much of the arid SW. It may have 2 litters annually of 5–8 young. Voice: sharp, shrill whistle of 1 or 2 notes—*sip* or *sip-ip*. Has been seen abroad in midwinter.

*Franklin's (*C. franklinii*): large; somewhat like a Gray Squirrel in appearance, but with shorter and less bushy tail, brownish body (nearly as dark below as above), and shorter ears. L. 15–16, t. 5½–6, wt. 13–16 oz. or more. Prairies, field and pasture edges, and even open woodland. The 5–8 young are born May–June. This is the 'gray gopher,' which is seldom numerous anywhere. It gives a clear bird-like whistled twitter. It is below ground from fall until about Apr., and much food is stored.

Rock (*C. variegatus*): large, with relatively long bushy tail; general tone brownish to blackish-brown, somewhat broken into a fine mottled pattern. In some parts of its range head and foreparts are nearly black, others elsewhere have the black extending over most of the back also; underparts are buffy or grayish. L. 13–21, t. 7–10½. Rocky canyons and slopes; often sits on boulders. There may be 2 litters annually, in May–June and in Aug.–Sept. Litter size is 5–7. Voice: a single loud shrill whistle, uttered at irregular intervals. It climbs trees and bushes well and has been seen abroad in winter. A captive lived nearly 10 years.

*California (*C. beecheyi*): shaped like the preceding; brown, with buffy flecks on upperparts; sides of head and shoulders whitish, extending backward as 2 stripes, and with a dark patch on the back between these; underparts buffy. L. 16–19, t. 5½–8. Prefers open or partly wooded slopes. Occurs on Catalina I. as well as the mainland. It breeds Feb.–early Mar. and has 5–12 young in the annual litter. Voice: a high-pitched sharp bark, a variety of chirps, and an explosive growl. It climbs trees and shrubs with ease. Has been seen abroad in winter.

Gray-tailed Antelope (*C. harrisii*): small and stocky; upperparts pinkish-cinnamon, more or less darkened with brown, and a narrow white stripe on each side from shoulder to hip; upperparts mouse-gray in winter; in all seasons underparts paler; tail mixed black and white above and below. L. 9–10, t. 3–3¾, wt. 4–5 oz. In sparsely vegetated desert country. The only striped Ground Squirrel within its range. Said to breed from mid-Jan. to Mar. Litter size: 6–9 young. Voice: a shrill rapid chitter. Climbs bushes and cacti. This and the following 2 are nervous, active, and Chipmunk-like; they run with tail straight up or curved along the back, hence often are called 'Antelope Chipmunks.' ***White-tailed Antelope** (*C. leucurus*): same pattern, but paler than the preceding; undersurface of tail white, bordered with blackish—the white showing conspicuously as the mammal runs with tail curved over its back. L. 7½–9½, t. 2–3. Arid desert. Said to breed in Apr. and again in July. Habits like the preceding. **San Joaquin Antelope** (*C. nelsoni*): buffy or pinkish, with creamy-whitish line on each side of body and same color on undersurface of tail—which shows when the mammal runs with tail curved over its back. L. 8½–9½, t. 2½–3. In San Joaquin Valley, Calif.

Mohave (*C. mohavensis*): small and unstriped; general tone cinnamon-gray; underparts paler; tail brown above and white below—the white showing as the mammal runs with tail curved over its back. L. 8–10½, t. 2–3½. In Mohave Desert. There may be 2 litters annually. Voice: a sharp insect-like whistle without vibration or trill. ***Round-tailed** (*C. tereticaudus*): small, unstriped and with no contrasting colors; salmon-colored cast to upperparts; underparts slightly paler; undersurface of tail drab or buff (never white). Occurs in cinnamon and grayish-brown color phases. L. 9¼–10½, t. 3½–4. Dry desert. Voice and habits quite like the preceding; probably neither hibernates.

*Golden-mantled (*C. lateralis*): in appearance and habits like an oversized Chipmunk with *unstriped* face. General tone orange-brown to buffy; generally a tawny area on head and shoulders (the 'mantle'); a wide white stripe from shoulder to hip, usually bordered on each side by a black one, and center of back gray or fawn; underparts buffy. The black stripes are reduced in some parts of the range. Included here is *C. saturatus* of the Cascades, which is somewhat darker and with less well-defined mantle. L. 9–12½, t. 2½–4½, wt. 6–10 oz. Open forests on foothills and mts., among rocks and fallen timber. The annual litter contains 2–8 young. This rather slow-moving mammal occasionally climbs trees or bushes, but usually is seen sunning quietly on a rock or log. It can utter a shrill bird-like whistle, also chirp, buzz, and grunt. A ticking note is accompanied by a nervous flicking of the tail. Often it feeds at camp sites and becomes quite tame. Most are below ground by Sept.

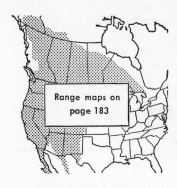

Western Chipmunks
Eutamias
Plate 22

GENERAL REMARKS: These are small ground-dwelling Squirrels, with clean delicate lines, a general grayish or tawny tone, 5 dark and 4 lighter stripes (some of either or both may be reduced or obscure) that *appear about equal* in width and extend from shoulders to flank or farther, and a light stripe above and one below the eye; underparts usually grayish-white; the furred tail is rather slender. Tracks are similar in pattern to the Eastern Chipmunk's (diagram page 185). This group is distributed from the Yukon southward, but only in and w. of the Great Lakes region do ranges of a Western and the Eastern Chipmunk overlap; see discussion under Least Chipmunk (p. 182). The Thirteen-lined, Mantled, and the 3 Antelope Ground Squirrel species have striped bodies and, all except the first, rather Chipmunk-like habits, but all have unstriped faces.

Western Chipmunks occur from low valleys to quite high mt. elevations and from deserts to cool n. forests. They are active by day and are rather social. Sometimes 2 species occur in the same locality, even about the same rock or tree, but usually they are kept more apart by habitat preferences. Since markings and color may be

(Within image: Range maps on page 183)

quite similar, in some cases it is far from easy to make accurate sight identifications. Differences in voice sometimes indicate whether more than one species is present —even before they have been observed carefully—but voices have not been described adequately for enough species to present such data here. In general, Western Chipmunks have 3 types of notes: a low-pitched resonant bark, usually uttered at long but regular intervals; high-pitched chipping notes, generally uttered more often and irregularly; and a mixture of guttural and wiry notes, given when fleeing from danger.

Two litters annually may be the rule, although some may have only one. Young are born hairless, with eyes closed, soon develop the adult pattern, and are reared by the female. Litter size is about 2–8. Winter sleep is not profound, there being periods of activity below ground when stored food is eaten.

Food includes nuts, fruits, berries, seeds, soft parts of plants, mushrooms, and many insects. Most species climb bushes or even trees quite readily. Having large internal cheek pouches, they carry and store much food in the burrow. These burrows are elaborate underground systems, and the earth is packed as the Chipmunk digs, leaving no mound at the entrance. Most of them live away from cultivated areas and seldom come into direct conflict with man's interests.

Latest monograph: A. H. Howell, *U. S. Dept. Agric., N. Am. Fauna* 52 (1929); it is followed here, with some modifications. Closely related species are grouped in paragraphs below.

CHIPMUNK (*Eutamias*) **species: Alpine** (*E. alpinus*): a small gray species; dark stripes on body warm brown. L. 7–8 in., t. 2¾–3½, wt. 1–1¾ oz. Sierras, from timber line down to about 8,000 ft.

*Least (*E. minimus*): very variable geographically; in general, larger and darker in N. and E. and smaller and paler in W. and S.; stripes continue to tail base; in general, a grayish species, but tone varies from tawny to cool gray to pale pinkish-buff; median dark stripe blackish; central pair of light stripes grayish-white. L. 6½–9, t. 3–4⅖, wt. 1–2½ oz. In E., range overlaps that of Eastern Chipmunk (p. 184), which is a larger species with reddish rump and stripes not extending to tail base. Other Western species within its range are larger and differ in color. The Least prefers open glades and rocky areas in mixed woodland or conifers; to over 11,000 ft. elevation in some areas. An expert climber, it often lies sunning on a tree branch. Its *chip* note is rather distinctively high-pitched and weak.

*Yellow Pine (*E. amœnus*): bright-colored, with very distinct stripes; general tone varies from tawny in N. to pinkish-cinnamon farther S.; dark of back stripes often has tawny or cinnamon intermixed; outer pair of light stripes usually clear white; rump usually tawny. L. 7⅖–10, t. 3–4¼, wt. 1⅓–2 oz. Mainly yellow pine forests; to 9,000 ft. elevation in some areas. **Panamint** (*E. panamintinus*): general tone bright tawny, with gray head and rump. L. 8–9, t. 3½–4, wt. 1½–2⅖ oz. Piñon pine and junipers of desert ranges of se. Calif., and sw. Nev., at about 6,000–9,000 ft. elevation.

*Colorado (*E. quadrivittatus*): general tone tawny-buff; whitish stripe below eye continues as a conspicuous patch behind base of ear; 3 central dark stripes blackish and 2 outer ones only faintly indicated; 2 central light stripes grayish and outer pair whitish; head and rump gray; tail relatively long, dull brown below, and nearly black above toward tip. L. 8–9½, t. 3¾–4½, wt. 1¾–2½ oz. Yellow pines and above; to 10,000 ft. in some areas. Common in w. mts. within its range. Mapped with it are 2 others that are very similar but sometimes listed as separate species: *E. adsitus* of Beaver Mts. of Ut. and Kaibab Plateau in n. Ariz.; *E. calipeplus* of Mt. Pinos, Calif. Similar in pattern also are the first 2 of the 4 following species. **Uinta** (*E. umbrinus*): l. 7¾–9½, t. 2¾–4½. At 7,000–10,000 ft., above yellow pine belt, in

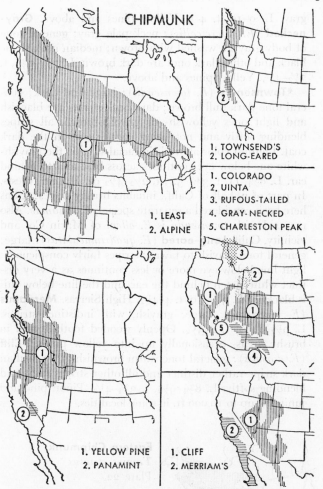

CHIPMUNK

1. TOWNSEND'S
2. LONG-EARED

1. COLORADO
2. UINTA
3. RUFOUS-TAILED
4. GRAY-NECKED
5. CHARLESTON PEAK

1. LEAST
2. ALPINE

1. YELLOW PINE
2. PANAMINT

1. CLIFF
2. MERRIAM'S

mts. of ne. Ut. and s. Wyo. **Charleston Peak** (*E. palmeri*): l. 8½–9, t. 3½–4. Conifers at 7,000–12,000 ft. on Charleston Peak in s. Nev.

Rufous-tailed (*E. ruficaudus*): large and bright-colored; shoulders and sides bright reddish-brown; rump

gray. L. 9–10, t. 4–5. Yellow pines and above. **Gray-
necked** (*E. cinereicollis*): neck pale gray; general tone
of body grayish, washed with brown; median dark stripe
black and other dark ones are dark brown. L. 7¾–9¾, t.
3½–4⅗. Yellow pines and above.

*Townsend's (*E. townsendii*): large and dark; general tone dark dull brown; dark back stripes are blackish
and light ones yellowish- or grayish-brown, all stripes
blending softly and not being conspicuous in the dark
coat. Lightest color above is in facial stripes; the grayish-
white one below eye continues across base and to behind
ear. L. 8¾–11, t. 3¾–5, wt. 2½–4½ oz. Humid forests.
In part of n. half of Calif., inhabits brushy slopes; it has
here been considered a separate species, *E. sonomae*. Also
mapped with *townsendii* is *E. alleni* of Marin Co. and
vicinity, Calif. **Long-eared** (*E. quadrimaculatus*): large;
general tone grayish to tawny; stripes fairly conspicuous;
light line below eye more or less continues as a very distinct white patch behind the ear, and the line below this
is blackish. L. 9¼–10, t. 4–4½. High Sierras. **Merriam's**
(*E. merriami*): large; grayish, with indistinct stripes.
L. 9½–11½, t. 4–5½. Openly wooded foothills and in
brushy areas, occasionally up into yellow pines. ***Cliff**
(*E. dorsalis*): general tone warm brownish-gray; median
dark stripe rather distinct and all other stripes faint and
blending softly. L. 8¾–9½, t. 3¾–4½. Piñon pine and
junipers; up to 10,000 ft. in some localities.

Eastern Chipmunk
Tamias striatus
Plate 22

A small ground-dwelling
Squirrel, having striped face
and 5 dark and 4 lighter
body stripes—the outer (or
lower) pair of light stripes being white or nearly so.

Stripes appear *unequal* in width. General tone tawny, with rump tending toward reddish and shoulders grayish; underparts white; internal cheek pouches large. L. 9–11 in., t. 3½–4, wt. 2½–5 oz. Compare with the smaller Least Chipmunk (p. 181) of the Western group, also with the Thirteen-lined Ground Squirrel (p. 177); their ranges overlap part of the Eastern Chipmunk's. This mammal usually is seen running about or sitting on

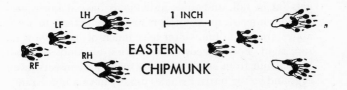

a rock or log; it is not conspicuous when motionless, but attention often is attracted to it by its loud *chip* note.

HABITAT: Deciduous forests and brushy areas, preferably on rocky ground or with fallen logs and stone walls.

REPRODUCTION: Adult females give birth in Apr.; summer litters may be offspring of preceding year's young that did not breed earlier. Breeding is from Mar. onward, and gestation requires 31 days. The 3–5, occasionally to 7, young are born in a lined chamber in the burrow system and are reared by the female. At birth they are naked, have eyes closed, and weigh about ⅛ oz. The striped coat begins to show in 8 days, fur grows rapidly in the fourth week, eyes open in 31 days, and they behave like adults soon thereafter. Probably they are weaned before 40 days old, but remain at home for some time longer. Life span ordinarily may be 2–4 years, but a captive lived 8.

HABITS: This Chipmunk is active by day and climbs trees readily. Its behavior reveals a mixture of nervous activity, curiosity, and shyness. Individuals dwelling near each other tend to be somewhat social, but the sexes are together only to breed. Tunnels go straight down, then turn laterally; the builder packs the earth as it goes, pushing up no mound at the entrance. The loud *chip* note may be repeated at regular intervals for many minutes; a soft musical *cuck* also may be repeated regularly. The body jerks as these are uttered. A startled Chipmunk gives several rapid *chip* notes and then a rapid trill.

Much food is carried in the cheek pouches for storage underground. This little mammal sometimes is not seen above ground for several weeks during hot weather. It gets fat in fall, and some individuals have a fairly profound winter sleep, but others are more active; to see it above ground in midwinter over much of its range is no rare sight. Food: seeds, nuts, berries, all kinds of small animal life from small Mice to snails and insects, even eggs and young birds. Females usually have a home range 80 yds. or less in greatest length, males a somewhat larger one. The population fluctuates markedly, peak numbers occurring at intervals of several years.

ECONOMIC STATUS: Bulbs and various parts of ornamental and garden plants are occasionally eaten, but generally this Chipmunk does not conflict with man's interests and is valued for its aesthetic appeal. In some localities, ticks carried by it may transmit spotted fever.

Gray Squirrels
Sciurus (part)
Plate 25

The familiar Gray Squirrel of parks and woodlands. **1. —*Eastern** (*S. carolinensis*): grayish above, in summer with brownish hair tips; white or pale gray below; tail long, bushy, and usually with whitish fringe. In parts of its range there are many melanistic (black) individuals. L. 15½–21 in., t. 7½–10, wt. ¾–1½ lb. **2.—Western** (*S. griseus*): somewhat larger—l. to 24 in., with

dusky feet and narrower tail. **3.—Arizona** (*S. arizonen-
sis*): in general like the Eastern, but belly sometimes
yellowish; tail ⅕ longer and with considerable black in
it, making the whitish fringe more conspicuous. L. 19–23,
t. 10–12.

The more slender Grays lack the squarish head of the
heavier Fox Squirrels—a character which holds regardless of color phase of either Gray or Fox. Leaf nests in
trees, especially noticeable in winter, are common Gray
Squirrel signs. When leaping, sets of tracks (diagram, p.
194) are about 20–24 in. apart.

HABITAT: The Eastern Gray prefers hardwoods; the Western and Arizona Grays are found mainly in oaks and
pines. The Eastern has been introduced and become
established in N. Am. at points as far from its natural
range as Seattle, Wash., and Stanley Park on Vancouver
I.; also abroad.

REPRODUCTION: Eastern Gray. Females first breed in their
second summer and thereafter in spring or twice annually. In SE., at least, there are 2 breeding seasons—Dec.
or Jan. and late May. Gestation requires about 44 days,
and litter size is 1–4, usually 2–3. Young are hairless and
have eyes closed at birth. Eyes open in 37 days, and well-
furred young come out in about 6 weeks to eat green
food; probably they are weaned soon thereafter. Then
either the female leaves or they drive her away. When a
second litter is raised in a season, after the mother departs, probably they quite often occupy the nest through
the winter. Captives have lived over 10 years. The Western Gray has a litter of 3–5 young, born in late winter or
early spring; there may be 2 litters annually in s. part of
its range.

HABITS: The various Grays differ but little; these remarks
pertain to the Eastern. It spends considerable time on the
ground, foraging for or storing food. Items are hidden
separately. Considerable buried food is not dug up again.
Dens in tree cavities are more or less permanent homes,
being occupied perhaps by a succession of individuals or,

in winter, even several together. A Squirrel may build a number of leaf nests in a season, mainly for shelter in feeding areas. Spherical in shape, they consist of a platform of twigs, an outer shell of leaves and twigs, and a lining of closely packed plant material. The entrance is at the side. Food remains often are found in them. After a tree den is fouled, the mother sometimes moves her young to a clean leaf nest.

When startled or irritated the Gray utters a rapid series of rasping *quack* notes ending in a drawn-out, rolling *a-a-a-a-a*. This is also given by both sexes when the mating urge is on them. Nasal, throaty grunts, a scolding *chur-r-r*, and a loud chattering of teeth are other sounds. This Squirrel does not hibernate. Food: nuts, seeds, buds and flowers of trees, mushrooms, insects, and some garden crops. Home ranges usually are several acres in extent, often overlapping. Evidently the population increases when food is plentiful, then may decline rapidly when it becomes scarce. Failure of the nut crop in an area when the population is high probably accounts for emigrations of thousands of Grays. Such movements, during which they cross streams and rivers, have been recorded at intervals for over a century in ne. N. Am. Usually Red and Gray do not live together peacefully, the former chasing its larger relative frequently, but some Grays are not much disturbed by this.

ECONOMIC STATUS: Gray Squirrels are important game mammals and are excellent eating. Hunters should not shoot into leaf nests, for they wound Squirrels that they do not bag. The Gray carries off many ears of corn at times, eats other garden food, flower bulbs, and buds. Its pruning of trees can be a nuisance, also its persistent attendance at bird feeding stations. In the NE. it may do a million dollars' damage annually by eating insulation off electrical cables. Where the population is to be encouraged, den trees should not be cut. Nest boxes can be provided. Grays are ornamental in parks.

Tassel-eared Squirrel
(Abert's and/or Kaibab
Squirrel)
Sciurus aberti
Plate 24

A large, heavy-bodied tree
Squirrel with broad ears, having tall tufts Jan.–June, and
very broad bushy tail. Color phase called Abert's: generally grizzled gray above; blackish ear tufts; back with
broad band of chestnut or rusty-red (lacking in some
Colo. specimens); a black line on lower sides; underparts
usually pure white; tail usually white below, but also
ranges from gray to black, with white-tipped hairs above.
The Kaibab color phase—of Kaibab Plateau, an area 40
mi. long by 20 wide on n. side of Grand Canyon in Ariz.
—differs in that underparts are mainly black, ear tufts
brownish-black, and tail usually all white. The Tassel-
eared Squirrel varies greatly, brownish or blackish (melanistic) Abert's being common in Colo. Abert's often has
a black belly like the Kaibab; the latter sometimes has a
gray tail like Abert's. L. 19–21 in., t. 8½–9½, wt. 1½–2
lb. Bulky leaf nests in trees or, in winter, large tracks in
snow reveal its presence.

HABITAT: Conifers, mainly yellow pines.

REPRODUCTION AND HABITS: Since young appear out of nests
Apr.–Aug., perhaps 2 litters are produced annually—at
least when food is plentiful. Litter size is 3–4. This Squirrel is rather deliberate in manner; the tail is waved
gracefully. It is rather gregarious, several often playing in
a tree. Usual utterance is a barking *chuck-chuck,* sug-
gesting a Fox Squirrel's notes, but it also grunts, chatters,
and has a variety of scolding notes. It does not hibernate,
but is inactive at times during cold weather. It builds
bulky nests of twigs with needles attached, lined with
grass and bark shreds, the whole being on a tree branch
and about one bushel in volume. Food: conifer seeds,

acorns, bark, tree flowers, various fruits, herbs, and mushrooms.

ECONOMIC STATUS: It is legally hunted in some areas. It is confiding when protected—a conspicuous and desirable mammal in parks and about camps. Many are hit by automobiles.

Fox Squirrels
Sciurus (part)
Plate 25

1.—*Eastern (*S. niger*):* largest e. tree Squirrel; heavy-bodied, and with squarish facial profile. Color varies greatly. Over much of its range, general tone of upperparts is rusty-brown; tail edged with buffy-brown; nose, underparts, and feet vary from yellowish-brown to orange-rusty. In a coastal strip, Del. into Va. and extending inland some distance, it is usually gray (no brown), with white nose, underparts, and feet. In SE. mainly, body is grayish with slight brownish overcast; tail edge whitish-gray; most of head blackish; nose and underparts whitish; feet buffy-brown. In La.–Tex., upperparts (including nose) are rather uniformly suffused with black; underparts and feet tend toward cinnamon. In some areas, both buff- and gray-phase Fox Squirrels occur; black (melanistic) ones are numerous in SE. and some places elsewhere. These are black, except nose, lips, and ears, which are nearly white (these parts also are black in melanistic Gray Squirrels). Intermediates occur between all variations described here. L. 19–28 in., t. 10–12¼, wt. 1½–3 lb. **2.—Mexican** (*S. apache*): a smaller and more graceful species. Upperparts blackish-gray; eyelids, underparts, and limbs salmon-brown; tail black, with creamy-orange fringe. L. 22, t. 11. Included with it here is *S. chiricahuae* of se. Ariz.

HABITAT: The Eastern prefers open woodlands, especially of oaks, longleaf pine, gum, or cypresses at swamp edges; introduced at points outside its natural range, as at Boise, Ida. The Mexican occurs in oak and pine forests, preferably near water.

REPRODUCTION: Eastern Fox Squirrel. Females born in spring first breed late the following winter; those born in summer breed the following spring or summer. The winter nest is in a tree cavity or is a lined outside leaf structure; summer nests used for denning are substantial also, while many flimsy structures are built then for feeding or resting shelters. Gestation requires about 45 days. Two peaks of breeding occur, in winter and late spring, probably indicating that many adults have 2 litters annually. Litter size: 1–6, usually 2–4. Young at birth have eyes closed and weigh about ⅔ oz. They have a fine hair coat in 10 days; eyes open in 40–44 days. They begin coming out of the nest in 6 weeks, eat green food at 8 weeks or earlier, and soon thereafter are independent. Captives have lived 6 or more years.

HABITS: Eastern Fox Squirrel. It is a slow and deliberate walker and somewhat clumsy as a climber. The tail is waved rather than flicked. It is not an early riser in the morning, but it does not cease foraging until after dusk. Males lead solitary lives most of the year. A favored den tree is used for many years, the entrance being gnawed to keep growing wood from restricting its size. Leaf nests for winter have an outer layer of twigs with leaves attached, a series of inner layers of damp leaves pressed together, then a lining of shredded bark and leaf fragments. These nests last several years. Voice: a barking series of several dry *quak* notes given rapidly, then a shrill drawn-out *qua-a-a-a;* there are variations of this, also grunts, snarls, and a chattering of the teeth. Much food is hoarded, items being placed in separate holes in the leaf mold or soil. Food: various nuts, berries, fruits, buds, twigs and bark, mushrooms, and corn. Home range usually is about 10 acres at any one time but is altered with the seasons,

(CONT. ON PAGE 193, AFTER PLATES)

NOTES ON PLATES

SCALE: All figures on Plates 1–3 are to same scale; so also are those on Plates 38–40. In between, Plates 4–37, figures on each pair of facing plates are to same scale.

AQUATIC MAMMALS: Colors are of these mammals when dry; many aquatic mammals look quite dark and color-less when wet. See especially Plates 16–19. (Whales, Dolphins, and Porpoises are shown in black and white on pages 333, 335, and 337.)

POSES: Variety is used within a group—Ground Squirrels, for example—to give some idea of range of poses seen in life.

YOUNG: Where 'young' are shown, color or pattern (or both) differs markedly from that of fully adult individuals. The coat shown may be shed before nursing ceases, as in Elk, or, at the other extreme, a mammal may breed in 'young' coat, as in Deermice. Not all cases are illustrated wherein young differ markedly from adults.

PAGE REFERENCES: Those on plates refer to where a species illustrated is discussed in text. If a species is one of a group treated under one heading in text, be sure also to read the opening paragraphs dealing with the group. Example: On Plate 30 under Golden Deermouse, page reference is 229; since this is one of the Deermice (*Peromyscus*), turn back also to beginning of Deermice section and read the opening paragraphs.

BIG BROWN BAT
p. 68

**LITTLE BROWN
MYOTIS** p. 61

**EASTERN
PIPISTRELLE**
p. 67

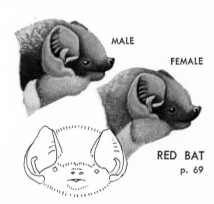

MALE

FEMALE

RED BAT
p. 69

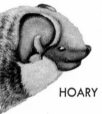

HOARY BAT p. 71

EVENING BAT
p. 72

**SILVER-HAIRED
BAT** p. 66

PLATE 1

EASTERN YELLOW BAT
p. 72

**EASTERN
LUMP-NOSED
BAT** p. 73

**CALIFORNIA
LEAF-NOSED BAT**
p. 57

PALLID BAT
p. 75

**MEXICAN
FREE-TAILED
BAT** p. 76

**PETERS' LEAF-CHINNED
BAT** p. 57

PLATE 2

LONG-TONGUED BAT p. 59

LONG-NOSED BAT p. 60

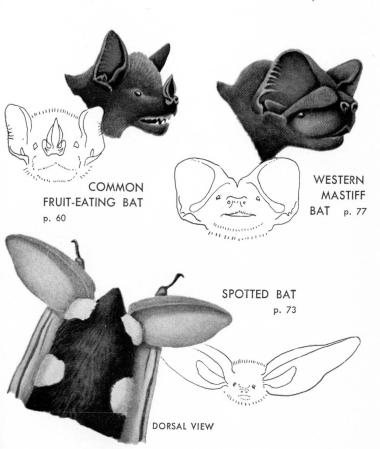

COMMON FRUIT-EATING BAT p. 60

WESTERN MASTIFF BAT p. 77

SPOTTED BAT p. 73

DORSAL VIEW

PLATE 3

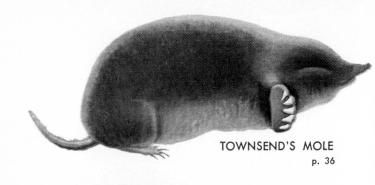

TOWNSEND'S MOLE
p. 36

HAIRY-TAILED MOLE
p. 38

EASTERN MOLE
p. 39

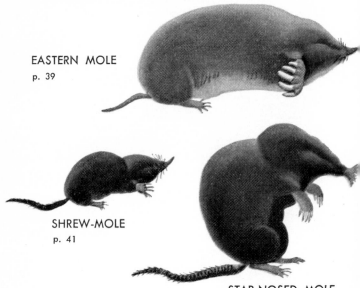

SHREW-MOLE
p. 41

STAR-NOSED MOLE
p. 42

PLATE 4

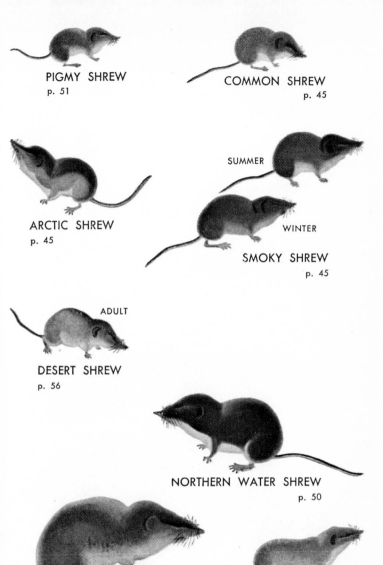

PIGMY SHREW
p. 51

COMMON SHREW
p. 45

ARCTIC SHREW
p. 45

SUMMER

WINTER

SMOKY SHREW
p. 45

ADULT

DESERT SHREW
p. 56

NORTHERN WATER SHREW
p. 50

BIG SHORT-TAILED
SHREW p. 54

LITTLE SHORT-TAILED
SHREW p. 52

PLATE 5

POLAR BEAR p. 88

BIG BROWN
BEAR p. 85

PLATE 6

'BLUE' PHASE

BLACK PHASE

BLACK BEAR
p. 79

CINNAMON PHASE

GRIZZLY BEAR
p. 83

PLATE 7

WOLVERINE
p. 109

RIVER OTTER
p. 111

SEA OTTER
p. 114

PLATE 8

MARTEN
p. 96

FISHER
p. 98

RACCOON
p. 90

BADGER
p. 122

PLATE 9

MALE,
WINTER

FEMALE, SUMMER

LEAST WEASEL
p. 103

FEMALE, SUMMER

MALE, WINTER

SHORT-TAILED WEASEL
p. 100

MALE, SUMMER
NORTHEAST

FEMALE, SUMMER
NORTHEAST

LONG-TAILED WEASEL
p. 104

SOUTHWEST

BLACK-FOOTED FERRET
p. 108

MINK   p. 106

PLATE 10

IN HAND-STAND POSE

(WEST)

(EAST)

SPOTTED SKUNK
p. 116

STRIPED SKUNK
p. 118
FULL-STRIPED
INDIVIDUAL

HOODED SKUNK
p. 121
NARROW-STRIPED
INDIVIDUAL

HOG-NOSED
SKUNK p. 121

PLATE 11

COYOTE
p. 134

RED WOLF
p. 136

BLACK PHASE

WHITE PHASE

GRAY PHASE

GRAY WOLF
p. 136

PLATE 12

KIT FOX
p. 128

GRAY FOX
p. 129

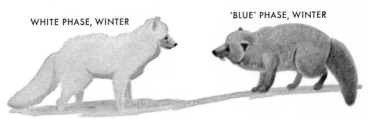

WHITE PHASE, WINTER

'BLUE' PHASE, WINTER

ARCTIC FOX p. 131

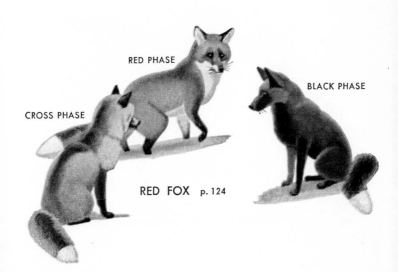

RED PHASE

BLACK PHASE

CROSS PHASE

RED FOX p. 124

PLATE 13

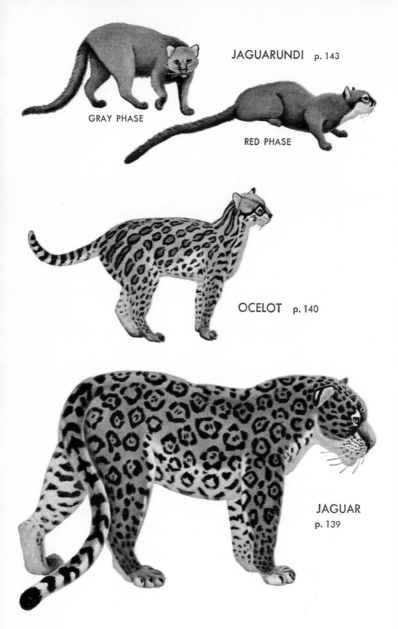

JAGUARUNDI p. 143

GRAY PHASE

RED PHASE

OCELOT p. 140

JAGUAR
p. 139

PLATE 14

LYNX
p. 144

BOBCAT
p. 146

MOUNTAIN LION
p. 141

ADULT

YOUNG

PLATE 15

BULL. SNOUT
DEFLATED

BULL, CHALLENGING,
SNOUT INFLATED

ELEPHANT SEAL
p. 165

COW

BULL

WALRUS
p. 154

COW

CALF

PLATE 16

COWS

PUP

BULL

NORTHERN FUR SEAL
p. 148

GUADALUPE
FUR SEAL p. 151

BULL

BULL

COW

NORTHERN
SEA LION p. 152

BULL

COW

CALIFORNIA SEA LION p. 153

PLATE 17

RINGED SEAL p. 158

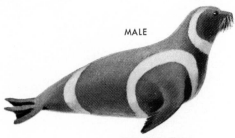

MALE

RIBBON SEAL p. 157

ADULT (DRY)

HARBOR SEAL p. 156

PUP

PUP, SHEDDING
WHITE FIRST
COAT

MALE

GRAY SEAL p. 162

PLATE 18

MALE

PUP

FULLY
MATURE
FEMALE

HARP SEAL p. 159

YOUNG FEMALE

MALE

HOODED SEAL p. 163

BEARDED SEAL
p. 161

PLATE 19

UINTA GROUND
SQUIRREL
p. 176

GRAY PHASE

TOWNSEND'S
GROUND SQUIRREL
p. 173

COLUMBIAN
GROUND SQUIRREL
p. 176

CALIFORNIA
GROUND
SQUIRREL
p. 178

FRANKLIN'S GROUND
SQUIRREL p. 177

PLATE 20

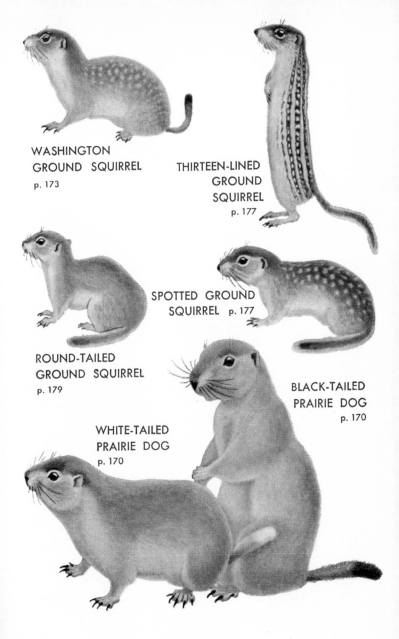

WASHINGTON
GROUND SQUIRREL
p. 173

THIRTEEN-LINED
GROUND
SQUIRREL
p. 177

SPOTTED GROUND
SQUIRREL p. 177

ROUND-TAILED
GROUND SQUIRREL
p. 179

BLACK-TAILED
PRAIRIE DOG
p. 170

WHITE-TAILED
PRAIRIE DOG
p. 170

PLATE 21

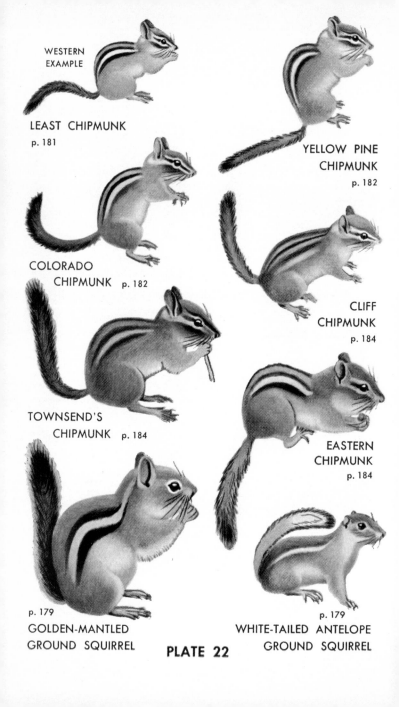

WESTERN EXAMPLE

LEAST CHIPMUNK
p. 181

YELLOW PINE
CHIPMUNK
p. 182

COLORADO
CHIPMUNK   p. 182

CLIFF
CHIPMUNK
p. 184

TOWNSEND'S
CHIPMUNK   p. 184

EASTERN
CHIPMUNK
p. 184

p. 179
GOLDEN-MANTLED
GROUND SQUIRREL

p. 179
WHITE-TAILED ANTELOPE
GROUND SQUIRREL

PLATE 22

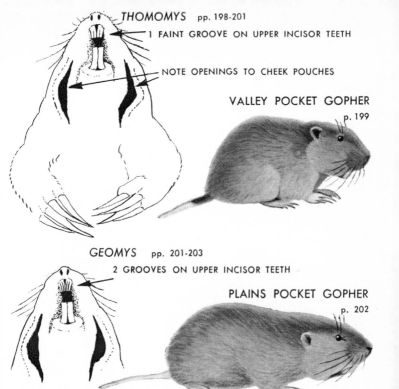

THOMOMYS pp. 198-201

1 FAINT GROOVE ON UPPER INCISOR TEETH

NOTE OPENINGS TO CHEEK POUCHES

VALLEY POCKET GOPHER
p. 199

GEOMYS pp. 201-203

2 GROOVES ON UPPER INCISOR TEETH

PLAINS POCKET GOPHER
p. 202

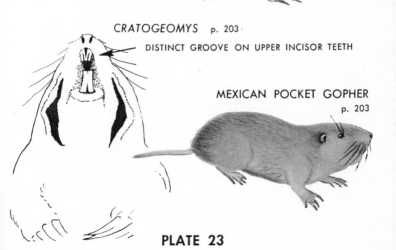

CRATOGEOMYS p. 203

DISTINCT GROOVE ON UPPER INCISOR TEETH

MEXICAN POCKET GOPHER
p. 203

PLATE 23

SOUTHERN FLYING SQUIRREL p. 196

PERCHED

GLIDING

WINTER

WINTER

SUMMER

SUMMER

DOUGLAS SQUIRREL p. 193

RED SQUIRREL p. 193

ABERT PHASE

KAIBAB PHASE

TASSEL-EARED SQUIRREL p. 189

PLATE 24

EASTERN GRAY SQUIRREL p. 186

MELANISTIC

EASTERN FOX SQUIRREL p. 190

MELANISTIC

BROWN

GRAY

PLATE 25

FLORIDA WATER
RAT p. 257

MUSKRAT
p. 258

BEAVER
p. 216

PORCUPINE
p. 272

PLATE 26

PIKA p. 275

APLODONTIA
p. 266

HOARY MARMOT
p. 169

YELLOW-BELLIED MARMOT
p. 169

WOODCHUCK
p. 167

PLATE 27

EASTERN WOODRAT
p. 235

WHITE-THROATED
WOODRAT
p. 236

BUSHY-TAILED
WOODRAT
p. 237

BLACK RAT
p. 261

BROWN RAT
p. 261

PLATE 28

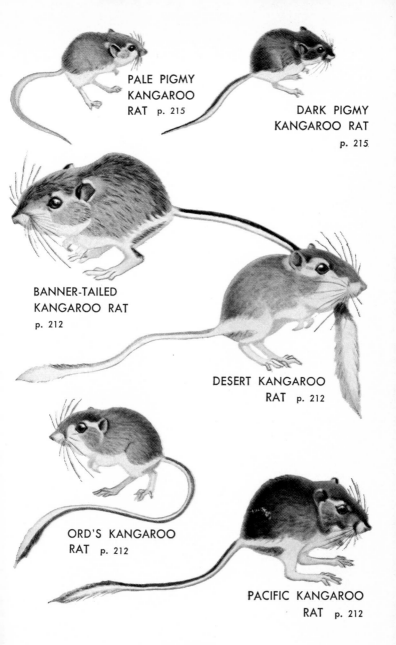

PALE PIGMY
KANGAROO
RAT p. 215

DARK PIGMY
KANGAROO RAT
p. 215

BANNER-TAILED
KANGAROO RAT
p. 212

DESERT KANGAROO
RAT p. 212

ORD'S KANGAROO
RAT p. 212

PACIFIC KANGAROO
RAT p. 212

PLATE 29

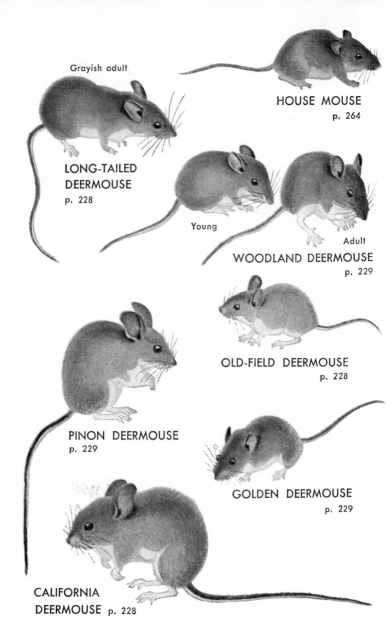

Grayish adult

HOUSE MOUSE
p. 264

LONG-TAILED
DEERMOUSE
p. 228

Young

Adult

WOODLAND DEERMOUSE
p. 229

OLD-FIELD DEERMOUSE
p. 228

PINON DEERMOUSE
p. 229

GOLDEN DEERMOUSE
p. 229

CALIFORNIA
DEERMOUSE p. 228

PLATE 30

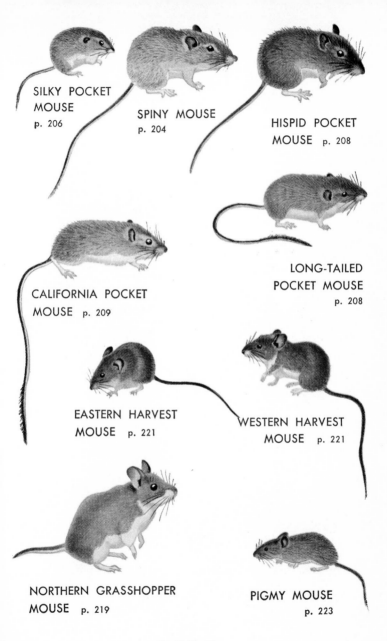

SILKY POCKET
MOUSE
p. 206

SPINY MOUSE
p. 204

HISPID POCKET
MOUSE p. 208

LONG-TAILED
POCKET MOUSE
p. 208

CALIFORNIA POCKET
MOUSE p. 209

EASTERN HARVEST
MOUSE p. 221

WESTERN HARVEST
MOUSE p. 221

NORTHERN GRASSHOPPER
MOUSE p. 219

PIGMY MOUSE
p. 223

PLATE 31

SUMMER

**GREENLAND VARYING
LEMMING** p. 242

WINTER

FOREFOOT
IN WINTER

BROWN LEMMING
p. 240

FOREFOOT

**SOUTHERN LEMMING
MOUSE** p. 238

ALASKA VOLE
p. 252

MEADOW VOLE
p. 249

SAGEBRUSH MOUSE
p. 254

PLATE 32

RED SPRUCE-MOUSE
p. 244

NORTHERN SPRUCE MOUSE p. 244

PINE MOUSE
p. 255

NORTHERN RED-BACKED MOUSE
p. 246

WOODLAND JUMPING MOUSE
p. 270

NORTHERN JUMPING MOUSE
p. 269

COMMON COTTON RAT p. 233

RICE RAT p. 231

PLATE 33

PIGMY RABBIT
p. 278

EASTERN
COTTONTAIL
p. 279

SWAMP RABBIT
p. 281

DESERT
COTTONTAIL
p. 281

WINTER

SUMMER

VARYING
HARE p. 283

WINTER

SUMMER

ARCTIC HARE
p. 285

BLACK-TAILED
JACK RABBIT
p. 286

SUMMER

WINTER

WHITE-TAILED
JACK RABBIT
p. 286

PLATE 34

RINGTAIL
p. 94

OPOSSUM
p. 33

FEMALE

MALE

COATI
p. 93

NINE-BANDED ARMADILLO
p. 320

ANTELOPE
JACK RABBIT
p. 287

COLLARED PECCARY
p. 289

PLATE 35

PRONGHORN
p. 306

BUCK

KID

DOE

BULL

COW

CALF

BISON
p. 309

PLATE 36

BULL, AUTUMN

ELK
p. 291

COW
AND CALF,
EARLY SUMMER

BULL,
AUTUMN

COW AND CALF,
EARLY SUMMER

MOOSE
p. 300

PLATE 37

RAM

EWE AND LAMB

WHITE PHASE

DALL'S SHEEP
p. 314

GRAY PHASE, RAM

BLACK PHASE, RAM

BIGHORN SHEEP
p. 314

RAM

EWE

NANNY

KID

BILLY

MOUNTAIN GOAT
p. 317

PLATE 38

MUSKOX
p. 311

BUCK, AUTUMN

WOODLAND
CARIBOU
p. 303

REINDEER p. 303

BARREN GROUND
CARIBOU p. 302

DOE, AUTUMN

BUCK, AUTUMN

PLATE 39

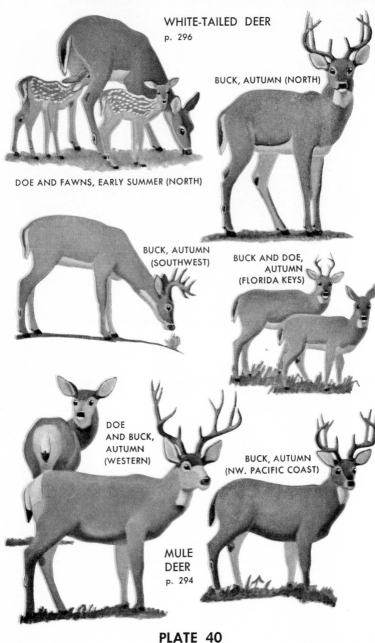

WHITE-TAILED DEER
p. 296

BUCK, AUTUMN (NORTH)

DOE AND FAWNS, EARLY SUMMER (NORTH)

BUCK, AUTUMN (SOUTHWEST)

BUCK AND DOE, AUTUMN (FLORIDA KEYS)

DOE AND BUCK, AUTUMN (WESTERN)

BUCK, AUTUMN (NW. PACIFIC COAST)

MULE DEER
p. 294

PLATE 40

so that several times this area may be used in a year. It is not unusual for an individual to travel a mile from its den.

ECONOMIC STATUS: Eastern Fox Squirrel. It provides good hunting and fine table meat and becomes wary when hunted. Leaf nests should not be shot at by hunters; a wounded occupant seldom is bagged. Some damage is done by foraging in cornfields and by gnawing bark or completely girdling trees. Being more gentle than the Gray, it is more easily tamed.

Red Squirrels
(Chickarees)
Tamiasciurus
Plate 24

Small tree Squirrels with fairly bushy tails; ears somewhat tufted in winter. General tone of upperparts varies from tawny to brownish to olive-brown, more drab in winter. Usually a blackish line on sides in summer; but winter adults and young may not show it. In the order given here they become progressively somewhat larger, but all are within this size range: l. 11½–14 in., t. 4–5¾, wt. 5–11 oz.

SQUIRREL (*Tamiasciurus*) **species: 1.—*Red** (*T. hudsonicus*): underparts whitish; tail usually with tawny fringe. **2.—*Douglas** (*T. douglasii*): underparts rusty; tail fringed with yellowish or white. **3.—Pine** (*T. fremonti*): white underparts and tail fringe. The three probably represent a single varying species. The lively habits and chatter of these Squirrels make them conspicuous. Their cone cuttings on stumps and rocks are common, and tracks in snow are numerous where the Squirrels occur. Chipmunks also climb trees, but they have distinctive back stripes. In rapid bounds, front tracks are between hind; in slow bounds, as in the accompanying diagram.

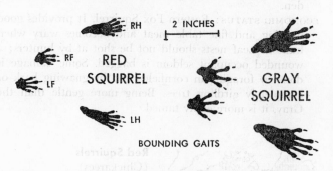

RH
2 INCHES
RF   RED
SQUIRREL
LF
GRAY
SQUIRREL
LH

BOUNDING GAITS

HABITAT: Conifers, especially spruces and firs, are preferred, but they are also found in other types of woodland.

REPRODUCTION: Red Squirrel. Females born in spring breed the following spring, and summer-born ones probably the following summer. Thereafter many, in s. part of the range at least, may have 2 litters annually. The nest, of shredded bark and other vegetation, may be in a natural tree cavity, a Woodpecker hole, or in a burrow in the ground. Spherical nests about a foot in diameter also are used, these usually being placed on a conifer limb near the trunk. Birds' nests of Crow size are roofed over and used. Breeds Mar.–early Apr., and gestation may require about 40 days; a second litter may be born Aug.–Sept. Litter size: 3–6, usually 4. Eyes are closed, and young weigh about ¼ oz. at birth. A fine hair coat appears by the ninth day, eyes open in 27 days, and they are weaned in less than 5 weeks; they often climb before being weaned. Weaned young drive the mother away and occupy the home for a while before separating. A captive lived 9 years.

The annual litter of the Pine Squirrel is born late spring–early summer, and litter size is 1–4; the Douglas Squirrel in spring has a litter of 4–7 (usually 4) young.

HABITS: All 'species' are curious, full of activity, and noisy at times. They are agile climbers and also spend much time on the ground. They are active by day and on moonlit nights. They dig burrows in the ground, packing most of the earth and not leaving dirt mounds at the many entrances. Mounds of cone fragments are common about burrows. They have several nests and other hiding places and always seem aware as to which retreat is nearest. They swim readily and well. Each individual has its home range, which it knows in detail. They do not hibernate, but are rather inactive in spells of cold or wet weather.

All have an extensive vocabulary. The chattering *tcher-r-r-r*, often much prolonged, is practically a 'trademark.' There are explosive grunts, growls, clucks, and other notes, sometimes all given in rapid and jumbled fashion, with much twitching of body and tail. All are great hoarders, storing cones in caches in the ground and mushrooms on tree limbs. The Douglas Squirrel has been known to store 8–10 bushels of cones in one hoard. Later, after 'ripening,' these are brought out, the scales cut, and only the seeds eaten. Not all stored food is consumed, hence these Squirrels are distributors and planters of seeds. Food: seeds of spruce, pine, maple, and other trees, berries, nuts, buds, mushrooms, lichens, and some animal food such as nestlings, bird eggs, and insects. Tree branches are tapped for sap. Home range is about ½–1 acre. The population fluctuates markedly, with peak numbers at about 5- to 6-year intervals.

ECONOMIC STATUS: In parts of Canada and Alaska some Red Squirrel skins are sold as fur. The meat is good eating. The planting that they do in some localities is desirable. At times they prune trees, cutting off twigs by the bushel. A Squirrel in a camp upsets anything it can move and gnaws window frames and other woodwork. In some areas they are hosts for ticks. The Marten eats many Red Squirrels, but is not dependent on them to a degree that population fluctuations coincide.

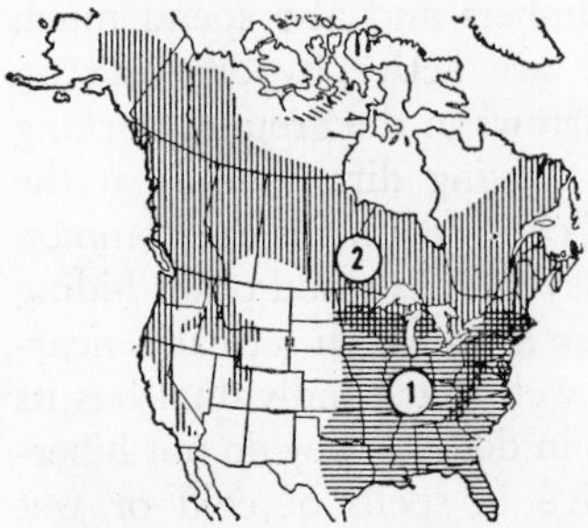

Flying Squirrels

Glaucomys

Plate 24

Small nocturnal tree Squirrels with furred membrane joining front and hind limbs; flattened tail and large eyes. Color of upperparts ranges from warm brown to cool gray, underparts whitish or creamy, and tail colored like back. **1.—*Southern** (*G. volans*): the smaller species; comparatively small ears; hair on underparts (except hind legs and gliding membranes) white to the base. L. 8½–10¼ in., t. 3⅖–4⅖, wt. 1¾–4 oz. **2.—Northern** (*G. sabrinus*): larger, with more than proportionately larger ears and eyes, and light hair of underparts lead-colored at the base. L. 10½–14½, t. 4⅖–7¼, wt. 3–6½ oz. Though often numerous, Flying Squirrels are nocturnal and seldom seen, except when brought in by a cat, caught in a trap, or found in an attic or camp. In snow the small Squirrel tracks are bunched and the furred lateral membranes leave an imprint.

HABITAT: The Southern prefers hardwoods, the Northern mixed woods or conifers.

REPRODUCTION: Some females of the Southern breed first at one, but others probably not until 2 years old. Dens are in Woodpecker holes, natural cavities, or outside spherical nests of leaves and shredded bark. The Southern begins breeding in Feb. and continues well into the summer, 2 litters being produced. Gestation requires 40 days, and litter size is 2–6. The Northern breeds in late winter, having 1 litter in the n. and 2 farther s. Gestation is unrecorded. In both species, perhaps mates sometimes associate more or less throughout the breeding season.

Southerns at birth are hairless, pink, have eyes closed, weigh ⅑–⅕ oz., and the gliding membranes are translucent. They are partly furred in 2 weeks, eyes open in

26–28 days, and they are weaned in 5 weeks or longer. If young are in danger, the mother sometimes moves them, holding one at a time by her teeth as she glides. Young make short glides in 8 weeks. The family may stay together until near time of birth of the next litter, which may be the following year. A captive Southern lived over 10 years.

HABITS: These nocturnal Squirrels are extremely fast climbers and agile gliders. Glides of up to 125 ft. are recorded. Before taking off, usually they sway the head and body from side to side as far as possible several times—evidently a range-finding maneuver. They land with an audible thump—a common sound on woodland camp roofs—and then climb to a higher point and glide again, swinging upward to alight. There is some control over the aerial course. Each species is gregarious, many sometimes being found in a tree cavity outside the breeding season. They do not hibernate, but are inactive during spells of cold, windy, or wet weather. Dr. E. P. Walker has observed that the Southern Flying Squirrel, a light sleeper, sleeps lying on its side, back, curled up in a ball, or hanging vertically—either head up or head down—most of the wt. being on the fingernails or toenails. This particular habit may have evolved from their clinging to the rough interior walls of large tree cavities that had no satisfactory bottom. Vocal sounds are a sharp, sibilant *tseet* like a small bird, a louder version of this when alarmed, and a squeal when in distress. Food items are buried individually. Food: nuts, berries, tree buds and catkins, insects, fungi, nestlings and bird eggs. Much foraging is done on the ground at night. Both species like meat and feed on any carcasses they find. A high population would be several per acre, when individual home ranges overlap greatly.

ECONOMIC STATUS: Both species occasionally are a nuisance in attics and in cornfields. The Northern, in seeking the bait, springs many traps set for valuable furbearers. Both make interesting pets.

POCKET GOPHERS Family Geomyidae

Range maps on page 200

Western Pocket Gophers
Thomomys
Plate 23

GENERAL REMARKS: Stout burrowing rodents; slits in cheeks lead to fur-lined pouches or pockets that are reversible; curved yellow upper front teeth have a *single* faint groove down front surface. They have small eyes and ears, short legs, very long front claws, short fur, and sparsely haired tail. Color varies from whitish or pale cream (in arid SW.) through mouse gray and brown to nearly black; in many localities fur approximates color of the soil occupied. Summer coat is brighter than winter. Use of brief descriptions and range maps (to eliminate species not in your area) will aid in identification, but some are so nearly alike that any specimens obtained should be referred to a mammalogist. By April 1941, a total of 266 names had been proposed for 'species' and 'subspecies' of *Thomomys* throughout its range (includes Mexico); the present list treats those n. of the border under 7 species headings.

In comparison, *Geomys* (p. 201) has 2 grooves down each of the 2 upper front teeth, and *Cratogeomys* (p. 203) has a single *distinct* one, but otherwise they appear quite like *Thomomys*. A Gopher mound (there may be many per acre) is larger than a Mole's; the soil is finely broken; the hole leading to it is larger and generally toward the side underneath (not near the center). Usually it is kept plugged. Ground Squirrels are called 'gopher' in many places, as is also a turtle in Ga. and Fla.

HABITAT: Many soil types are occupied, from sea level to

above timber line at 13,000 ft. in some areas. They are found in deserts, prairies, open forests, grasslands, and meadows.

POCKET GOPHER (*Thomomys*) **species: Northern** (*T. talpoides*): grayish, washed with brown; nose brownish or blackish; ears rounded, with a black patch behind each. L. 6¾–9½ in., t. 1¾–3, wt. 3–5 oz. Low areas to high mts. **Pigmy** (*T. umbrinus*): small; yellowish-brown to dark chestnut. L. 6½–7⅖, t. 2–2⅖. A mt. species. **Sierra** (*T. monticola*): small; yellowish- to dark smoky-brown; nose and patches behind pointed ears blackish; some whitish on tail and feet. High mts. **Townsend's** (*T. townsendii*): large; grayish, with faint buffy overcast; often whitish around mouth, also on tail and feet. Moist valley soils. ***Valley** (*T. bottae*): varies much geographically in size and color; usually brownish, but ranges from nearly black in n. Calif. coastal areas to nearly white in Imperial Desert; larger in valleys and smaller in s. desert mts. L. 6¾–10¾, t. 2–3¾. This species is especially difficult to delimit; *fulvus* is included with it here, while the next one following, for present purposes, is listed separately. **Bailey's** (*T. baileyi*): buffy- to reddish-brown; hard to distinguish from the preceding. L. 8–8½, t. 2¼–2½. Foothills. **Giant** (*T. bulbivorus*): large; sooty-brown. L. 11–12, t. 3¼–3¾. Rich soil in Willamette Valley, Ore.

REPRODUCTION: Males wander and seek females in burrows. There is a limited breeding season in n. (1 litter) and longer one farther s. (2–3 litters); year-round breeding (2–3 litters) has been reported for *T. bottae* in irrigated fields in Calif. Also, females of some species may have 2 litters in rapid succession if forage is abundant. Gestation, for the genus, has been estimated at 1 lunar month; litter size usually is 2–4. Newborn young *T. bottae* are 2 in. long, weigh ⅐ oz., and may be exceptional within the genus in having cheek pouches present even before birth (not mere slits at birth and pouches later). The mother

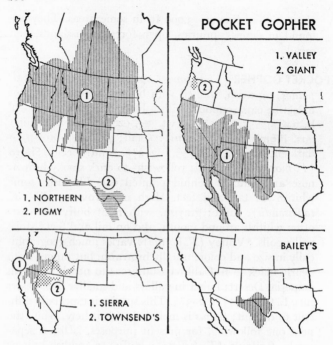

POCKET GOPHER

1. NORTHERN
2. PIGMY

1. VALLEY
2. GIANT

1. SIERRA
2. TOWNSEND'S

BAILEY'S

rears the young, which become solitary as soon as weaned.
HABITS: These remarkably efficient burrowers come to the
surface mainly at night and on cloudy days. They cannot
swim. Tunnels are clean-cut and of a size merely to allow
passage of the occupant. The Gopher breaks up through
at various points, spreading dirt fanwise in a mound and
then plugging the exit from within. There may be several hundred feet of tunnels at about the same level,
usually ½–3 ft. below the surface, made when seeking
food. Much food is stored in side chambers. From the
upper tunnel system a shaft may drop several feet to a
much less extensive lower one; here in a side chamber is
a grass-lined nest; other chambers are for food, also one
for a toilet, which is sealed off when soiled. In winter,
Gophers push cores of earth up into snow tunnels; these

are seen on the ground after the snow is gone. Some even make surface nests in winter and forage a great deal on the ground under the snow.

They are solitary except when mating. Generally they are silent, even when handled. Food: all forms of plant material. The front paws are used to stuff food into the fur-lined cheek pockets for transportation to storage or an eating place. Paws are rubbed along the sides of the face to push the food out. Nesting material and perhaps dirt, also, are transported. Pouches can be turned inside out to clean them; they are pulled back in place by a special muscle. Populations fluctuate markedly. Home range consists mainly of the burrow system. The Badger, a faster digger, catches many Pocket Gophers.

ECONOMIC STATUS: Pocket Gophers work and rework the soil. Sometimes they do much damage by tunneling through dikes, eating crops, cutting roots of trees, or gnawing bark.

Eastern Pocket Gophers
Geomys
Plate 23

Generally similar to Western Pocket Gophers (p. 198), except that the 2 curved upper front teeth have *two* grooves each: a large one down the front surface and a smaller adjacent one toward the inner side. These Gophers vary greatly in size and color but tend to divide into 2 color types: brown and black. Some have a darker streak on the back. Wt. 5–16 oz. Many 'species' names have been applied, but it seems best to treat the genus under 2 headings here. See comparative remarks and description of mounds under Western Pocket Gophers.

POCKET GOPHER (*Geomys*) **species: 1.—*Plains** (*G. bursarius*): varies from pale to rich brown to gray to nearly black; white-spotted to fully albino individuals are not rare. L. 7½–13 in., t. 2–4½. If several species actually are involved here, then only a specialist with series of specimens for comparison could assign specific names to them. **2.—Southeastern** (*G. pinetis*): usually brown or black. L. 8–13, t. 2½–3¾. Technical species names applied to it include *tuza* and *floridanus;* a vernacular one is 'salamander' (from 'sandy-mounder'), in Ga. and Fla. where 'gopher' is applied to a turtle.

HABITAT: Both prefer deep soil, dry to very damp. The Plains Pocket Gopher occurs mainly in treeless areas, the Southern in open woodland, especially pines, and also in fields.

REPRODUCTION: Female Plains Pocket Gophers may attain breeding age in about 3 months. Young are produced Feb.–Aug. in S. (probably 2 litters) and Apr.–May in N. (1 litter). Litter size is 1–5, and young probably leave the home nest at age of 30–35 days to begin solitary lives. The Southeastern has 1 litter of 2–6 (usually 4) young born in Mar.–Apr. Its newborn young are 2 in. long, weigh about ⅕ oz., have facial vibrissae ('whiskers'), a few hairs on upperparts, and make a resonant squeaking noise. Eyes, ears, and cheek pouches are not open; a wrinkle shows where a pouch will be. In e. Tex. and La. those living in damp soil make mounds up to 2 ft. high x 6 in diameter; within such a mound, chambers for the nest, food storage, and the toilet are made.

HABITS: In wasteland near Manhattan, Kans. the tunnel system of a female Plains Pocket Gopher was excavated. Diameter averaged about 2¾ in. Shallower foraging tunnels (not over 10 in. down) made up 90% of the system, the balance being deeper living quarters. There were 510 ft. of tunnel and 105 mounds. Plant roots and rootstalks were stored in 2 chambers, one of which also contained a 7-in. spherical nest of grass and some feathers. The Pocket Gopher's tail is a tactile organ. The Gopher can travel forward and backward in its tunnels, but can turn around only at intersections.

ECONOMIC STATUS: Land under intense cultivation is more or less avoided, but *Geomys* is a pest at times in alfalfa and hayfields; it also eats sugar cane, sweet potatoes, peanuts, and peas.

Mexican Pocket Gopher
(Chestnut-faced Pocket Gopher)
Cratogeomys castanops
Plate 23

Generally similar to Western Pocket Gophers (p. 198), except that there is *one distinct* groove on the middle front surface of the 2 curved upper front teeth. General tone varies from warm tan in N. to reddish-brown farther s., but usually appears rather yellowish. L. 10–11 in., t. 2½–3. Prefers deep soil. See general remarks on the Western group for comparison and for description of Gopher mounds; range of several other Gophers overlaps that of the present one. Litter size is 1–3, and habits, in general, appear to be quite like those of *Thomomys*.

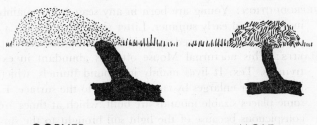

GOPHER MOUND   **MOLE** HILL

POCKET MICE, KANGAROO RATS, AND ALLIES
Family Heteromyidae

Spiny Mouse
(Texas Spiny Mouse)
Liomys irroratus
Plate 31

A large Mouse; slits in cheeks lead to fur-lined pockets; tail long and hairy; fur, especially on neck and shoulders, if rubbed the 'wrong' way, feels spiny because of the stiffened guard hairs; *no grooves* in upper front teeth. Upperparts are salt-and-pepper gray; a light brownish wash along sides; underparts pale creamy-white. L. 9–10 in., t. 4½–5, wt. about 1 oz. Pocket Mice (*Perognathus*) have pouches and some also have bristly fur, but those that might be confused with *Liomys* are yellowish, stouter in build, have markedly broad heads, and grooved upper front teeth.

HABITAT: Brushy field borders, under bushes, and in woodlands; a burrower, but occurs even up in trees along the Rio Grande when ground habitat is flooded for a short time.

REPRODUCTION: Young are born in any season, but mainly in spring and early summer. Litter size: 3–5 (usually 4) young, which are furred at birth, but the 'spines' are soft.

HABITS: This nocturnal Mouse often is abundant in extreme s. Tex. It lives mainly in ground tunnels, which it repairs or enlarges by carrying earth to the surface. In some places sizable mounds are built, which at times are conspicuous because of the light soil brought to the surface; the entrance is at the side. Food includes blackberry, ebony, and other berries, also seeds of mesquite beans, papaya, and pomegranate. Food is carried to stor-

age in the fur-lined pouches. This Mouse has eaten garden crops in a few places.

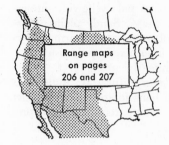

Range maps
on pages
206 and 207

Pocket Mice
Perognathus
Plate 31

GENERAL REMARKS: Small to
large Mice (l. 3¾–9⅗ in.);
cheek slits open into fur-
lined pouches; head decidedly broad; upper front
teeth *grooved;* never a strik-
ing color pattern. Most have brownish or grayish upperparts and white or pale buffy underparts. Young are
grayer than adults. In the Tularosa Basin, N. Mex., a
race of *P. intermedius* living on lava flows is nearly
black; a race of *P. apache* found on white sands in that
area is pale gray above and pure white below.

Pocket Mice tend to fall into 2 groups: small to medium-sized, with soft fur; and medium to large, with
guard hairs, especially on the rump, stiffened as spines or
bristles. All are arranged here under 18 headings. Note
that fur is soft in the first 12, harsh in the next 2, and
with spines on rump in the last 4; also, the terminal third
of the tail does not have a hair crest in the first 10 and
the 13th, but is crested otherwise. Range maps should be
used in conjunction with descriptions when attempting
to assign species names.

In comparison, Kangaroo Rats have much longer hind
legs, usually a white band across the thigh, and most are
much larger. Pigmy Kangaroo Rats, of limited distribution, have long hind legs and the tail is enlarged in the
middle. See also the Spiny Mouse (p. 204) of s. Tex.
Pocket Mice make small mounds, usually in weedy or
brushy places.

HABITAT: Arid and semi-arid country.

POCKET MOUSE (*Perognathus*) **species: Wyoming** (*P. fasciatus*): fur very soft; upperparts drab gray, with yellowish spots on ears and wash on sides; underparts white. L. 5–5⅓ in., t. 2¼–2½. Occurs on plains. **Plains** (*P. flavescens*): fur soft; upperparts pale yellowish; underparts white. L. 4¼–5⅓, t. 2–2⅗. Sandy plains. **Merriam's** (*P. merriami*): fur soft; upperparts warm yellowish-brown, with dark hairs intermixed; yellowish patch behind ear; underparts white. L. 3¾–4¾, t. 1½–2. Sandy plains. ***Silky** (*P. flavus*): fur soft; upperparts pale yellowish, with blackish hairs intermingled; distinct yellowish patch behind ear; underparts white. L. as pre-

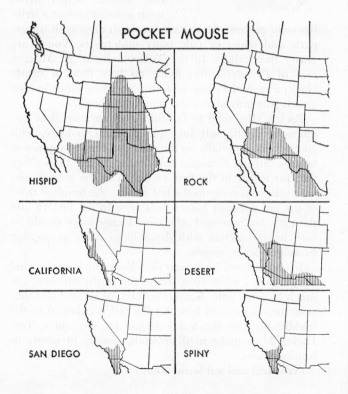

POCKET MOUSE

HISPID

ROCK

CALIFORNIA

DESERT

SAN DIEGO

SPINY

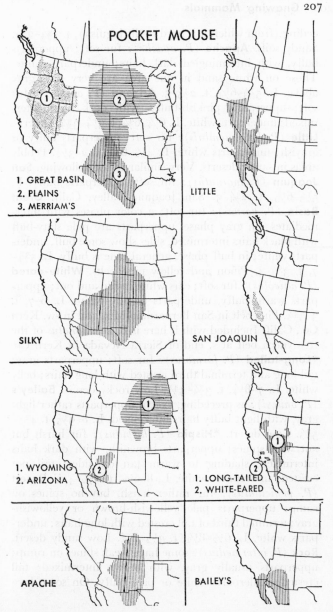

POCKET MOUSE

1. GREAT BASIN
2. PLAINS
3. MERRIAM'S

LITTLE

SILKY

SAN JOAQUIN

1. WYOMING
2. ARIZONA

1. LONG-TAILED
2. WHITE-EARED

APACHE

BAILEY'S

ceding (from which it is hard to distinguish), t. 1¾–2¾. Sandy soils. **Apache** (*P. apache*)*:* fur soft; upperparts buffy, with intermingled dark hairs; underparts white. Those on white sand in one area are very pale gray above. L. 5⅓–6¼, t. 2⅗–3. **Arizona** (*P. amplus*)*:* fur soft; upperparts pinkish-buffy, with dark hairs intermixed; underparts white. L. 6¼–6¾, t. 3¼–3¾. Deserts. **Little** (*P. longimembris*)*:* fur soft; upperparts buffy or grayish; underparts white. L. 4½–6⅓, t. 2–3½. Pebbly areas in sandy deserts. Very similar to the following. **San Joaquin** (*P. inornatus*)*:* fur soft; upperparts buffy. L. 5⅓–6⅕, t. 2¾–3. San Joaquin Valley, Calif. **Great Basin** (*P. parvus*)*:* fur soft; 2 color phases with intermediates—in gray phase, upperparts are pale slaty-buff with black hairs intermixed, sides show some buff, underparts white; in buff phase, general tone is buffy. L. 5¾–7, t. 3¾–4. Piñon and yellow pine belts. **White-eared** (*P. alticolus*)*:* fur soft; ears white inside and out; upperparts warm buffy, underparts usually white. L. 6–7, t. 3–3⅗. Pine belt in San Bernardino Mts. and in sw. Kern Co., Calif. Included with it here is *P. xanthonotus* of the tree yucca belt at s. end of Sierra Nevada in Kern Co. ***Long-tailed** (*P. formosus*)*:* fur soft; upperparts gray; tail long and terminal third crested with long hairs; belly white. L. 7–8¼, t. 3¾–4⅘. Low rocky desert. **Bailey's** (*P. baileyi*)*:* as preceding, except upperparts rather light gray, with light buffy hairs intermixed. L. 8–9⅗, t. 4⅖–5⅖. Low desert. ***Hispid** (*P. hispidus*)*:* fur harsh but not with spines; upperparts brownish, with dark hairs intermixed, shading to warm tan on sides; tail not crested; underparts white. L. 8–9½, t. 3½–4½. **Desert** (*P. penicillatus*)*:* fur rather harsh, but no spines on rump; upperparts pale yellowish-brown or yellowish-gray; terminal third of tail crested with long hairs; underparts white. L. 6½–8½, t. 3½–4⅘. Low sandy desert. **Rock** (*P. intermedius*)*:* some have weak spines on rump; upperparts usually gray, with brown intermixed; tail crested; underparts white or pale buffy. On some lava flows in s. N. Mex. it is blackish all over. L. $6\frac{1}{5}$–$7\frac{4}{5}$, t. $3\frac{1}{4}$–4. Desert lava and rocky slopes. Included with it as perhaps not separable is *P. nelsoni* of the Big Bend region, Tex. **San Diego** (*P. fallax*): spines on rump; upperparts dark brown, with deep fulvous intermixed, and a yellowish-brown line on sides; tail crested; underparts white. L. $6\frac{1}{2}$–$7\frac{1}{3}$, t. 3–$3\frac{4}{5}$. Low deserts and foothills in s. Calif. ***California** (*P. californicus*): spines on rump; upperparts dark brownish-gray, with yellowish-brown intermixed; the long tail is crested; underparts creamy- or buffy-white. L. $7\frac{1}{5}$–$9\frac{1}{5}$, t. 4–$5\frac{4}{5}$. Coastal s. half of Calif. **Spiny** (*P. spinatus*): spines on rump; upperparts a mixture of pale browns; tail crested; underparts buffy-white. L. 6–8, t. 3–$4\frac{1}{2}$. Arid desert in se. Calif.

REPRODUCTION: Young are found throughout the warmer months, mostly early in the season in sw. states, and mainly early June–Aug. in Pacific NW. They are born in a nest in the tunnel system. More than one litter annually may be the rule, but some in N. have only one. Gestation is not recorded for any species. Reported range of litter size is 1–8, with 4 perhaps usual. A captive Little Pocket Mouse lived at least $7\frac{1}{2}$ years.

HABITS: Pocket Mice are nocturnal and somewhat gregarious. Tunnels usually go down steeply, beside a rock or under shrubbery. The entrance is often a tiny round hole in the ground, but quite frequently a mound is kicked together there. Several openings may be made, leading to an elaborate tunnel system having food-storage and other chambers. Entrances are usually plugged just below the ground surface, and wind-blown sand obliterates them and tracks also. Voice is a high thin squeak. Some of these Mice do not come above ground for long periods in winter, and captives are quite torpid at low temperatures. They can go without drinking, since, like some other arid country dwellers, they can manufacture water within themselves from starchy foods eaten.

Food consists mainly of a wide variety of seeds. Green

parts of plants are eaten in spring and pulp of prickly pear at various seasons. Insects and other invertebrates are consumed in considerable quantity. Ordinarily there are several underground caches of food to tide the owner over periods of drought and, perhaps, winter. Populations fluctuate markedly. The Badger digs out Pocket Mice; some Deermice, also Grasshopper Mice, catch and eat them.

ECONOMIC STATUS: Pocket Mice dig up garden seeds, eat growing plants, and sometimes cut the tops off grains. Occasionally they injure livestock range by selectively eating grasses, which then may be replaced by weeds. They seldom do much damage.

Range maps on page 213

Kangaroo Rats
(Pocket Rats)
Dipodomys
Plate 29

GENERAL REMARKS: From large Mouse to Rat size (l. 8¼–15 in.); cheek slits open into fur-lined pouches; head broad and eyes large; hind legs extremely long; front legs and feet small; tail very long, usually with a crest of hairs on terminal portion, a tufted end, and lateral white stripe; upperparts vary from very pale sandy to dark brown, with facial marks of white and, usually, some degree of blackish; in almost all species a white band crosses the flank and merges with a lateral white stripe on the tail; lower body surface, front legs and feet, and upper surface of hind feet pure white. Young are darker (more slaty) than adults. Variation is mainly in degree of color intensity and number of hind toes. Some are next to impossible to identify on the basis of external characters alone. They are treated here under 16 headings.

In comparison, Pigmy Kangaroo Rats (*Microdipodops*) are smaller, have the tail enlarged in the middle, and occupy a limited geographical area. Pocket Mice have shorter tails and hind legs and plain faces. Most Kangaroo Rats make mounds, from mere handfuls of dirt up to 15 ft. in diameter and 4 ft. high. These have many entrances, also narrow paths radiating outward.

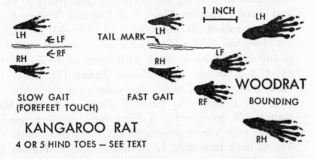

1 INCH

TAIL MARK

LH   LH   LH

LF   LF

RH   RF   RH

RF

SLOW GAIT
(FOREFEET TOUCH)

FAST GAIT

WOODRAT
BOUNDING

RH

KANGAROO RAT
4 OR 5 HIND TOES — SEE TEXT

Mounds are conspicuous from a distance. Paired tracks of hind feet, made when hopping, show 4 or 5 toes; often the tail makes a mark. In slow gait the front feet sometimes leave a mark.

HABITAT: Dry areas, with or without scattered brush or trees, some species preferring loose soil and others even digging in rocky soil.

KANGAROO RAT (*Dipodomys*) **species: Heermann's** (*D. heermanni*): 4 or 5 (usually 4) hind toes; varies geographically in general tone from pale sandy to tawny-olive; tail-tip white or dusky. L. 10½–13½ in., t. 6½–8½. One of several species that is not always identifiable with certainty on basis of external characters only. Valleys, also live-oak and pine areas; parts of upper two-thirds of Calif. and lower Ore. **Morro Bay** (*D. morroensis*): darkest; white flank stripe incomplete or absent. L. 11¼–12½, t. 6½–7½. Limited to a sandy area less than 4 mi. sq. in immediate vicinity of Morro Bay, Calif. **Mohave** (*D. mohavensis*): 5 hind toes; general tone

212 Gnawing Mammals

pale. L. 11–12, t. 6–7. Mohave Desert. **Panamint** (*D. panamintinus*): 5 hind toes normally; general tone rather dark. L. 11⅓–12½, t. 6⅓–7½. Yuccas and scattered trees in s. coastal half of Calif. **Stephens'** (*D. stephensi*): 5 toes; general tone dark. L. 11½–12¼, t. 6½–7¼. San Jacinto Valley and vicinity, Calif. **Giant** (*D. ingens*): 5 hind toes; general tone warm buff. L. 12½–14, t. 7–8. Semi-arid strip along sw. border of San Joaquin Valley and nearby Carrizo Plain and Cuyama Valley, Calif. ***Banner-tailed** (*D. spectabilis*): 4 toes; rich coloration; very long tail, with white lateral stripes ending well short of tail tuft, which is black with large white tip. L. 12–15, t. 7–9. Brushy arid terrain. **Texas** (*D. elator*): 4 hind toes; general tone clay color; tail-tip white. L. 11½–13, t. 6½–7½. Parts of Okla. and Tex. **Merriam's** (*D. merriami*): 4 hind toes; smallest species; general tone varies geographically from pale sandy yellow to dark brownish. L. 9–10¼, t. 5–6¼. **Fresno** (*D. nitratoides*): 4 toes; size small; general tone dark. L. 8¼–10, t. 4¾–6. San Joaquin Valley. ***Ord's** (*D. ordii*): either 4 or 5 hind toes; varies geographically from very pale to bright buffy-brown; 2 lower front teeth rounded (not flat) across the front. L. 9–10½, t. 5–6. ***Pacific** (*D. agilis*): 5 hind toes; general tone dark dull brown. L. 10½–13, t. 6¼–8. **Santa Cruz** (*D. venustus*): 5 hind toes; dark rich coloration; ears large. L. 11¾–13½, t. 7–8. A cent. coastal area of Calif. **Big-eared** (*D. elephantinus*): 5 hind toes; dark rich coloration; terminal third of tail markedly bushy and mainly white. L. 12½–13, t. 7–8. Chaparral-covered slopes of s. part of Gabilan Range, Calif. **Great Basin** (*D. microps*): 5 toes; general tone varies from pale buffy to dusky; 2 lower front teeth flat across the front. L. 9½–12¼, t. 5½–7¼. Mainly sagebrush and greasewood areas. ***Desert** (*D. deserti*): 4 hind toes; general tone very pale warm brown; tail has white tip and lacks any dark ventral stripe (white continues from side to side). L. 12–15, t. 7–8½. Warm sandy desert.

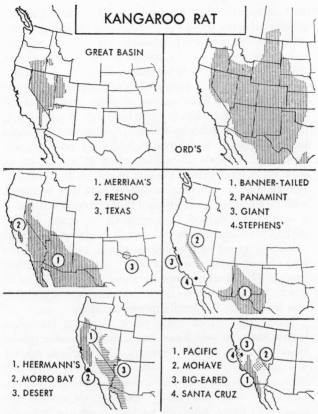

KANGAROO RAT

GREAT BASIN

ORD'S

1. MERRIAM'S
2. FRESNO
3. TEXAS

1. BANNER-TAILED
2. PANAMINT
3. GIANT
4. STEPHENS'

1. HEERMANN'S
2. MORRO BAY
3. DESERT

1. PACIFIC
2. MOHAVE
3. BIG-EARED
4. SANTA CRUZ

REPRODUCTION: They are said to breed the year following birth. Young are born in a lined nest chamber in the tunnel system. Breeding occurs late winter–early fall, with peak in spring, and some have at least 2 (if not more) litters annually. Litter size for most species, so far as known, varies from about 1–6, usually 2–4, and gestation is unrecorded. Young of the Bannertail are born hairless and with eyes closed; a dark coat, showing adult pattern, is partly developed in 10 days, and eyes open at an unknown later date.

HABITS: Kangaroo Rats are nocturnal. They travel mainly by bipedal leaps, using the long tail as a balancing organ. It is used as a prop when standing. They are not gregarious. Some of the smaller species do not build mounds, their tunnel entrances being flush with the unaltered surface. Others build a mound in a cleared space; it may have a dozen or more entrances, large enough for the occupant to enter when erect on hind legs. A mound may be added to for years by successive occupants, additions being dirt excavated from below, food remains, and droppings. Tunnels within are often in several layers, with small food-storage pockets in the walls, as well as storage chambers. Several bushels of food may be stored, with added small caches buried in the ground outside. If a mound is disturbed, frequently the occupant thumps with its hind feet or raps with its tail. Main vocal sounds: a buzzing growl of warning or alarm, chuckling notes and chirps given when foraging, and a high-pitched squeak. The gland between the shoulders, common to all species and to both sexes, produces an odor that probably aids individuals in identifying one another.

Food: all sorts of seeds, plant parts cut into short lengths, insects, and some fungi. Some smaller species rarely store any food. Merriam's (and perhaps others) is parasitic, for it enters galleries of larger kinds and steals stored food; it may be kicked and killed if caught. Lizards, snakes, and many invertebrates occupy the mounds at times. Although perhaps Kangaroo Rats are not above ground much in very hot or cold weather, they have no profound seasonal sleep.

ECONOMIC STATUS: Sometimes they eat seeds of cattle forage plants, so compete locally with livestock. By stirring the soil around their dens, they actually caused a fivefold increase in amount of sheep forage in one area in Calif.

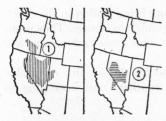

Pigmy Kangaroo Rats
Microdipodops
Plate 29

Like the larger Kangaroo Rats (p. 210) in general appearance, including fur-lined cheek pouches, but smaller, with plainer pattern, and the short-haired tail has largest diameter in middle and no end tuft. Young are darker than adults. **1.—*Dark** (*M. megacephalus*): upperparts brownish- to grayish-black; underparts pale grayish or white; tail-tip blackish. L. 5¼–7¼ in., t. 2¼–3¼, wt. ⅖–¾ oz. **2.—*Pale** (*M. pallidus*): upperparts pale creamy-buff; underparts pure white; no blackish on tail. Measurements almost same as for preceding. The characters given distinguish these rodents from large Pocket Mice or small Kangaroo Rats. Paired hind tracks are miniatures of those of the larger Kangaroo Rats. In rapid bounding, the tail is carried high and seldom leaves a mark; in slower gait, the forefeet occasionally leave a mark and the tail drags more often.

HABITAT: Dry sandy or mellow soil with scattered sagebrush or other low vegetation.

REPRODUCTION: Both species. Young are born in burrows, mostly in May–June. Counts have revealed 1–7 (usually 3–4) embryos; there may be 2 litters annually.

HABITS: These nocturnal Mice of sand and sage are jumpers. Burrow entrances are usually under a bush, and the doorway generally is plugged in daytime. Drifting sand fills the space above the plug, obliterating all evidence of a burrow. For size of the occupant, the hole is very small. The enlarged mid-section of the tail of these rodents gives it added weight as a balancing organ; Kangaroo Rats (*Dipodomys*) effect the same result by having tails more elongated. Voice: a high-pitched squeal when captured. They have no seasonal sleep but may not be active above ground in winter. Food: seeds and insects, quantities of the former being stuffed in the cheek pouches and carried down tunnels to storage. They probably do not drink water. In some areas and seasons they are really abundant.

ECONOMIC STATUS: These rodents do not live on arable land. They are gentle in captivity and interesting to study.

BEAVER　Family Castoridae

Beaver
Castor canadensis
Plate 26

Our largest rodent; a stocky mammal with scaly, naked, and horizontally flattened paddle-shaped tail; hind feet webbed. Coat is deep brown in N. and pale yellowish-brown in SW., everywhere with paler underparts. L. 3–4¼ ft., t. 9–12 in. long and to 6 in. wide, wt. to 70 lb. or more. Beaver signs include the familiar dams, lodges, canals, and tree cuttings. An alarmed Beaver slaps the water with its tail as it dives, making a loud noise and sizable splash. A swimming Beaver has a very squarish head profile; the Muskrat's is less angular and the Otter's is definitely rounded. Also see track diagrams of Beaver and Muskrat (p. 259).

NOTE: Family Capryomidae. **Nutria** (*Myocastor coypus*); introduced; a large aquatic S. Am. rodent; occurs in widely separated U.S. localities; centers of abundance are marshes of La. and Ore. L. 30–42 in., t. 12–17, wt. 12–20 lb. The tapering rounded tail is sparsely haired;

front teeth orange-red; hind feet webbed. Because the head is shaped like a Beaver's, this rodent looks like a Beaver when tail is not visible. Gestation requires 100–125 days, longer in nursing females, and the several litters per year average 5 young. They are born furred, are able to get about in a few hours, and are weaned in 7–8 weeks. After expensive processing, fur is a fair substitute for Beaver.

HABITAT: Beavers prefer waterways having nearby poplar (aspen) trees. There have been many transplantings of Beavers into areas where they had been trapped out, also introductions into places not previously occupied. Introduced 1929–31 on Kodiak and Raspberry I., Alaska.

REPRODUCTION: Females first breed when about 2½ years old and probably mate for life. Young are born in a lodge or a hole in a bank. Breeding occurs in winter (later with younger ones), and gestation may require 3 months. Kits, numbering 1–6, usually 3–4, generally are born Apr.–May, but sometimes as late as July. A kit at birth is about 15 in. long, has a 3½-in. flat tail, weighs ½–1½ lb., eyes are open, and it is covered with soft fur. Weight is 10–15 lb. at 6 months, 16–21 lb. in 9 months, and 20–27 lb. as a yearling (Mich. data). Mates share the lodge, but the male may wander and breed with other females. Young stay in the lodge into their second year, when either they leave or are driven out before the mother gives birth to the second litter following. The Beaver has lived 19 years in captivity.

HABITS: Beavers are rather gregarious. They are abroad mainly at dusk or later. Gait on land is slow, but they swim at fair speed, using the webbed hind feet. Oxygen can be stored and used so economically that a Beaver can remain submerged at least 15 minutes. The split nail on each second hind toe evidently is used as a comb. When swimming or working, Beavers make no vocal sounds, but one can hear various moaning and sighing notes within a lodge by canoeing quietly up to it. Glands in the groin, very large in males, give off a pleasant musk which is deposited on piles of mud or stones. These 'sign heaps' probably serve to inform other Beavers of presence and sex of the individual.

Dams average about 75 ft. long, but one in Mont. measured 2,140 ft. Often they are poorly situated, hence unnecessarily long, or frequently washed out and hence abandoned. An entire family plus other Beavers may join in dam-building. A foundation is made of mud and stones, then peeled and unpeeled brush and poles are laid on (butt ends upstream) and plastered down with mud, stones, and soggy vegetation. In this fashion the dam is built to above water level and may be kept in repair for years. The lodge is built in much the same fashion and added to, mainly in fall, as long as occupied. It may grow many feet high and to 40 ft. in base diameter. One or more exits are under water, so can be used in winter when the Beavers go out under the ice to feed on bark of anchored sticks and logs. Within is a sleeping platform above water level; some vegetation is added as bedding for the kits. Some Beavers live in holes that they excavate in banks.

Food consists of the bark and adjacent outer layers of poplars (aspens), alders, birches, willows, and other trees. Various parts of many aquatic plants are eaten. In cutting a tree, a Beaver (sometimes with a helper) uses its upper front teeth for leverage, the cutting action being by the lower ones only. There is no control over which direction the tree will fall. Large trunks are peeled where they fall, and smaller sections are dragged to water and towed to storage. In level country, long shallow canals are often made for towing logs to deep water. A Beaver will utilize a poplar of 1- to 3-in. base diameter per night. An acre of poplars can support a family of 6 for 1–2½ years, depending on many factors. Several families often live near each other. They get on amicably, although there is some fighting at breeding time. Unlike most rodents, Beavers do not have more or less periodical and pronounced population fluctuations.

ECONOMIC STATUS: Beaver fur, after guard hairs are

plucked, is noted for its lustrous beauty. The pelt is prime in late winter and spring. Much of the exploration of N. Am., beginning early in the 1600's, was incidental to the quest for Beaver pelts. So great was the demand that Beavers were extirpated from many areas. Under protection they have become plentiful. They flood and damage woodlands and highways, cut timber, and dam and block routes of migrating salmon. Dams on trout streams result in higher water temperature. In many dry areas in W. their reservoirs hold water and prevent erosion. Generally speaking, even in settled areas, their presence in small numbers is desirable.

MICE, RATS, VOLES, AND LEMMINGS
Family Cricetidae

For Old World Rats and Mice (Muridae), see pages 261–265.

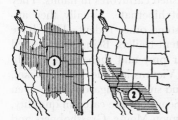

Grasshopper Mice
Onychomys
Plate 31

Stocky Mice, with rather short, thick, tapering tails giving the appearance that part was cut off. Fur fine and dense; pattern bicolored—white underparts sharply divided from darker upperparts. **1.—*Northern** (*O. leucogaster*): varies from slaty-gray with brownish overcast to pale sandy to warm reddish-brown. L. 5–7½ in., t. 1⅛–2⅖, wt. to 2½ oz. **2.—Southern** (*O. torridus*): smaller and more trim; varies from light pinkish-cinnamon to tawny; slightly longer tail. L. 4¾–6½, t. 1½–2½, wt. to 2 oz. Young of both species are gray above. Where ranges overlap, the Southern usually occurs at lower elevations. The club-like tail identifies these Mice.

Signs of their presence are small pairs of 5-toed footprints spaced 2–3 in. apart in running gait, hearing either their whistle or 'bark' at night, or perhaps finding remains of their mammal victims.

HABITAT: Sandy sagebrush country, short-grass areas, and weedy places are preferred in N., but farther s. habitat varies from barren creosote-bush plains to grasslands, mesquite areas, and even limestone cliffs.

REPRODUCTION: In the Northern species females breed when 3 months old. Young are born in a burrow, Apr.–Sept., mostly in spring and early summer. Gestation requires 32 days, or 33–47 in females giving milk. Litter size is 2–6, usually 4 (and 3–4 in the Southern species), and there is more than 1 litter annually. Young at birth are pink, hairless, have eyes closed, and weigh ⅟₁₀ oz. or less. They are furred in 12 days, eyes open in 19 days, and they are weaned soon after. A gray coat is worn 5–6 months.

HABITS: Most rodents eat mammal carcasses, but Grasshopper Mice are accomplished carnivores in habits. They are nocturnal and do not hibernate. Usually they appropriate a hole dug by some other rodent. They have keen senses and are persistent trailers. Being short-legged and stout, they stalk their prey and then, with a rush, seize it and kill by biting. Victims include Voles, Pocket, Harvest, and Deermice, and small Kangaroo Rats—even other Grasshopper Mice. Scorpions are eaten in quantity, hence the local name Scorpion Mouse. Grasshoppers and other insects comprise about one fifth of the diet. Seeds are eaten when animal food is scarce. Like true carnivores, they eat large meals. With mouth open and nose pointing skyward, they utter a shrill clear *screek* of about one second duration and often repeated several times; although it may be mistaken for an insect sound, it is more like a miniature Wolf howl and audible for at least 50 ft. It has a ventriloquistic quality. In protest or anger, they utter a series of notes like the barking of a tiny Terrier.

ECONOMIC STATUS: Some grains and beneficial insects are eaten. They destroy scorpions, noxious insects, and many young and adult rodents, which is to their credit from man's viewpoint.

Range maps on page 222

Harvest Mice
Reithrodontomys
Plate 31

Small Mice (l. 4¼–7⅕ in.), with long, scantily haired tails and conspicuous ears. The usual pattern is brownish or grayish on the back, shading to orange-buff or gray sides, and white or gray underparts. The deep groove on the front surface of the curved upper front teeth is a certain means of identification. Young are darker than adults. Harvest Mice are somewhat like small House Mice, but usually more brown or buffy, have lighter feet, more hairy tail, and grooved upper front teeth. Signs of their presence are baseball-sized grass nests, usually up off the ground in low vegetation. By using range maps and descriptions one can identify most adults.

HABITAT: Almost any situation having dense low cover, but preferably weedy fields, grassy garden borders, salt- and fresh-water marshes, stream borders, and irrigation ditches; also even in dry sandy uplands.

HARVEST MOUSE (*Reithrodontomys*) **species: *Eastern** (*R. humulis*): fairly dark brown, shading to paler and somewhat grayer underparts. L. 4¼–5½ in., t. 1¾–2½. Se. U.S. **Plains** (*R. montanus*): pale grayish with orange-buff overcast and often a poorly defined darker streak down back; underparts white. L. 4¼–5⅗, t. 2–2⅗. Cent. U.S. ***Western** (*R. megalotis*): upperparts range from

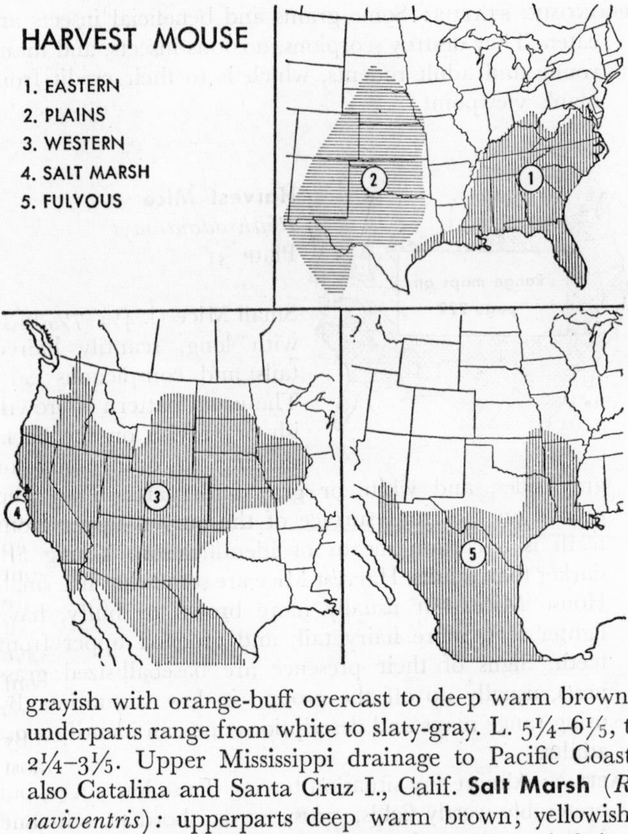

HARVEST MOUSE

1. EASTERN
2. PLAINS
3. WESTERN
4. SALT MARSH
5. FULVOUS

grayish with orange-buff overcast to deep warm brown; underparts range from white to slaty-gray. L. 5¼–6⅕, t. 2¼–3⅕. Upper Mississippi drainage to Pacific Coast, also Catalina and Santa Cruz I., Calif. **Salt Marsh** (*R. raviventris*): upperparts deep warm brown; yellowish-brown overcast is clearer on underparts. L. 4¾–6⅗, t. 2¼–3⅖. Salt marshes of San Francisco, San Pablo, and Suisun Bays, and lower San Joaquin and Sacramento rivers, Calif. **Fulvous** (*R. fulvescens*): largest; grayish-brown above, shading to rich orange-buff on sides; underparts white. L. 6⅕–7⅕, t. 3¼–4. Parts of s. U.S. w. of Mississippi River.

REPRODUCTION: Western Harvest Mouse. Some females breed at 4¼ months of age, when still in darker young coat. Young are born in a woven spherical nest. Gestation requires 23–24 days, and breeding may occur all year (several litters), but mainly Apr.–Oct. Counts have revealed 1–7 (average 4) embryos. Young at birth weigh about ⅟₂₅ oz., are hairless, and about ¼ in. long. Eyes and ears open in 7–8 days; young can leave the nest in 10 days, are weaned in about 2 weeks, and in another week or more they disperse. Adult wt. is attained in about 5 weeks. Little is known about reproduction in other species.

HABITS: These nocturnal and slightly gregarious little Mice are nimble climbers. They make no runways on the ground but use those of other rodents. Their most conspicuous trait is weaving spherical nests which are used the year round by the non-hibernating occupant. Vegetation is gathered at the site, woven upward into a cup, enclosed at the top, and lined with plant fibers. Usually it is off the ground some distance, in grass, tall weeds, or a bush, but occasionally it is under a log, in a bird's nest, up a tree, or even in a ground tunnel. A high-pitched rather ventriloquistic bugling, almost above range of human hearing, has been heard. Diet is seeds and green shoots of vegetation mainly, with some insects. These Mice climb to cut fruiting heads of grains and other plants, but probably most food is fallen seeds gleaned from the ground. Some food remains occur in nests, but there is no storage.

ECONOMIC STATUS: Some grain is eaten, but usually these Mice are entirely harmless.

Pigmy Mouse
Baiomys taylori
Plate 31

A tiny Mouse, with very slender tail, delicate feet, and very small eyes. Upperparts are grayish-brown with darker hairs intermixed; some-

times a very small obscure brownish streak on sides; belly
has gray hairs with white tips; tail somewhat lighter below. L. 3½–4⅓ in., t. 1⅖–1⅗. Only young of other
Mice are as small as an adult Pigmy Mouse; the combination of very small eyes, very slender limbs and tail,
and no well-defined bicolored pattern ought to distinguish it even from young House and Harvest Mice.
Signs of its presence are tiny runways, also very small
holes in matted, prostrate grass.

HABITAT: Grassy and weedy areas having matted, fallen
vegetation.

REPRODUCTION: At 2½ months of age both sexes are able
to breed. Young are born in a surface nest of fine dry
grass. A captive female produced 9 litters in 202 days,
or an average of 1 per 25 days. In Tex. this Mouse breeds
all year. Gestation requires 20 days or less, perhaps longer
with females already giving milk. Litter size is 1–5,
usually 3. Young at birth weigh about ½5 oz., are pink
and hairless. They attach to the mother's nipples and
may remain attached, being dragged about at times, for
18–22 days, when they are weaned. Eyes open in 12–14
days. Their dark gray fur is replaced by adult fur, beginning at about 46 days of age. Unlike most rodents,
the male parent helps care for the young and will carry
them back to the nest if they become detached from the
female outside it.

HABITS: This small Mouse, which is active all year, is
rather gregarious. Probably it forages mainly after dark.
It uses the runways of other rodents and also makes its
own tiny ones. The nest is in a small depression in the
ground or under a log. Voice is a high-pitched squeal.
Food probably consists of seeds, various green plant parts,
and some insects. Home range is less than 100 ft. in
diameter, and a fair population is 6–8 adults per acre.
There must be many predators on so prolific a mammal,
but they are unrecorded.

Range maps
on pages
226 and 227

Deermice
(White-footed Mice)
Peromyscus
Plate 30

GENERAL REMARKS: Medium
to large Mice (l. 4¾–10⅖
in.); bicolored pattern; ears
and eyes large; short-haired
tail often as long or longer
than head and body. Up-
perparts vary from gray or
sandy to deep or golden brown, usually sharply de-
marcated from white or whitish underparts (lower face,
belly, part of legs, feet, and usually underside of tail). In
general, inhabitants of cool woods are grayish, some se.
species are richly colored, and those of open or arid terrain are pale. Range of almost every mainland species is
overlapped by that of one to several others, but local
habitat preferences tend to keep them apart. In some
species there is much color variation over the geographical range, or even wide variation within a local population. Regardless of adult coloration, young, until nearly

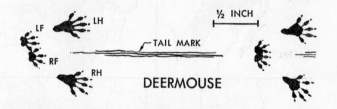

LF LH
TAIL MARK
RF
RH
½ INCH

DEERMOUSE

adult size, are grayish. These matters often render identification difficult, and the beginner should refer specimens to a mammalogist. Still useful is the monograph by
W. H. Osgood, *U. S. Dept. Agric., N. Am. Fauna* 28
(1909); more up-to-date studies of parts of the genus
have been published.

DEERMOUSE

PIÑON

COTTON

OLD-FIELD

CANYON

FLORIDA

DESERT

BRUSH

CALIFORNIA

1. GOLDEN
2. ROCK
3. OAK

DEERMOUSE

1. LONG-TAILED
2. SITKA

WOODLAND

Tracks, also nests (often untidy) situated in all manner of more or less concealed situations, or sight of these nocturnal mice reveal their presence.

HABITAT: Practically everywhere throughout the continent s. of tree line and on various islands. See below under species.

DEERMOUSE species: Common names are not uniform, although they combine readily with 'Deermouse'; all are white-footed. **Desert** (*P. eremicus*): ears large; pale gray upperparts with orange-buff overcast that is clearest on sides; tail long, thinly haired, and its color above and below not markedly different. L. 7–8 in., t. 3⅘–4⅖. Arid regions, preferably with cactus.

*California (*P. californicus*): largest, with appearance of an undersized Woodrat; upperparts cool grayish-brown with some buffy-brown on sides; ears fairly large; tail blackish above. L. 8¾–10⅖, t. 5–5¾, wt. to 2½ oz. Mainly s. half of Calif.; prefers brushy areas such as edge of dense chaparral. **Canyon** (*P. crinitus*): varies from grayish-buff to buffy; fur long and lax; tail fairly long in relation to head and body length, well haired, and with small end tuft. L. 6½–7⅔, t. 3½–4⅓. Mainly in rocky canyons. *Long-tailed (*P. maniculatus*): most variable and occupying largest geographical area; varies from clear gray (young and adult alike) to grayish-buff to warm buffy-brown (grayest in n. forest areas); tail colored above like back and below white, sharply divided. L. 4¾–9, t. 2–5. Cool n. forests to prairies to wide range of vegetation types in w. U.S. In parts of range difficult to tell from other species there. **Sitka** (*P. sitkensis*): dark brownish-gray, shading to deep brownish on sides; poorly differentiated from *maniculatus* of the mainland. L. 8¼–9, t. 4–4½. Baranof, Chichagof, and Forrester I., Alaska; Prevost I. in Queen Charlotte group, Brit. Columbia. *Old-field or Beach (*P. polionotus*): pale pinkish-cinnamon; tail relatively short. L. 5–6⅕, t. 1⅗–2⅖. Se. U.S.; rocky fields and sandy beaches.

***Woodland** (*P. leucopus*): wide-ranging; varies from more or less reddish-brown to deep gray with some brownish-buffy overcast on sides. Reddish and brownish-gray adults often occur in the same locality. L. 6–8$\frac{1}{5}$, t. 2$\frac{2}{5}$–4. Mixed or hardwood areas and brushland. Often difficult to distinguish from other species. **Cotton** (*P. gossypinus*): dark sooty- to tawny-brown with blackish hairs intermixed; tail usually dark above and markedly paler below. L. 6$\frac{1}{3}$–8$\frac{1}{5}$, t. 2$\frac{3}{4}$–3$\frac{3}{5}$. Mainly se. U.S.; wooded low ground and swamps. **Brush** (*P. boylii*): varies from soft grayish- to medium brown, becoming more or less buffy brown on sides; tail well haired. L. 7–8$\frac{3}{5}$, t. 3$\frac{3}{5}$–4$\frac{2}{5}$. Arid SW. and W.; brushy terrain. **Oak** (*P. pectoralis*): pale grayish-buff; white of foot includes ankle. L. 7–8, t. 3$\frac{1}{2}$–4$\frac{2}{5}$. Big Bend region, Tex. ***Piñon** (*P. truei*): very large ears; cool sooty-brown, with buffy overcast becoming fairly clear down on sides; tail very dark above and light below. L. 7–8$\frac{3}{4}$, t. 3$\frac{1}{3}$–4$\frac{4}{5}$. Sparsely wooded rocky foothills and lower mt. elevations. **Rock** (*P. nasutus*): very like preceding, including large ears; where their ranges overlap, tail of Rock Deermouse usually is equal to or greater than its head and body length. L. 7$\frac{1}{4}$–8$\frac{2}{5}$, t. 3$\frac{3}{5}$–4$\frac{2}{5}$. Arid rocky and brushy terrain.

***Golden** (*P. nuttalli*): beautiful rich orange-brown, becoming paler on sides, and not sharply differentiated from white underparts. L. 6$\frac{1}{3}$–7$\frac{3}{5}$, t. 3–3$\frac{3}{5}$. Se. U.S.; brushy and hardwood areas. Arboreal in habits. **Florida** (*P. floridanus*): dull buffy-brown with dusky overcast, shading to pale orange-buff on sides, and sharply divided from white underparts; tail relatively short. L. 7$\frac{1}{2}$–8$\frac{4}{5}$, t. 3$\frac{1}{5}$–3$\frac{4}{5}$. Fla.; occupies burrows of other animals on sandy ridges.

REPRODUCTION: Laboratory data mainly. In some species, at least, both sexes begin breeding while still in subadult gray coat. A female Woodland may breed at 46 days, a Long-tailed at 48, but the Cotton not until about 70. Breeding continues throughout the warmer months in

N. and, farther s., perhaps all year in some species, or except coldest and/or hottest months. Gestation periods: Desert, 21; California, 21–25; Long-tailed, 22–27; Woodland, 22–25; Cotton, 23; Piñon, 25–27; if lactating (giving milk), periods are often considerably longer.

For Deermice collectively, range of litter size is 1–9, usually about 4, but the Desert, California, and probably Canyon species have smaller and fewer litters. Also collectively, eyes usually open in 12–15 days, but species vary slightly. Weaning occurs at 22–37 days in the Woodland and Long-tailed; in the Desert and California it is always prolonged—44 days in one instance in the latter. In some species the pregnant female may tolerate a nursing litter and the male in the nest until near birth of her next litter, or even continues to do so thereafter in the California Deermouse.

Instances of paternal care, such as warming, washing, and guarding young, have been noted in the Woodland and Long-tailed species. In most species studied, weaned young either are driven from the nest or the female abandons it and makes a clean one for her next litter. Most Deermice probably survive only one or two breeding seasons.

HABITS: Volumes have been written about these nimble nocturnal Mice. Most species are noted for exploring their home area thoroughly, often including ground surface, holes below, and more or less vegetation above. Individuals of a species tolerate each other in some measure and have overlapping home ranges that vary in size, depending on food supply and safety factors. Nests of dry vegetation, lined with plant down or shredded material, may be in tunnels they dig, as with several species, in turtle burrows as in the Florida Deermouse, in logs, stumps, crannies in cliffs, or may be roofed-over bird nests, or heaps of mattress stuffing or other soft material in camps and houses. A soiled nest is abandoned; although one may be used all winter, a number are needed annually.

Voice is a thin squeak, also a shrill buzzing or so-called song; evidently all species except the California Deermouse, when excited, thump rapidly with the front feet to produce a drumming sound. Both sexes do it. Internal cheek pouches are better developed in n. species, and much food is carried to storage. They do not hibernate. Diet includes all sorts of seeds, fruits, berries, nuts, many insects, numerous other small invertebrates, and carcasses of dead creatures. Populations fluctuate markedly, peak numbers occurring about every 3–5 years.

ECONOMIC STATUS: Some grain is eaten in fields and in storage; also, at times when they are abundant, these mice may eat the annual crop of tree seeds in some areas needing reforestation. As laboratory mammals that produce litters in rapid succession, they have been valuable in heredity studies. Indoors and out they have proved useful in theoretical and applied studies of animal populations, behavior, ecology, reproduction, and evolution.

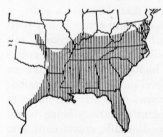

Rice Rat
Oryzomys palustris
Plate 33

A slender Rat, with sparsely haired long scaly tail that is much lighter below than above. Color of upperparts grayish- or warm buffy-brown with blackish hairs intermixed; underparts and feet are whitish-gray (creamy-white in s. Tex.) and quite clearly delimited from upperparts. L. 9–12 in., t. 4–6¼, wt. to 3 oz. Most readily confused with Cotton Rats, which have longer, grizzled fur and shorter, stouter tails. The sparsely haired scaly tails of the introduced Brown and Black Rats are uniformly dark all around or nearly so. A Mexican species of Rice Rat (*O. couesi*) occurs n. to the vicinity of Brownsville, Tex., where it is found in grassy places in mesquite brush. It differs mainly in cranial characters.

Rice Rat signs are feeding platforms of dinner-plate size, made by bending over vegetation, also their woven grassy nests a little larger than a large grapefruit, or even 12–18 in. in diameter, or tracks in mud of fresh- or salt-water marshes.

HABITAT: Marshes, also drier areas of grasses or sedges.

REPRODUCTION: Females breed when about 7 weeks old. Young are born in the spherical woven nests, in aquatic vegetation above water, and in drier situations. Breeding continues Mar.–Nov. in n. part of range and probably all year in S. Following are mainly La. data. Gestation requires 25 days, and the female breeds again within a few hours after giving birth. Litter size: 1–7, usually 3–4. Newborn young have fine hair on upperparts, eyes are closed, and they weigh about ½ oz. They are well furred in 6 days, eyes open in 8; they have a high-pitched squeak, leave the nest to run about and feed at 10 days, are weaned in 11–13 days, and are full grown in 4 months. Probably most of them do not survive a year.

HABITS: The Rice Rat, rather social and active at any hour the year round, is abundant in the great coastal salt marshes. It does not have well-defined runways. It swims and dives readily. Voice is a high-pitched squeak. Woven nests are above high-water level in clumps of vegetation; in drier situations short burrows evidently are made in soil. Food: parts of green plants—cuttings being found on feeding platforms; also seeds, snails, crustaceans, and other invertebrates, since remains of these also are found at feeding sites.

ECONOMIC STATUS: Because of its usual habitat preference, this rodent rarely comes into direct conflict with man. It breeds readily in captivity and may become a useful laboratory mammal.

It is desirable to keep captives in a humid environment, with water readily available, and an adequate supply of green foods and vegetables.

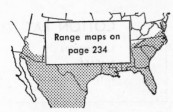

Cotton Rats
Sigmodon
Plate 33

Medium-sized Rats; blackish fur of upperparts has more or less brownish tips that give a coarse grizzled appearance; tail scaly, finely haired, blackish above, somewhat lighter below, and shorter than head and body; ears partly hidden in fur. Young have adult pattern but shorter hair. The grizzled coat distinguishes the Cotton Rats; see comparisons under Rice Rat (p. 231). Commonest signs are a maze of surface runways and some shallow burrows under grasses and similar cover.

HABITAT: Preferably damp situations with tall grass or other ground cover, but often perfectly dry ground. See below.

COTTON RAT (*Sigmodon*) **species: 1.—*Common** (*S. hispidus*): general tone of upperparts brownish, varying to blackish in Fla., where hairs are darker basally and brownish tips are shorter; underparts grayish-white; tail sparsely haired. L. 9–13 in., t. 3¼–5¼, wt. 4–8½ oz. Damp meadows, ditches, broom-sedge fields, weedy places, grassy forest glades. **2.—Least** (*S. minimus*): upperparts blackish, grizzled with pale buff; underparts buffy-brown; tail decidedly hairy. L. 7–9, t. 3½–4. Damp and dry grassy areas in mts. **3.—Yellow-nosed** (*S. ochrognathus*): upperparts grayish-black, grizzled with orange-buff that is nearly a solid color on nose, face, and rump; underparts whitish-gray. L. 10½, t. 4½. Grassy areas in foothills and mts.

REPRODUCTION: Common Cotton Rat. Females begin breeding at age of 30–40 days, males at 20–30. Young are born in a nest of grass or weedy trash in the runway system. Litters are produced from late winter through summer

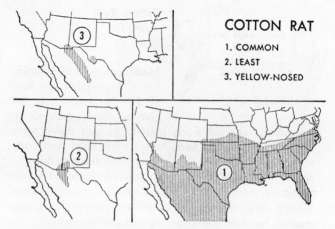

COTTON RAT

1. COMMON
2. LEAST
3. YELLOW-NOSED

into fall in N. and perhaps all year in S. if food is adequate. Gestation requires 27 days, and 2–8 hours after giving birth the female is bred again. Litter size: 2–10, usually 5–6. Young at birth have a hair coat. Eyes usually open in 18–36 hours. Evidently young are weaned in 15–25 days, or even much earlier, and then disperse. Growth continues about 50 days. Probably few individuals live a year.

HABITS: Common Cotton Rat. Usually this is the most abundant mammal on s. farmlands. It is active the year round and more or less at any hour, traveling in its runways and burrows and eating vegetation, all kinds of small animal life, and any carcasses it finds. Males, especially, are excitable and fight a great deal. Voice is a sort of squeaky squeal. Home range of an individual is perhaps usually under 80 ft. in greatest length. The population fluctuates greatly.

ECONOMIC STATUS: The Common Cotton Rat cuts sugarcane stalks and eats all kinds of garden crops, even digging sweet potatoes. Quail eggs and chicks are eaten. A host of other creatures, in turn, feed on it. As a laboratory mammal it has proved very useful in studies of medical bacteriology.

Range maps on page 236

Woodrats
(Pack, Trade, or Cave Rats)
Neotoma
Plate 28

Rat-like, with large well-haired ears, large protruding eyes, soft fur, and fairly long hairy (not scaly) tail. In the non-bushy or round-tailed species the tail has short, close-lying hair; that of the bushy-tailed is fairly bushy but not Squirrel-like. Most species are western. Color above varies from pale creamy-buff or cool gray to deep brown, more drab in winter; underparts are buffy or whitish. Females are smaller than males. Upperparts of young are grayer than those of adults.

Woodrats are too evenly colored to be confused with larger Ground Squirrels; the well-haired tail and fine fur distinguish them from other Rat-like mammals. Their houses or nests, of all sorts of woody growth and debris, are situated as follows: on plains, to about 4-ft. base diameter, on ground among cacti or in brush; in mts., usually on ledges or against cliffs, on Pacific Coast often off ground in live-oaks. See track diagram on p. 211.

HABITAT: Varies; see under species. To high elevations in Sierras and s. Rockies.

WOODRAT (*Neotoma*) **species:** Only the last species listed, *N. cinerea,* is bushy-tailed. ***Eastern** (*N. floridana*): large; upperparts grayish-brown or brown, lighter and warmer on sides; throat, belly, and feet white or nearly so; tail like back above, white or nearly so below, and shorter than head and body. L. 14–17 in., t. 6–8, wt. 7–12 oz. Rock slides, cliffs, caves, swamps, also on plains. **Southern Plains** (*N. micropus*): upperparts cool gray; throat, chest, and feet white; belly grayish; tail very dark

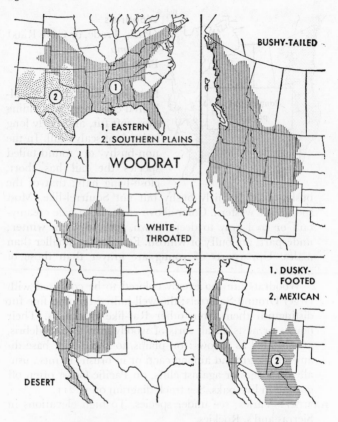

above and gray below. L. 13–15, t. 5½–6½, wt. 7–13 oz.
Arid plains. ***White-throated** (*N. albigula*) : upperparts
gray with strong buffy-brown suffusion; throat hairs
white clear to base; belly white or grayish; feet white;
tail brownish-black above and white or nearly so below.
L. 13–16, t. 5½–7¼. Arid SW. **Desert** (*N. lepida*):
small; upperparts vary from pale gray with buffy overcast (deserts) to medium gray with bright buffy overcast
to grayish-brown (s. Calif.) ; underparts grayish to buffy;
hairs on throat slate-colored basally. L. 10⅓–13½, t.

4⅓–6½. **Mexican** (*N. mexicana*): upperparts gray, with warm buffy-brown overcast, but nearly black on some lava flows; underparts grayish-white; tail blackish above, white below. L. 12½–14¼, t. 6–6½. Mainly rocky terrain. **Dusky-footed** (*N. fuscipes*): large; upperparts deep dull brown; belly white or grayish; tail long and nearly uniformly dark; tops of hind feet have clearly defined dusky areas. L. 14¼–17⅔, t. 6¾–8⅔. A climber, often nesting in live-oaks. ***Bushy-tailed** (*N. cinerea*): only Woodrat with a decidedly bushy tail; fur rather long and lax; upperparts vary from light buffy-tan, with darker hairs intermingled, to blackish-brown; undersurface, including tail, white. L. 12¼–17, t. 5¼–7⅓. An agile rock climber; varied habitat, but especially rocky places, also woods at fairly high elevations.

REPRODUCTION: Probably all species breed when less than a year old. There is a lined nest in a house or rock cranny. Reported or estimated gestation periods, followed by litter size in parentheses: Eastern, about 36 days? (1–4, but up to 6 embryos noted); Southern Plains, 33 (2–3); White-throated, less than 30? (1–3); Dusky-footed, 33 (2–4). Number of litters may be one in spring in N., but most have more than one, and some in S. may breed nearly all year and have several. Following data are for the White-throated. Young at birth have whiskers, scant hair on back, and weigh about ⅓ oz. They are well furred when eyes open in 15–19 days. In 62–72 days they are weaned. Before this the mother may have another litter, but permits the older young to suckle at times. They either depart voluntarily or she drives them away. They have adult body size and are capable of breeding in about 300 days. Captives have lived 3–4 years.

HABITS: Woodrats are mainly nocturnal and perhaps somewhat colonial. In W. their most notable trait is building bulky houses, often looking like a small edition of a Beaver lodge on land. This is added to as long as it is occupied by one owner or a succession of them. Most species build on the ground, some quite often in trees in some localities, and a number regularly build smaller nests in protected rocky places. A Woodrat may line the sides of its paths close to its lodge with cactus spines for added security. It often drops whatever it is carrying to its nest and picks up some more attractive object—especially a shiny one: coins, watches, spoons, other metal objects, even false teeth. Voice: a squeal and a shrill chatter; chirps are uttered at mating time. They thump with one or both hind feet, or even vibrate the end third of their tails, to communicate warning.

Food is mainly vegetable matter: fruits, berries, seeds, bark of twigs, herbs, grasses, and pulp of cactus joints. A few insects are eaten. Food may be eaten where found or carried to storage in the house for winter use. Foraging is done on the ground or by climbing bushes and trees. Waste, such as food remains and droppings, is cleaned out of the house at intervals. Those on deserts may not drink water. Home range usually extends only about 20–25 yds. from the house, but it may be larger when food is scarce nearby. Populations fluctuate markedly.

ECONOMIC STATUS: Usually Woodrats do not conflict with man's interests. When other food is scarce, they may damage fruit or nut trees by gnawing bark. Their flesh is edible.

Lemming Mice
(Bog Lemmings)
Synaptomys
Plate 32

Resembling small Voles (*Microtus*), but with short tails, relatively massive head, long loose fur, and curved upper front teeth that have a *shallow* groove at the outer edge. **1.—*Southern* or Cooper's** (*S. cooperi*): upperparts brownish with a salt-

and-pepper effect; underparts lighter and grayer. L. 3¾–5 in., t. ½–⅘, wt. ¾–1⅓ oz. **2.—Northern** (*S. borealis*): varies from pale to deep rich brown, often quite dark (especially in Ungava); averages longer than the preceding; tail to about 1 in. and slightly stouter. Both have longer winter fur. The Northern then has elongated *thick* claws on front toes, especially the 2 middle ones; winter claws of the Southern are quite long and sharp, but not thickened.

Age for age, Lemming Mice are darker than most Voles (*Microtus*), but 'bobbed' tail is best identifying character. Lemming Mice have surface runways and sub-surface tunnels, as do Voles. *Synaptomys* perhaps never is detected for certain except by trapping.

HABITAT: The Southern: bogs, swales, grassland, thickets, forest floor. Northern: both damp and dry situations, with or without woody growth. Spotty known occurrence of these rodents makes a general map of their ranges seem particularly misleading.

REPRODUCTION: Both begin breeding before they are full grown, and have litters from spring well into fall. Embryo counts: Southern, 1–7 (usually 3); Northern, 1–5 (usually 3).

HABITS: Lemming Mice are often local, but quite plentiful, and absent from seemingly identical nearby areas. They do not hibernate and are active at any hour. Surface runways and short-cut lengths of grass stalks are like those of Voles (*Microtus*). Their powerful jaw muscles undoubtedly are useful when cutting through tangles of roots and soil or beds of moss. I have captured the Southern in dry and very wet Star-nosed Mole tunnels. They commonly use tunnels and runways made by other small mammals. Voice: a short sharp squeak. Undoubtedly each sex makes its presence known by secretion from the large glands in the groin, in males proportionately as large as the Beaver's; males also have small hip glands that are more developed in the breeding season. Food: vegetable material, mainly green parts of low vegetation, and probably slugs, snails, and other invertebrates. Home range perhaps rarely exceeds 100 ft. in greatest length, and many individuals may occur on an acre of ground. Populations fluctuate greatly, the Mice being locally plentiful some years and nearly nonexistent others.

Brown Lemming
Lemmus trimucronatus
Plate 32

A stocky little rodent; tail very short; ears nearly hidden in fur; general tone brownish the year round. L. 4¾–6½ in., t. ⅔–¾, wt. 1½–4 oz. Adults in summer are richly colored, brown above, often with grizzled grayish foreparts, and medium to pale warm brown or cream below. Often there is a poorly defined darker streak from nose to back of head (not down back). Adults in winter have very long fur, warm brown above and paler below; hair on wrists and ankles is much lengthened, giving more foot surface and probably added protection to haired soles of feet. Claw on the thumb is long, flat, and most conspicuous in winter. Young are an even dull brown above and pale brown below. On St. George I., Bering Sea, this Lemming has blackish hind feet and has been named *L. nigripes*.

In comparison, Varying Lemmings, also bob-tailed, have grayer summer coat with more or less distinct streak down center of back; in winter they are white; and the gray young have a conspicuous black streak from nape to rump. Both kinds make surface runways, burrows, piles of dung pellets, snow tunnels, and occasionally trails on the snow surface. They use each other's summer runways and winter burrows. In bounding gait (of either species), tracks are paired; front and hind overlap, as in the left-hand diagram for Meadow Vole (p. 248).

HABITAT: Mostly beyond timber line in N.; in general, this species prefers wetter areas than the Varying Lemming, but dry areas with varied plant growth are often utilized.

REPRODUCTION: Breeding begins before full growth is attained. The nest, a spherical ball of plant materials lined with moss, shredded plant fibers, and hair or feathers, may be among vegetation on the ground surface, under a rock, or in a burrow. There are several litters annually, with breeding from spring into fall, or even reported for winter. Gestation period (unknown) probably is about 20–22 days. Counts have yielded 3–9, usually 4–7, embryos.

HABITS: The Brown Lemming is active at all hours and seasons. A cornered one sits on its haunches, squeals, and chatters its teeth; it strikes with the forefeet in self-defense. Lemming emigrations are best known in Scandinavia, but are reported to occur on a smaller scale in N. Am. The population builds up for 3–4 years, when the tundra swarms with them. This build-up may be rather local or over a wide area. Vegetation is riddled or, in places, almost entirely consumed as they move in search of food. They swim readily and are swallowed by fish. Those that travel do not return. They are drowned, killed by a host of creatures, or die of disease within a few weeks, so that the population is nearly wiped out. Then Foxes, Weasels, Owls, Hawks, Ravens, and other creatures that eat them (and other rodents that likewise have vanished) must find other food or starve. Following a 'crash' in the small rodent population in N., there are southerly flights of the Snowy Owl, Great Gray or Northern Shrike, and Rough-legged Hawk, as well as less conspicuous movements by other creatures.

The Brown Lemming makes surface runways and sub-surface tunnels. Winter tunnels under snow tend to hug the ground surface. At times it travels under snow on sea, lake, and river ice. Food: sedges, grasses, bark, leaves, berries, blossoms, and various roots. When winter snows have melted, one often finds several quarts of dung at a runway intersection. In summer bulbous roots are carried under stones or down burrows for winter use.

ECONOMIC STATUS: Brown and Varying Lemmings and Vole (*Microtus*) species are more or less collectively called 'mice' in the N. A die-off of these rodents is followed by a diminished number of mammals that feed on them, notably of Foxes. Rodents thus are a key link in the number of furs harvested. An abundance of rodents may result in the lichen ground cover being riddled by them, which even affects Caribou movements.

Varying Lemmings
(Collared Lemmings)
Dicrostonyx
Plate 32

Generally like the Brown Lemming (which see), but stouter in form and with striking seasonal color change. Brownish in summer. Winter coat *white* (but see exception below), with fur dark at base; even soles of feet have white hairs; third and fourth front toes develop a bulbous underportion to each claw, which is shed in spring. Young are dull gray-ish-brown above, with conspicuous dark spinal stripe, and pale gray or buffy below. **I.—Ungava** (*D. hudsonius*): in summer, upperparts buffy gray with indistinct spinal stripe; belly grayish-buff. L. 5½–6 in., t. ¾. **2.—*Green-land** (*D. grœnlandicus*): W. and n. of Hudson Bay, upperparts a mixture of grays and browns with narrow darker spinal stripe and belly creamy-buff; in Alaska, larger and grayer; does *not* turn white in winter on the 2 Aleutian islands from which it is known: Unalaska and Umnak. L. 5–6½, t. ⅗–⅘, wt. to 3½ oz. **3.—St. Law-rence Island** (*D. exsul*): St. Lawrence I., Alaska. See comparison and data on indications of presence under Brown Lemming on p. 240.

HABITAT: Mainly beyond tree line; dry sandy or gravelly areas with more or less plant cover; less often in wet places or where there is some tree growth.

REPRODUCTION: The nest is often in an underground burrow. Adults have at least 2 litters in the warmer months. Varying Lemmings definitely are known to breed in winter at times. Gestation period is unrecorded (20–22 days ?). Counts have yielded up to 11 embryos, usually 3–4. Week-old young are well haired above; eyes open in about 14 days.

HABITS: In many habits and in population behavior the Varying Lemmings are much like the Brown (which see). Each travels in, and forages in and about, its own and the other's runways. Voice: a chuckling sound and a squeal. The method of defense is similar to the Brown's. Summer nests may be in burrows, or on the surface under a bush, rock, or debris. Nest burrows are rather short, often with a side chamber for a toilet. Unlike the Brown, in winter Varying Lemmings regularly tunnel through drifts; vegetation is often carried into such a tunnel, and a winter nest is made inside a snowbank. The double claws are useful in scratching through hard-packed snow.

ECONOMIC STATUS: See under Brown Lemming.

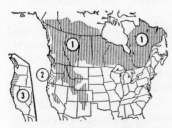

Spruce Mice
Phenacomys
Plate 33

Much like Voles (*Microtus*) or Red-backed Mice (*Clethrionomys*) in general appearance, but with rather long, very fine fur. Most diagnostic characters are internal. Combination of fur texture, color pattern, and tail length may distinguish these Mice, but recourse to tooth pattern—see A. B. Howell, *U. S. Dept. Agric., N.*

Am. Fauna 48 (1926)—may be necessary for positive identification.

The first species listed has medium-length tail. **1.— *Northern** (*P. intermedius*): upperparts vary—bright chestnut to dark brown in Ungava, pale grayish-brown in w. Ontario to Rockies, and darker grayish-brown in Canadian Rockies and w. U.S.; underparts paler. Nose is yellowish, except in Canadian Rockies and w. U.S., where it is not differentiated in color. L. 5–6¾ in., t. ⅞–1⅝, wt. 1–1½ oz. Following are long-tailed species. **2.—Coast** (*P. albipes*): upperparts deep rich brown; face sooty; underparts clear gray (with buffy tinge in winter). L. 6¼–7⅗, t. 2½–2¾. **3.—*Red** (*P. longicaudus*): upperparts rich orange-brown. L. 6¼–7½, t. 2⅖–3¼. Included with it here is the warm brownish *P. silvicola,* known from Tillamook and Benton Co., Ore.

Young *Phenacomys* are darker above than adults and dull slaty below. Ground runways in suitable habitat may be used by them or other similar-sized Mice. The Red Spruce-Mouse makes small spherical nests from low down to high up in conifers, usually out away from the trunk.

HABITAT: The Northern occurs in grassy forest glades or edges, mossy areas, heather, also sagebrush, and from low elevations to near summer snow fields in mts.; the Coast and Red species are both ground- and tree-dwelling, in humid coniferous forests.

REPRODUCTION: Young of the Northern are born in ground nests; embryo counts are 3–8. The Red (and probably Coast) builds spherical nests only on conifer limbs, so far as now known. The Red breeds all year, but mainly in warmer months, with litter size of 1–3. Probably all have at least 2 litters annually. Young Red Spruce-Mice are born with eyes closed and weigh ⅑ oz.; they have some fur in 4 days, are well furred in 15, eyes open in 19, and they are independent in a month.

HABITS: Few mammalogists have captured these Mice, which are usually rather scarce and local. Range of the genus *Phenacomys* coincides fairly well with that of spruce, hence the name Spruce Mouse is adopted here at the suggestion of Dr. Francis Harper.

The Northern is sometimes taken where there are no signs of runways, or in runways in grass or burrows that might have been made by several Mouse species. The Red Spruce-Mouse is best known. Males live in ground burrows or under surface debris, but go up trees to make small temporary nests there when they find females to be bred. Females live in trees, building larger nests, probably lower down, of twigs and uneaten portions of conifer needles. Sometimes an abandoned Squirrel nest serves as a foundation. For food, tender terminal fir twigs are cut. Each needle is bitten off and all but the tougher central portion and some surrounding material eaten. They eat at any convenient place; some cuttings are stored on top of the nest. At least one species of Jay is known to rip open nests to get the Mice.

Red-backed Mice
(Red-backed Voles)
Clethrionomys
Plate 33

Rather brightly colored Mice; usually with wide, more or less reddish-brown back stripe, either delineated clearly from or merging gradually with lighter sides; underparts usually grayish-white. Young tend toward dark slaty, but there is a reddish cast to upperparts in most cases where adults have any reddish. Reddish or orange-tan upperparts and medium tail length usually will identify these Mice.

In nw. N. Am. some *Microtus* are tan or buffy, not orange. The Spruce Mice (*Phenacomys*) differ in size and color, but some are quite easily confused with Redbacks. The gray phase, known in the Northern Redback from Alberta to Ungava, may be confused with some *Microtus* or the Northern Spruce Mouse. Pine Mice have rich brown silky fur. Often Redbacks leave no noticeable signs of their presence, or only obscure runways among lichens, mosses, or in forest litter.

HABITAT: In general, Redbacks may be considered as forest counterparts of the Voles (*Microtus*), even though some of the latter are woodland or mt. dwellers. On tundra or on mts. above tree line, Redbacks prefer shrubby ground cover in both dry and damp situations.

RED-BACKED MOUSE (*Clethrionomys*) **species: 1.—Tundra** (*C. rutilus*): rich reddish- to orange-brown back, merging into buffy-gray sides and belly; fur long and lax, especially in winter; tail short and thick. L. 5–6 in., t. 4/5–1½. Tundra, bogs, woodland. **2.—St. Lawrence Island** (*C. albiventer*): back brown; sides gray. St. Lawrence I., Alaska. **3.—*Northern** (*C. gapperi*): varies greatly over its wide range—reddish of back (or chestnut in se. Alaska and Brit. Columbia) always evident in 'normal' color phase—in N. clearly set off from grayer or yellowish-brown sides, but farther s. they blend together; tail slender. L. 5–6½, t. 1¼–2, wt. to 1½ oz. Mainly wooded terrain, dry or damp. From Labrador to well inland w. of Hudson Bay, color phases are: 'normal' (with dark reddish back stripe), gray with darker back stripe, and black. More than one phase may occur in the same litter; intermediates between phases exist. Gray ones may be difficult to distinguish from some other Mice on basis of external characters only. From se. Alaska to s. Brit Columbia, on islands and mainland, there are notably gray-sided, dark-backed Redbacks. Those of Ariz. and N. Mex. are large and dull-colored. **4.—Western** (*C. occidentalis*): very dark brown back, contrasting slightly with dark sides; belly whitish or buffy; feet light. L. 5–7, t. 1¾–2⅕. Mainly in moist coniferous forests.

REPRODUCTION: They breed the season they are born. Young

are born in a nest of shredded vegetation in ground litter, under a log, or in a stump. Following data (mainly Mich.) pertain to *C. gapperi*. Gestation requires 17–19 days. Several litters are born spring–fall, and the female may breed again while giving milk. Litter size: 3–8, usually 4–6. Young at birth have no hair except tiny whiskers, eyes are closed, and they weigh about 1/14 oz. Hair is noticeable in 4 days, eyes open in 11–15, and weaning occurs in 17–21 days. They probably disperse soon thereafter. Gestation was 18 days in a Western female that was bred 12 hours after giving birth to a litter.

HABITS: Redbacks are active at any hour and season. In many cool forested areas they are the most abundant rodent. They climb stumps and rough-barked trees readily and sometimes nest in crannies well above ground. In a Me. woods camp a *gapperi* had her nest in the bottom of a smooth pine box 18 in. tall. By placing her feet properly she could scurry up a right-angled corner of the box without faltering, and go down again after foraging. As is common with this Mouse, on not being disturbed she lost much of her shyness toward humans. Voice is a high-pitched and rather musical squeak. Food consists mainly of the soft parts of many plants, also seeds, nuts bark, lichens, fungi, and immature stages of many insects. Some food is carried to storage. An individual's home range usually is a fraction of an acre, varying in size with food supply and population pressure. High numbers occur at about 4-year intervals, when these Mice are truly abundant. From field experience I believe that, when this Mouse and the Big Short-tailed Shrew are abundant, the Mice do considerable climbing and foraging in trees—especially low conifers. Few have been seen in trees in the Shrew's range, but in Labrador one person saw it perched in spruces several times.

ECONOMIC STATUS: Redbacks occasionally damage a few trees by eating bark, especially in winter. They eat quantities of insect larvae, including those of forest pests. A host of creatures prey on these Mice.

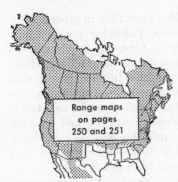

Range maps on pages 250 and 251

Voles
(Meadow or Field Mice)
Microtus
Plate 32

Rather stocky short-eared rodents with beady black eyes. They fall in the range of l. 3⅞–10¼ in. (mostly about 6) and t. ¾–3½ (mostly about 1½); ratio of tail to body length is often a useful identifying character. Upperparts vary from grayish through brown (commonly) to very dark brown to buffy or tan (nw. N. Am.); belly may be slaty or brown or buffy. Young are darker than adults.

Although most people know a Vole, or Field Mouse, sometimes a mammalogist must use internal characters such as tooth structure to identify species with certainty. In comparison, Lemming Mice look quite similar at a glance, but have short tails and grooved upper front teeth. Lemmings in any coat are stouter, with stubby tails. On external characters only, some Spruce Mice (*Phenacomys*) may be confused with them. The color and pattern of Red-backed Mice are distinctive, but some phases of the Northern may be hard to tell from some *Microtus*. The little Sagebrush Mouse is gray, with short tail. Pine Mice have silky fur and deep brown

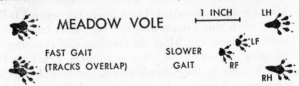

MEADOW VOLE   1 INCH   LH

FAST GAIT   SLOWER   LF
(TRACKS OVERLAP)   GAIT   RF

RH

upperparts. Commonest *Microtus* signs are surface runways in grass and other low plant growth, burrows in loose soil, tunnels under snow, or sight of the scurrying Voles themselves.

HABITAT: Most prefer grassy or sedgy places; some occur in rocky ones, or even low vegetation with forest overstory; in the Arctic and above tree line on mts. they occur in practically any low vegetation. Except for areas in the Gulf states (where the Common Cotton Rat fills their niches), generally present throughout the continent and on many adjacent islands.

VOLE (*Microtus*) **species: *Meadow** (*M. pennsylvanicus*): varies over its continent-wide range—dark brown upperparts in E. to gray with brown intermixed in W.; belly grayish-white or slightly buffy. L. 5¼–7⅗ in., t. 1¼–2⅗, wt. to 4 oz. Grassy areas, swales, woodland clearings, at any elevation. Perhaps actually the same species as *M. agrestis* of the Old World. Not always considered specifically distinct from *pennsylvanicus* are: *M. provectus* of Block I., R.I.; *M. nesophilus* (extinct) of Gull I. off e. Long I., N.Y.; and *M. breweri* of Muskeget I., Mass. **Mountain** (*M. montanus*): upperparts grayish-brown to brownish-black; feet usually dark. L. 5¼–7½, t. 1¼–2⅗. Mainly in mt. valleys. **California** (*M. californicus*): more or less grayish-brown, but varies from somewhat reddish in deserts to blackish on coast; feet pale. L. 6¼–8⅓, t. 1½–2⅔. Usually grassy areas, from sea level to high elevations. **Townsend's** (*M. townsendii*): large; upperparts brownish-black; belly grayish or grayish-brown; tail blackish; feet dusky. L. 6½–9, t. 1¾–2¾. Usually damp low areas, on mainland and various islands. **Tundra** (*M. œconomus*): fur long; upperparts vary from grayish to buffy-tan (over most of range) to tawny to brown, with paler sides merging into white or buffy underparts. Has longer tail than Alaska Vole. L. 6–8½, t. 1¼–2. Damp or dry grassy or sedgy areas mainly. Range includes various islands around Alaska: St. Lawrence, Big Punuk; in Aleutians to Amak and on Unalaska; Kodiak, Afognak, and some others e. and s. to Chichagof. **Long-tailed** (*M. longicaudus*): large; relatively long tail; upperparts vary from grayish to dark

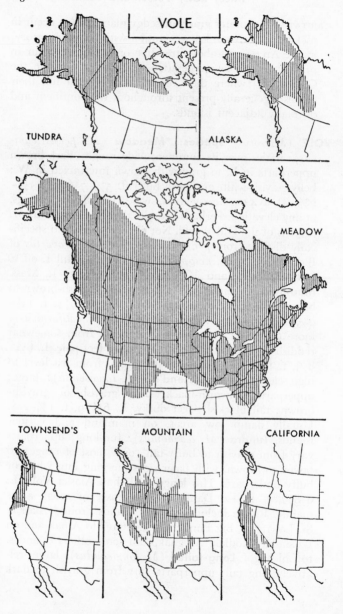

VOLE

TUNDRA

ALASKA

MEADOW

TOWNSEND'S

MOUNTAIN

CALIFORNIA

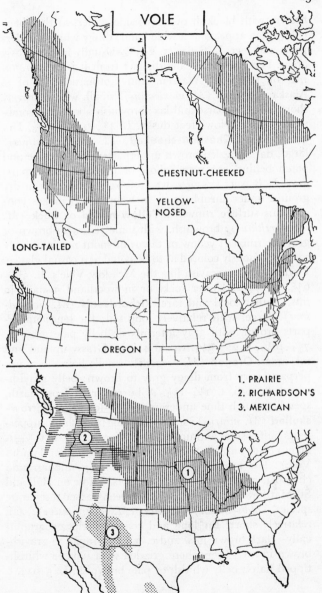

VOLE

CHESTNUT-CHEEKED

YELLOW-NOSED

LONG-TAILED

OREGON

1. PRAIRIE
2. RICHARDSON'S
3. MEXICAN

brown, with blackish overcast; sides paler, so that back color often appears as a wide band; dingy whitish under-parts and feet. L. 6–8⅝, t. 2–3½. Usually in dry grassy areas. Perhaps specifically distinct from it is *M. corona-rius* of Forrester, Warren, and Coronation Is. of s. Alaska. **Mexican** (*M. mexicanus*): small, with relatively short tail; fur coarse and lax; brownish above and some-what lighter below; feet dusky. L. 4¾–6, t. 1–1⅜. Dry grassy areas. **Chestnut-cheeked** (*M. xanthognathus*): large; dark grizzled-brown upperparts; sides of nose and patch behind ear rusty-yellow or chestnut; underparts gray. L. 8–9, t. 1½–2⅛, wt. to 6 oz. A burrower in dry ground under shrubbery or in woods; also makes con-spicuous surface runways. **Yellow-nosed** or **Rock** (*M. chrotorrhinus*): brownish, with some yellowish-brown or gray intermixed; yellow or tawny of snout not invariably so conspicuously colored as to be noted at a casual glance. Underparts are grayish like the Meadow Vole's. L. 5½–6⅘, t. 1¾–2. Under rocks or in woodland, usually in mts.; rather local and rare. **Richardson's** (*M. richard-soni*): large, with relatively long tail; fur long; upper-parts brown, with gray intermixed; belly pale gray. L. 7¾–10¼, t. 2⅓–3½, wt. to 4½ oz. Grassy upland and mt. areas. **Oregon** (*M. oregoni*): small; hair short; up-perparts vary from dingy gray to brown; belly grayish-white. L. 5–6, t. 1¼–1⅝. A burrower in loose earth, spending much time underground. ***Alaska** or **Narrow-skulled** (*M. miurus*): small; fur long; tail short; upper-parts buffy; sides and underparts paler. L. 3⅞–6, t. ¾–1. Damp or dry areas (tolerates more wetness than Tundra Vole); low ground to high in mts. Digs underground chambers and there stores plant roots. Those on Hall and St. Matthew Is., Bering Sea, have been named a separate species (*abbreviatus*). **Prairie** (*M. ochrogaster*): tail relatively short; fur long and coarse; varies geographi-cally—dark brown in s. and e. parts of range to grayish-brown in nw.; everywhere grizzled with tan- or whitish-tipped hairs; belly whitish or pale brownish. L. 5–6¾, t.

$7/8$–$15/8$, wt. to $13/4$ oz. Mainly prairies; often makes burrows where grass is sparse. Those occurring in a limited area in Tex.–La. have been named *M. ludovicianus*.

REPRODUCTION: *M. pennsylvanicus*. Females can breed at 25 and males at 45 days of age. The spherical nest of dry plant material may be in a clump of vegetation, under plant debris, or at times in a shallow burrow. Gestation requires 21 days. At first, litters are smaller; an adult has 6–8 (usually 5–7) young. The female often is bred again right after giving birth. In years of Meadow Vole abundance a female may produce litters at 3-week intervals for several months. They breed all year in S., but not in winter in N. Young at birth are hairless, have eyes closed, and weigh about $1/10$ oz. They are well haired in 7 days, eyes open in 8–9; they are weaned before 14, and usually stay with the mother a few days thereafter. Most do not survive a year. All *Microtus* that have been studied have at least several litters per year; known gestation periods are in a 20- to 22-day range.

HABITS: *Microtus* does not hibernate. Most species make well-defined surface runways under low vegetation. They swim and dive well. Several species regularly dig short burrows, especially if ground cover is scant, and some live in rock crannies. Voice is a high-pitched squeak. They are vegetarians, eating all sorts of plant material, including leaves, seeds, roots, and bark. Where grass or sedge stalks stand so close that they do not fall if cut at the base, a *Microtus* keeps cutting short sections until the fruiting head is pulled down within reach. This accounts for the piles of cuttings scattered along runways. A *Microtus* can eat its own wt. in green food in 24 hours. Some of the n. species store food, evidently for winter use; one, at least—*M. miurus*—gathers small piles of hay. A low population of the Meadow Vole is 15–40 per acre; this may increase to 60–250 in 3–4 years and then, in fall or winter, it drops again. Causes are not fully known, but disease plays a role in the decline. Cycles are well enough established so that years of population peaks are predictable. Similar ups and downs evidently occur in all *Microtus,* as also in Lemmings and some other rodents.

ECONOMIC STATUS: Occasionally a *Microtus* population attains plague proportions, as in 1907–08 in the Humboldt Valley, Nev. Alfalfa fields were ruined. Unlike Lemmings, *Microtus* do not emigrate during their plagues and so damage is usually rather local. These Voles eat growing or harvested grains. They girdle fruit and other trees, under snow in winter, which becomes a serious matter in years of *Microtus* abundance. They themselves, of course, are a very important part of the diet of many kinds of wildlife. Also see economic status under Brown Lemming (p. 242).

Sagebrush Mouse
(Sagebrush Vole)
Lagurus curtatus
Plate 32

A small, short-tailed, rather slender-faced Mouse with relatively long fur. Upperparts pale gray, sometimes with brownish cast, and with fine salt-and-pepper effect, the pattern being uniform on back and sides; belly grayish-white; tail whitish below. L. 4½– 5⅗ in., t. ¾–1, wt. ⅔–1 oz. Young are browner and slightly darker than adults. Pale gray color and short tail distinguish this little Mouse. Signs of its presence are tunnels under sage bushes, shredded bark and leaves there, or, at times, surface runways from bush to bush.

HABITAT: Dry sagebrush, rabbit bush, and short-grass areas; to 10,000 ft. elevation in a few localities.

REPRODUCTION: The nest, of shredded vegetation, is in a subsurface cavity; usually there are at least 2 entrances. Breeding evidently occurs all year. Embryo counts are 3–10 (usually about 6).

HABITS: This Mouse is active at all hours and seasons. Usually the entrances to its short burrows are under a bush, at the edge of a stone heap, or in any sort of rubble, or it occupies a tunnel system made by some other rodent at these sites. When the population is high, distinct surface runways lead from one bush to another. Summer food consists mainly of herbaceous plants. Under a snow blanket it climbs sage bushes, strips off the bark, and eats the cambium layer beneath, also some foliage. When the snow is gone, bark shreds and cut leaves litter the ground below.

Pine Mouse
(Pine Vole)
Pitymys pinetorum
Plate 33

A small Mouse, with fine fur having a pronounced sheen; ears small and nearly concealed; tail short. In ne. part of its range the back is uniformly rich chestnut-brown, the edges of this wide band being rather definitely set off from the more buffy sides; in Midwest it is bright chestnut above, shading gradually into sides; in s. Ga.–Fla. (where it is considered a distinct species—*P. parvulus*) it is tawny above, grading to cinnamon on sides. Underparts are gray, in some areas with cinnamon or tawny overcast. L. 4¼–5⅝ in., t. ⅝–1, wt. 1–2 oz. Young are darker and more lead-colored than adults. The combination of fine silky fur and short tail distinguishes it from Red-backed Mice (*Clethrionomys*) and Voles (*Microtus*) occurring in its range. Signs of its presence are small tunnels in leaf mold or dirt, often with surface above pushed up into a little ridge.

HABITAT: Main requisite is thick leaf mold or loose soil, in forests (deciduous or mixed, seldom in pines), orchards, fields, scrub areas, and gardens. Has been taken in about every plant association, from open fields to tamarack swamps.

REPRODUCTION: The spherical nest, of shredded vegetation, under a log or just below the ground surface, usually has several entrances. Gestation probably requires about 21 days. Litters of 2–5 young are produced spring–fall in NE. and all year (at least some years) from N.J. south. Young are born hairless, with eyes closed, and weigh about ½₂ oz. They are well furred in 7 days, eat solid food in 16, and are weaned in 17 days.

HABITS: This Mouse dwells where tunneling is easy. Its close fur has the Mole-like characteristic of lying well whether rubbed forward or backward—an obvious adaptation for traveling either way in tunnels. It uses its own tunnels, also those of Moles, large Shrews, and other Mice, and has surface trails that usually are close to upright objects. Harsh chirrs and chitters are uttered when individuals meet. A musical Thrush-like *cheer-cheer* is given in alarm, and a similar note is sometimes made in low 'conversational' tone. Food: many succulent roots and tubers, also seeds, leaves, nuts, bark, berries, and apples. Rootstalks and other foods are stored in tunnels. Population ups and downs are said to coincide more or less with those of the Meadow Vole (*Microtus pennsyl-vanicus*). It may be able to defend itself against the Big Short-tailed Shrew (*Blarina*) under most circumstances.

ECONOMIC STATUS: This Mouse eats flower bulbs, potatoes and other root crops, and bark. When bark is eaten off fruit-tree roots below ground, much damage may be done before any is detected. Winter girdling of trees above ground, but under snow, may not be discovered until spring. Because of its habit of traveling in subsurface burrows and surface runways, traps set in these places catch a good percentage of the individuals present. Because Pine Mice seldom wander from these routes, traps scattered at random in suitable occupied habitat generally catch few, if any, of them.

Florida Water Rat
(Round-tailed Muskrat)
Neofiber alleni
Plate 26

A fairly large and robust rodent; fur dense; ears small and
nearly hidden; tail round, scaly, and nearly hairless; hind
feet slightly webbed. Upperparts usually dark brown or
blackish; belly buffy to nearly white. L. 12–14 in., t. 4½–
6½, wt. 6–11½ oz. Fur of adults has a silky sheen when
dry; young are very dark slaty, without sheen. This rodent looks like a small Muskrat, with round instead of
vertically flattened tail.

Signs of its presence are globular nests, usually 14–24
in. in diameter, on shore, in shallow water, or on floating
vegetation; flattened piles of cut vegetation used as feeding platforms; surface runways in muck and shallow
water; ground honeycombed with tunnels just below the
surface; floating sections of cut vegetation; or small
Muskrat-like tracks in mud.

HABITAT: Mainland and islands; brackish waters of river
deltas, fresh-water bogs, swamps, 'prairies,' and lake
margins. More of a bog than a water mammal.

REPRODUCTION: Young are born in a lined nest that usually
has 2 entrances opening from below. There are at least
several litters annually; it probably breeds all year.

HABITS: This rodent is somewhat more terrestrial than
the larger Muskrat. It is active at times by day, as well as
after dark, and tends to be gregarious. Voice is a squeak.
The globular nest of marsh grasses and other vegetation
has a very small lined chamber inside. If the nest is on
mucky earth, 2 tunnels lead into the muck and away.
Some nests are in fields of broom sedge not too remote
from water; here there is a network of surface runways
through the sedge.

Nests are built in shallow water, or on bog vegetation,
or even on a heavy mat of floating vegetation, sometimes

at bases of bog shrubs or trees. On mangrove islands they are placed against the tree roots. Some are built in buttonbushes and used during high water, then deserted. In making burrows, earth is left in little piles at the entrances, often mixed with dung and food remains. Known foods include various rushes, sedges, flag, saw grass, maiden cane, sea purslane, sugar cane, floating heart, and mangrove bark. Food may be eaten where found, or in a tunnel or runway, or carried to a feeding platform or nest. Fluctuating water levels pose problems; the Rats must build higher nests and platforms during high water. Nests and platforms are sunning sites of snakes, especially cottonmouth moccasins, which eat the Rats.

ECONOMIC STATUS: Usually of no significance to man, but sometimes does damage to cane and other crops, such as tomatoes and beans. Some damage blamed on it may be work of the Cotton Rat.

Muskrat
(Musquash)
Ondatra zibethicus
Plate 26

A large robust rodent with dense glossy fur, small ears, nearly hairless, scaly, laterally flattened tail, and partly webbed hind feet. Upperparts usually are brownish, somewhat lighter on sides; underparts pale—to almost white on throat—and often with small dark chin patch. L. 16–25 in., t. 7–11, wt. 1½–4 lb. Color is rich and dark in NE., lighter farther s.; it is smaller and duller on Gulf coast. In NW. and down through the Rockies it is small and dark; it is even smaller, but paler and more grayish, in SW. Especially in the coastal area, N.J.–N.C., a blackish phase is about as common as the brown. The small dark Newfd. mammal has been named *O. obscurus.*

A swimming Muskrat might be mistaken for a small Beaver, but the latter has a very squarish head. Compare also with the introduced Nutria (p. 216), which prefers good Muskrat habitat. Muskrat signs are houses in marshes, feeding platforms of cut vegetation, channels in

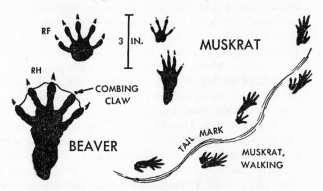

mud under shallow water leading to underwater or surface holes in banks, floating cut vegetation, and tracks. In spring and fall, Muskrats wander as far as several miles from water and are frequent highway casualties.

HABITAT: Fresh- and salt-water marshes; borders and island edges of all types of waterways except uncommonly in rapid rocky streams and rivers. Introduced on Vancouver I., in parts of Calif., and elsewhere at home, as well as abroad. In Alaska introduced 1925 on Long, 1929 on Kodiak, and later on Afognak and Raspberry I.; in Gulf of St. Lawrence in early 1930's (?) on Anticosti I.

REPRODUCTION: Young are born in a house or in a lined chamber in the earth. Gestation requires 29–30 days. Breeding continues early spring–fall in N.; in La. it breeds all year, but mainly Nov.–Apr. There are several litters annually, and the female is bred again while nursing. Litter size: 1–11, usually 5–7 in N. and 3–4 in S. Young at birth have eyes closed, some gray hair, are about 4 in. long, and weigh about ¾ oz. In a month they can fend for themselves and the mother soon drives them away.

HABITS: The Muskrat is active at any season or hour. It uses its hind feet when swimming, the tail having a waving motion or being held rigid as a rudder. It is rather awkward ashore. Houses are quite elaborate structures, often rising 2–3 ft. above water, of cut vegetation, with some bedding in the cavity, and one or more underwater entrances. A house is added to (except when there is ice) as long as used, as also are platforms where food is towed to be eaten. Much tunneling in banks is done, a 'rat' sometimes having several chambers, each with one to several underwater entrances. Houses and chambers are kept clean, the oval droppings being deposited outside on rocks and logs. Usually there is one adult per house, but several may live together amicably for a while when not breeding. Voice: a nasal moan, also squealing notes; teeth are chattered or ground at times. Musk glands in the groin give off a sweetish scent that identifies the sexes to each other.

Chiefly a vegetarian, the Muskrat eats stems and fleshy parts of many plants, including cattails, flags, arrowhead, three-square rush (*Scirpus*), and various grasses, also fresh-water mussels and some other invertebrates. If a marsh becomes overcrowded, there is much fighting, especially in fall and winter. Some individuals wander miles, even over land, searching for other living places. In Canada, population peaks are said to occur at about 9- to 10-year intervals. Aside from the trapper, the Muskrat has two major types of hazards: fluctuations in water level that strand or flood its dwellings, and a host of predators.

ECONOMIC STATUS: The Muskrat is first in importance in the fur trade; enormous numbers are trapped. Carcasses, often sold as 'marsh rabbit,' can be prepared for the table in many ways and are excellent eating. Muskrats eat growing corn in gardens near water. They burrow in irrigation banks and gnaw wooden gates. In the Brit. Isles and Europe, where it has been introduced, it has damaged earthworks and become a nuisance in water channels and fishponds.

OLD WORLD RATS AND MICE Family Muridae

Range maps on page 263

Rats
Rattus
Plate 28

*Brown (*R. norvegicus*), also called House or Norway Rat: has coarse fur, large naked ears, and sparsely haired, scaly tail that is shorter than head and body. Upperparts are usually gray-ish-brown, shading to pale gray or brownish underparts. L. 12½–19 in., t. 6–8½, wt. 8–24 (usually 10–12) oz. Laboratory strains range from white to black, and some in the wild are blackish. ***Black** (*R. rattus*), also called Ship, Roof, or House Rat: compared with the Brown, is more slender in form, has shorter nose, and the slender, sparsely haired, scaly tail is longer than head and body. Upperparts are gray-ish-black and underparts sooty. L. 13–17, t. 6½–8¾, wt. 5–10 oz. The gray-bellied form is brown above, shading to gray below; the white-bellied is brown above, sharply set off from white or pale yellow underparts.

In comparison, the Cotton Rats have coarse grizzled fur; the Rice Rat has longer fur, and underside of sparsely haired, scaly tail is light-colored; Woodrats have silky fur and well-haired tails. Signs of presence are the usual ratholes, dung, gnawed wood or various foods, trashy nests usually hidden in woodwork or in holes (or in trees in case of white-bellied Black Rat), or sound of the rats scurrying about.

HABITAT: Introduced from the Old World; N. Am. ranges are not recorded in detail. Alberta was said to be free of

BROWN RAT

introduced Rats in 1951. The cosmopolitan Brown occurs wherever man's works provide food and shelter, as in and about buildings and wharves, also in salt marshes and in cane and other crop fields. It is more of a burrower and a less agile climber than the Black. The ordinary Black and its gray-bellied form are primarily House Rats, although occurring on croplands and the like; the white-bellied form is mainly a s. tree-dweller.

REPRODUCTION: Brown Rats in the wild probably begin to breed when about 4 months old. Young are born in a nest of trash. Gestation requires 21–23 days, or longer if the female is giving milk when bred. Breeding continues throughout the warm months in N. and all year, although at reduced rate in winter, in S. Litter size: 1–15, usually 7–9. Young at birth have eyes closed, are hairless, weigh about ⅕ oz., and are 1⅘ in. long. Eyes open in 14–17 days, and they are weaned in about 21 days. Soon they disperse. In laboratory strains, females cease breeding at 18–24 months, and a 3-year-old Rat of either sex is aged. Far less is known of the Black Rat, which has smaller litters. The 2 species do not hybridize.

HABITS: Both species are active all year. They swim well. The ubiquitous Brown is known to most people. It is somewhat gregarious, but fighting occurs over available food at times. Its voice is a squeak or squeal; the Black's is more twittering. In N. there is a spring movement to

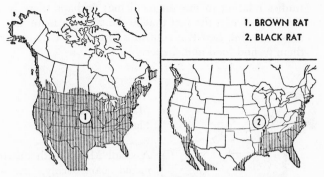

1. BROWN RAT
2. BLACK RAT

fields and a return in fall to buildings. Sometimes hordes of Rats leave an area, creating a Rat plague in their path. Common foods are garbage, grains, vegetables, meats, all sorts of packaged foods, soap, eggs and young of poultry and wild birds—and even dead rats. Insulation is gnawed from electric wiring, hence short circuits and fires may result. A Rat needs considerable water and will gnaw through lead pipe to get it. One may eat a third of its wt. in food per day and damage or waste much more than that. The agile Black is particularly at home aboard ship. Home range of the Brown may be part of a building or alley, or a much larger area, depending on food availability and density of the Rat population. In most centers of human population there are many more Rats than people.

ECONOMIC STATUS: The Brown Rat is the most destructive of all mammals to man's interests. In the U.S. alone this amounts to hundreds of millions of dollars annually. The aggressive Brown drives out the Black, which otherwise would be number-one pest in much more area. Both are a hazard to man in transmitting plague and typhus fever via Rat fleas. Zinsser's volume on *Rats, Lice and History* has amply shown that Rat-borne diseases have altered human destiny more than kings and armies. Laboratory strains of the Brown Rat have proved to be of great value to the geneticist, bacteriologist, and biochemist in

studies relating to human medicine; perhaps there is a
sort of justice in the fact that so damaging a mammal is
thus so useful. Best Rat control is to make it difficult for
them to find food and shelter.

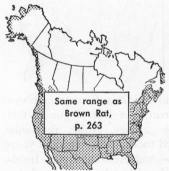

Same range as
Brown Rat,
p. 263

House Mouse
Mus musculus
Plate 30

A small Mouse with nearly
naked ears, scaly, nearly
naked, long tail, and close-
lying fur. Upperparts are
grayish-brown to brown,
shading to lighter brown or
buffy belly. L. 6–8 in., t. 3–
4, wt. ½–1 oz. Young are
grayish. Deermice, which often come indoors, have white
or nearly white underparts, clearly divided from color of
upperparts, at any age. The House Mouse may be confused with **Harvest Mice** (where they occur), but the
latter have grooved upper front teeth. House Mouse
signs are small dung pellets on shelves, floors, and in cup-
boards, also the holes it gnaws and tooth marks it leaves
on food items and woodwork.

HABITAT: Introduced from the Old World; occurs in and
about buildings from Greenland, n. Canada, and Alaska
southward. In N. largely an indoor mammal, though
often summering in fields and thickets; in S. occurs all
year in and at a distance from human dwellings.

REPRODUCTION: Females begin breeding when about 40 days
old. The nest, of anything soft, is concealed in woodwork
or a hole. When outdoors, it nests in debris, corn or grain
shocks, or various kinds of crannies, building a somewhat
domed nest. Gestation usually requires 19 days. Litters
are born in warmer months in N. and all year in S., the
female again being bred while giving milk. Litter size:

4-11, usually 5-7. Young at birth have eyes closed and are hairless. They are furred in 10 days, eyes open in 14, and they are weaned in 3 weeks, at ½ adult wt. They then disperse. Some captives have lived 6 years.

HABITS: The House Mouse is active at any hour or season. It climbs well and readily jumps from high places, thus getting on tables or other sources of food. It swims well. There is considerable fighting among males; females will fight to defend their holes. Voice is a variable rapid squeak, also faint Canary-like runs of chirps and chitters. Foods include grains, vegetables, meat, paste, glue, soap, and all sorts of stored items. Some food is hoarded. People usually are more aware of House Mice in fall, when many of them move indoors from fields. The Mouse population can build up rapidly, the offspring of one pair theoretically increasing to millions in a couple of years. Actual plagues of them occur at times, as in 1926-27 and 1941-42 in Central Valley of Calif. Evidently disease ends these irruptions rather quickly, but not before much damage to crops has been done. In the first of these plagues, the Mice multiplied in a dry lake bed under cultivation. They were plentiful in Nov. and by mid-Jan. an investigator found 17 Mice per sq. yd. over many acres, or over 82,000 per acre. They had so worked the sparsely vegetated soil that it appeared as if recently cultivated. From here they moved a short distance into adjoining terrain. Grain bins had literally thousands of Mice swarming around them, haystacks sheltered thousands, and millions more were in the fields.

ECONOMIC STATUS: This Mouse eats much food and spoils more. It leaves a musty odor. Its fleas harbor typhus, and it is suspected of being involved in several other diseases affecting man. The white strain makes a mild-mannered, though unsanitary, pet. Hundreds of thousands of these Mice have been used in biological experiments.

APLODONTIA   Family Aplodontiidae

Aplodontia
(Mountain Beaver)
Aplodontia rufa
Plate 27

A large, stocky, short-limbed rodent, with small eyes, short rounded ears, many long whiskers, and only the stub of a tail. Front claws are elongated and strong. Fur is dense, short, and erect; color varies from cinnamon to a cool brown, with black hairs scattered chiefly on back; underparts are grayish, and some individuals have white patches. L. 13–18 in., t. 1, ht. at shoulder when standing about 5, wt. 2–3 lb. Males are slightly larger than females. Size, uniform color, and apparent lack of tail distinguish this mammal from any other in its range.

Indications of its presence are saplings and bushes trimmed and topped (Rabbits and Hares do not cut so high) and ground honeycombed with tunnels, the many entrances being 6–10 in. in diameter and having fan-shaped mounds.

HABITAT: Damp forest and dense vegetation (shrubs, fern patches) with soil suitable for tunneling, usually on a slope near water. Sea level to over 9,000 ft. elevation.

REPRODUCTION: Breeding begins at about 2 years. Nests are in enlargements of tunnels or in side pockets, 1–2 ft. below ground surface, lined with dry vegetation and of about 18-in. diameter. Gestation is said to require about a month; the annual litter of 2–6, usually 2–3, young is born Mar.–Apr. Newborn young have very straight, fine, pale brown hair that lies close to the body; eyes are closed for 10 days; the head proportionately is very large.

The rough adult coat is attained in a month. Nursing ends about June, and the young then leave the mother. They attain about ¾ adult wt. by end of first winter.

HABITS: The Aplodontia looks and acts quite like a Pocket Gopher. It is not a Beaver, and it usually occurs in lowlands. Although mainly nocturnal and crepuscular, it is also abroad on overcast days and probably is active below ground at any hour. The long whiskers serve as feelers when it travels in tunnels or enclosed spaces. It swims well.

An elaborate underground tunnel system may have several hundred feet of tunnels and many surface openings, but contains only a single adult. Several or many Aplodontias in an area merely indicate adequate food and burrowing conditions, not gregariousness. Tunnels are cleaned or worked on regularly, the dirt, droppings, and old nest material being pushed out of the openings. Stones are carried out and left near the entrances. If a tunnel is flooded by rain, the mammal swims in it. There is much burrowing beneath snow, and some travel on crust in winter. Noises include a rapid chattering of teeth, a rough breathing sound, and, when captured, a variety of whines and squeals. A musky odor, detected at tunnel openings, undoubtedly serves as a means of communication. Because of the short legs, its slow gait looks like a creep; it also has a hurrying sort of gallop. Two projecting pads on each front foot aid in handling food, as the Aplodontia sits up, Squirrel-like, when eating.

Food: almost any green plant material. Herbaceous items are eaten entire; bark is peeled from woody plants. Sword-fern fronds are a favorite food, the tips being cut and stacked at burrow entrances or carried below ground. So much more food is stored than eaten that some of it spoils and later is taken outside. Saplings and trees are stripped of bark, especially in winter, under snow. Cuttings up to several feet long are dragged to tunnel entrances, cut in sections, and carried below. Twigs and small saplings are cut by one slanting tooth-stroke. Small piles of vegetation left in exposed places in summer probably are bedding material (not food) drying in the sun. The Aplodontia cannot climb by the usual rodent methods, but does go up shrubs and saplings as up a ladder, from branch to branch, cutting these off as it ascends; then the top is lopped off and it backs down the trunk. It drinks considerable water.

ECONOMIC STATUS: Tunnel systems of the Aplodontia are shelters for many other mammals. This rodent cuts and prunes in forest plantations, thus being a nuisance there. Its pruning in extensive forests helps maintain openings where food for Deer or other wildlife can grow. It has a fondness for cabbages, also raspberry bushes and pea vines, which are eaten in gardens near forest edges. Occasionally it has tunneled in walls of drainage ditches, causing cave-ins.

JUMPING MICE Family Zapodidae

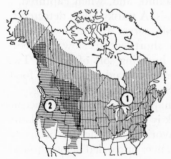

Meadow Jumping Mice
('Kangaroo Mice')
Zapus
Plate 33

Small-bodied Mice, with much elongated hind legs and tail; end portion of tail not white. Sides are dull yellowish-brown with scattered darker hairs; the broad back stripe from nose to tail is more or less brownish-black with scattered lighter hairs; belly white or tinged with buff, sharply defined from sides; tail bicolored (lighter below). Each of the 2 upper front teeth has a groove on front surface.

JUMPING MOUSE (*Zapus*) **species: 1.—*Northern** (*Z. hudsonius*): as described above. L. 7¾–9¼ in., t. 4½–5¾, wt. ⅖–1 oz. **2.—Western** (*Z. princeps*): usually larger, darker in N. and generally brighter in S.; in some areas the back band is not well defined at edges, also there is more buffy tinge to underparts. L. 8–10¼, t. 4¾–6¼. Young *Zapus* have the adult pattern but are duller.

In comparison, the Woodland Jumping Mouse has a white tail-tip; Harvest Mice have shorter tails and quite uniform upperparts; Pocket Mice, Pigmy and the larger Kangaroo Rats have slits in cheeks leading to pouches ('external' cheek pouches), while *Zapus* does not (it has 'internal' ones). Occasionally these jumpers are startled from grassy or boggy places.

HABITAT: Meadows, swales, swamps, bogs, and forest glades, from sea level to high mt. elevations. Also sagebrush flats, thickets, and open woods.

REPRODUCTION: Northern Jumping Mouse. Young of early litters breed in their first summer when about 2 months old; those born later breed the following year. The nest, a small ball of plant material, is usually in a protected spot, such as in a hollow log or stump, under some protecting object, or in an underground burrow, but may be in vegetation on or slightly above ground. Gestation requires about 18 days, and the female is often bred again while nursing. Young are born early June–Sept. or later, at least 2 litters of 5–8, usually 5–6, young being produced annually. At birth they are hairless except for tiny whiskers, have eyes closed, are about 1¼ in. long (tail then is short in relation to body length), and weigh about ⅟₃₀ oz. They are well furred in 17 days and make short hops. The black stripe appears in 15–19 days, eyes open in 22–25, and they lose their dull coat in 23–27 days. At this time they venture from the nest and eat solid foods. They are capable of an independent existence in 4 weeks.

HABITS: The Northern and the Western Meadow and the Woodland Jumping Mouse are commonly called 'Kanga roo Mice' because of their jumping ability. The Northern, here discussed, is often common in suitable habitats but has a very spotty local distribution. It tends to be nocturnal, rather solitary, and makes no runways. When startled, it may make a leap of several feet, then progress by shorter jumps on an erratic course. It swims readily and well. The shallow burrows are inconspicuous, there being no mound at the entrance. Young have a sucking note and a high-pitched squeak; adults are rather silent but have a clucking note and squeak at times. Much wt. is added in fall, and the fattest ones go into hibernation first, in a lined burrow below frost line. In spring this species does not emerge until the season is well advanced. Food: grass seeds, fleshy fruits, and insects; it needs considerable water. A dozen of these Mice per acre in early fall, with overlapping home ranges, probably is a high population. Even in good habitat, they are scarce some years and quite abundant in others.

Woodland Jumping Mouse
('Kangaroo Mouse')
Napaeozapus insignis
Plate 33

A small-bodied Mouse, with much elongated hind legs and tail; end portion of tail white. Sides are bright yellowish-brown with scattered darker hairs; broad back stripe from nose to tail is blackish-brown with scattered lighter hairs; belly white, sharply defined from sides; tail bi-colored (white below) and has white end portion of varying length—unless an individual has lost it through ident. Each of the 2 upper front teeth has a groove on surface. Internal cheek pouches are present. L. ¼ in., t. 4⅗–6⅖, wt. ⅔–1 oz. Young are duller dults. In comparison, Meadow Jumping Mice

(*Zapus*) do not have a white tail-tip. One finds this jumper by startling it.

HABITAT: Mainly in woodlands (preferably with ground cover) and edges of glades, in dry to moist situations, from sea level to considerable mt. elevations.

REPRODUCTION: Probably young are born more often in a nest in a burrow than is the case with *Zapus*. Gestation (not accurately known) requires 23 days or less. Perhaps male and female remain together for some time in summer. A litter of 3–6, usually 4, young is born in early summer; some females have another in early fall. Young at birth lack the tiny whiskers common to newborn of many rodent species.

HABITS: This beautiful Mouse is rather nocturnal, evidently not as solitary as *Zapus*, and makes no runways. It probably makes longer jumps than the latter. When traveling it prefers to keep under overhanging brook banks, low vegetation, or other shelter. The small round holes of its burrows have no earth mound and are kept plugged in daytime. Although generally silent, it does utter soft squeaks. In fall the fattest go into hibernation first, in a lined burrow, and emergence occurs when spring is well advanced. Food: seeds, fleshy fruit, various plant parts (especially fleshy rootlets exposed by water action along brook banks), and insects. Females have home ranges of 1–6½ acres, males 1–9, and ranges overlap, so that many of these Mice may occur in a small area. Populations fluctuate markedly.

ECONOMIC STATUS: Neither *Zapus* nor *Napaeozapus* is recorded as having any appreciable effect on its habitat. They both eat insects. Few persons have firsthand knowledge of their existence, except that most farm hands within their range have startled these jumpers in or about hayfields or swales.

PORCUPINES   Family Erethizontidae

Porcupine
('Hedgehog')
Erethizon dorsatum
Plate 26

A large, stout, quilled rodent, with small head, short legs, and stout tail. The quills, yellowish-white, tipped with black or brown (and up to 30,000 per individual) distinguish it; these are lacking on underparts and on portions of the face. In E. the dark, more or less whitish-tipped guard hairs usually are somewhat longer than the quills; in W. they are much more elongated and are yellowish at tips. L. 25–35 in., t. 5¾–12, wt. 8–15 or even to 35 lb., ht. at shoulder about 12 in. Young are usually blacker than adults. Signs include oval- to bean-shaped droppings about ⅝ in. long, often in quantity at den entrances; trees with bark removed at various heights; the toed-in tracks; or sight of this slow-moving mammal up a tree or on the ground.

HABITAT: Woodlands—those containing conifers or poplars (aspens) being preferred.

REPRODUCTION: Males breed in their second year and perhaps females also. Breeding occurs fall–early winter. The male wanders in search of a female, and there is an elaborate courtship. He utters high falsetto sounds, approaches the female, rubs her nose, and showers her with urine. She may squall loudly at his approach; in time she accepts him and offers no defense when he approaches from the rear for the actual copulatory act. After 7 months' gestation the single young is born Apr.– June. At birth the young is about 10 in. long, has eyes open, weighs 12–20 oz., and its quills harden within ½ hour. It accompanies its mother. All typical defense reactions are well developed. A clicking of the teeth is apparent in 3–5 days. Nursing is frequent, as the female sits on her haunches and tail. Little solid food is eaten the first month. Captives have nursed 4–5 months, by which time they weigh several pounds. A captive female lived over 10 years, evidently surviving past breeding age.

HABITS: Especially when shedding, a Porcupine may shake loose some quills that drop with no particular force. *It cannot throw them.* If alarmed and cornered, it turns its rump toward the source of danger, erects its quills, and the tail is swung rapidly against any object that touches it. The Porcupine never attacks. It is active mainly at night, and its series of groaning *unh* notes is a common woodland sound. It has well-trodden trails in vegetation and in snow. Several may den together in winter or use the same rest tree and trails, but the Porcu-

PORCUPINE,
WALKING

LH

LF

LH

LF

TAIL MARK

4 INCHES

RF

RH

pine tends to be solitary much of the time. It is active all year. An efficient climber, it also swims well. Summer food consists of herbaceous plants, including aquatic ones. In fall and winter it chips off the outer layer of tree bark and eats the succulent ones beneath, containing stored sugar and starch, and often feeds in the same tree for days. Pines, hemlocks, and aspens are favored, also sugar maples and elms. In spring, tree flowers and tender leaves are eaten. One Porcupine per 5 acres is a high population. Predators that attack it by way of its unprotected belly are the Fisher, Bobcat, and Mountain Lion.

ECONOMIC STATUS: A sparse population usually does insignificant damage to woodlands. Where the Fisher occurs, the Porcupine is seldom numerous. In a corn- or grainfield a Porcupine breaks down far more than it eats. It girdles valuable timber and some orchard and ornamental trees. It gnaws an entrance into woodland camps, then gnaws everything it finds that is salty from human perspiration or cooking fats. Items left outdoors, such as ax handles, canoe paddles, and saddles, are gnawed. I have eaten Porcupine liver often; the meat, however, of a young one had a rather unpleasant taste.

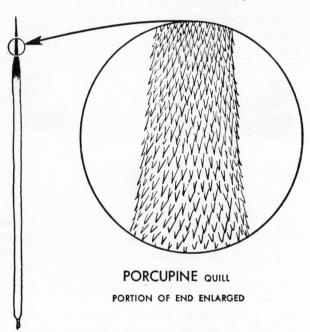

PORCUPINE QUILL

PORTION OF END ENLARGED

PIKAS, HARES, AND RABBITS
Order Lagomorpha

PIKAS   Family Ochotonidae

Pika
(Cony, Rock 'Rabbit')
Ochotona princeps
Plate 27

In general appearance quite like a medium-sized Guinea Pig; ears short and broad; hind legs very little longer than front; tiny tail appears to be lacking externally. Upperparts vary from grayish to cinnamon-buff and shade on lower sides to whitish, tinged with buff. Soles of feet are haired except for pads on toe ends. L. 7–8½ in., ht. at shoulder about 3½, wt. 4½–6 oz. In Alaska and adjacent parts of Canada, where the Pika has a faint grayish 'collar' on shoulders and underparts are creamy-white, it has been considered a distinct species—Collared Pika (*O. collaris*). Summer fur of the Pika is worn only about 2 months; winter fur, of some shade of dark gray, is worn the rest of the year. Young are darker than adults.

275

Marmots occur in Pika habitat, but they could hardly be confused.

Signs of the Pika are: sound of the bleating call, its 'haystacks' of curing vegetation, numerous tiny round dung pellets, or whitish urine streaks on rocks at its lookout stations. When crossing snow, the small triangular tracks it makes are like a miniature Snowshoe Hare's.

HABITAT: Rock slides and piles in mt. areas; old lava fields in ne. Calif., e. Ore., and sw. Idaho; up to 13,600 ft. elevation in N. Mex., but down almost to sea level n. of Columbia River.

REPRODUCTION: *O. princeps*. The 2–5 young are born in a nest under rocks, late May–early Sept.; there are probably 2 litters annually. Gestation requires 30½ days. Young at birth weigh about ⅓ oz. By the time they are ¼ to ⅓ adult size, they are weaned.

HABITS: The Pika is active by day, perhaps also by moonlight, and is rather solitary. When sunning on a rock, it blends well with its surroundings. A dry explosive *ka-ack* or *chre-e-e-e-k* is its alarm note; also, it gives a series of *ka* bleats at about 2-second intervals. With each call the body jerks forward and upward. After calling, the Pika darts rapidly out of sight. It makes short forays from its rocky retreat to clip and gather bundles of nearby vegetation. These are carried back in its mouth and added to a 'haystack' for curing, usually against or under a boulder but exposed to the sun. A pile may contain a bushel or more of dry material; it is carried in among the rocks for food, for winter and probably summer also. The Pika does not hibernate. Grasses, sedges, weeds, many of the larger flowering plants, and many woody plants are cut. Sometimes the Pika climbs a few feet up trees and out on low limbs to cut twigs. Foraging is done mainly within 100 ft. of home shelter, but in some places even several times this distance.

RABBITS AND HARES Family Leporidae

Range maps on page 280

Cottontails
(Cottontail Rabbits)
Sylvilagus
Plate 34

GENERAL REMARKS: Typical Rabbit form; medium to relatively short ears and hind legs; upperparts gray to reddish-brown, often with blackish intermixed; in most species underparts are light and underside of tail white, but important exceptions are noted below. Females are larger than males. Young have the adult pattern. In the latest monograph E. R. Hall, *Univ. Kans. Pub., Mus. Nat. Hist.*, vol. 5, no. 10 (1951), used a combination of range and both internal and external characters in making a key to species. For the most part, by use of range maps, descriptions of external characters, and knowledge of habitat, they can be identified.

Probably all Cottontails, except possibly the Pigmy Rabbit, have 'forms' (resting places) in which they spend much time. They use holes of other mammals regularly for shelter, but Hares rarely do this. Adults usually are silent, but may scream if injured. The Eastern Cottontail, at least, sometimes gathers in groups, especially when courting. In general, summer foods are herbaceous plants and winter food consists of bark and twigs, but the list of plant items eaten is nearly endless. Population fluctuations in those species that have been studied are very marked. Most Cottontails survive less than a year, but some Easterns have lived 5 years in captivity.

Vernacular names used are 'Cottontail' for some species and 'Rabbit' for others; in a technical sense all are Rab-

bits (as opposed to Hares), because young are born
naked, with eyes closed, and helpless, in a fur-lined nest
prepared for them. The domesticated Belgian 'Hare' is
a Rabbit also. On the other hand, so-called Jack and
Snowshoe 'Rabbits' are Hares; young are born fully
furred, with eyes open, and are able to move about in
a few minutes. Cottontails are smaller than Hares (some
of which have cottony tails), have smaller ears and much
smaller hind feet. Commonest signs are the small narrow

COTTONTAIL

10 INCHES

BOUNDING
GAITS

SNOWSHOE
HARE

footprints, round droppings, or sight of these familiar
mammals.

HABITAT: Varies; see under species.

SPECIES: *Pigmy Rabbit (*S. idahoensis*): smallest; broad
ears seem overly large for the body; upperparts grayish-
brown (almost bluish-gray in winter) with pinkish tinge;
tail dusky. L. 10–11⅗ in., t. ⅘–1⅕, ear from notch
1¾–2½, wt. ¾–1 lb. No white on underparts distinguishes it from young of the Mountain Cottontail. Prefers areas of tall dense sage- or rabbit brush on rough
terrain; to over 7,000 ft. elevation in Nev. Signs are its
burrows and tiny tracks. Young are born underground.
Litter size: 2–8, usually about 6; probably 2 litters annually. Young are born late May–early Aug. It digs its
own burrows or enlarges those made by other small mammals, the several 4-in. entrances being usually under a
bush. A den is used for years, and worn trails lead away
from it. This Rabbit scampers or scurries, rather than
bounds, and rarely ventures from under a brush canopy.

Sage leaves are eaten, especially in winter.

Brush Rabbit (*S. bachmani*): small; relatively short-eared; body rather uniformly dark brown or brownish-gray; underside of tail whitish. L. 12–14½, t. 1¼–1¾, ear from notch 2–2⅗, wt. 1¼–1¾ lb. Prefers dense brush and seldom ventures 15 yds. away from it; sea level to about 5,000 ft. elevation. Compared with the Mountain Cottontail, it is smaller, with shorter ears, and has less white on underparts (hairs on mid-ventral part of body gray, not white). Breeds Jan.–June; the 2–5 young per litter are born in a nest. Makes well-defined runways in brush.

Marsh Rabbit (*S. palustris*): small; relatively short-eared; coarse-haired; upperparts blackish- or reddish-brown; underside of tail brownish or dingy gray (not white) ; belly mostly not white; feet small, reddish-brown above. L. 14–17, t. 1⅓–1⅗, ear from notch 2¼–3, wt. 2–3 lb. Densely vegetated swamps, bottomlands, and coastal islands. Swims readily. No white in tail distinguishes it from other Cottontails within its range. Embryo counts: 3–4.

*Eastern Cottontail (*S. floridanus*): varies considerably, but upperparts tend toward brownish in summer and somewhat grayish-brown in winter, with considerable blackish intermixed; underside of tail white; feet pale—brownish, buffy, or whitish. L. 15–18, t. 1¾–2½, ear from notch 2½–3, wt. 2–4 lb. Thickets, weed patches, and forest edges are used as escape cover; often it feeds and nests nearby in the open. Widely transplanted and introduced. The Desert Cottontail of open terrain has longer ears; the smaller New England Cottontail, mainly of woodlands, has shorter ears. Swamp and Marsh Rabbits have darker feet, and the former a dingy (not white) tail. Breeding begins at age of 9–10 months. Courtship consists of pursuit by the male and various hopping antics by both sexes. The female digs a small cavity, or sometimes uses a natural one, which she lines with grass and with fur from her belly. Early in the season the site is

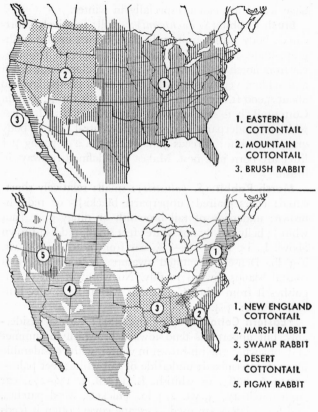

1. EASTERN COTTONTAIL
2. MOUNTAIN COTTONTAIL
3. BRUSH RABBIT

1. NEW ENGLAND COTTONTAIL
2. MARSH RABBIT
3. SWAMP RABBIT
4. DESERT COTTONTAIL
5. PIGMY RABBIT

often in a thicket, but later, when ground cover is better developed, it is often more in the open. Gestation requires 28 days; a female may be bred again before her young are a day old. Whether young are born in the nest, or whether elsewhere and carried there by the female, is a moot point. At intervals, usually many hours apart, the female crouches over the nest or nurses the young close to it. Litter size: 1–8, usually 4–5, with several litters born late winter–early fall. Young are furred in a week, eyes open in 6–9 days; they squeal in

10 days, venture from the nest in about 12, and leave permanently a few days later.

New England Cottontail (*S. transitionalis*): small; short-eared; upperparts reddish-brown in summer and reddish-gray in winter, overlaid at all seasons with considerable blackish; a dark area between ears. L. 15½–16½, t. 1⅗–2, ear from notch 2½, wt. 2¼–3 lb. Open forest with brushy understory, also brushy areas, mainly in hills and mts. Short-eared and smaller than the Eastern Cottontail and much smaller than the Varying Hare.

Mountain Cottontail (*S. nuttallii*): upperparts grayish suffused with pale yellowish; hind feet covered with dense long hair. L. 14–16, t. 1¾–2, ear from notch 2¼–2½, wt. 1½–3 lb. In n. part of range occurs in sagebrush, also timbered areas, and in s. part in forests, usually not lower down than pines. The only Cottontail in most of its habitat. The Desert Cottontail of plains and open country has larger ears. Embryo counts: 4–8.

*Desert Cottontail (*S. audubonii*): larger than the preceding, with longer ears and legs; upperparts pale grayish-brown suffused with yellowish; short hair on hind feet. L. 14–17, t. 2–2¾, ear from notch 2½–3¾, wt. 1¼–3 lb. Open arid terrain with scattered brush. Compare with the Eastern and Mountain Cottontails and Brush Rabbit. Embryo counts: 2–6.

*Swamp Rabbit (*S. aquaticus*): large, with rather coarse hair; upperparts blackish- or reddish-brown; underparts with some white; underside of tail white; hind feet brown above. L. 19–21, t. 2½–2¾, ear from notch 3½–3¾, wt. 3–6 lb. Wet bottomlands and cane jungles, also dry areas in Tex. A strong swimmer. The smaller Eastern Cottontail has lighter feet.

ECONOMIC STATUS: Cottontails provide more hunting than all big game combined; millions are shot annually. The Cottontails eat various garden crops and, especially in winter, girdle fruit trees and ornamental shrubs. A host of predators feeds on them; Rabbits and Hares, for example, collectively are listed first in order of volume in the Coyote's diet. Vast numbers of the Eastern Cottontail have been trapped and later released, in areas where the local population was at a low point in its fluctuations, or introduced into new areas. Benefits are small in terms of Cottontails harvested by hunters, and there is the danger of introducing tularemia or Rocky Mountain spotted fever.

Is it not possible that, if the shooting public ever is to be adequately informed on the nature of game fluctuations and the futility of trying to maintain consistently high populations of shootable species, they will come to accept these biological facts through firsthand experience with the fluctuating Cottontails? When this lesson is learned and applied to the extent that unsound practices in attempting to maintain any game species at a consistently high level cease, a step forward will have been made.

Cottontails are the principal source of tularemia or 'Rabbit fever.' Other sources are Hares, various rodents and other mammals, and some birds. A person may become infected by handling infected carcasses, or by being bitten by deerflies or ticks from them. Incubation period of the disease in man is 3–4 days. Symptoms include: a pimple-like swelling where the organism has entered the skin, enlargement of lymph nodes, fever, chills, weakness, and prostration. Duration of illness is 3 weeks to much longer; it is fatal in a small percentage of reported cases. A person who survives an attack is believed to have permanent immunity. Sick Rabbits should be avoided, and meat of wild Rabbits, whether obtained by hunting or purchased (it is marketed in some areas), should be thoroughly cooked. Most Rabbit livers are spotted in some measure; *many fine spots* are an indication of tularemia, but large spots are not.

Varying Hare
(Snowshoe Hare or
'Rabbit')
Lepus americanus
Plate 34

Typical Rabbit form; hind
feet large; between the Cottontails and the Jacks in
general size. In summer, up-
perparts vary from yellowish- to grayish- to rusty-brown,
with black intermixed; underparts, including underside
of tail, white. Winter coat is white (hair dark at base)
with dusky ear-tips, except in w. Ore. and Wash. and n.
to Fraser River, Brit. Columbia, where the winter coat
is very like the summer one. L. 17–21 in., t. 1½–2, ear
from notch 3¼–4, wt. 2½–4½ lb. Females are larger
than males. Pattern of young is essentially that of summer adults.

In comparison, Arctic Hares have tail all white (not
just underside) and, when in white coat, the long hair
is white to the base. Jack Rabbits have much longer
ears; the White-tailed Jack, in winter coat only, has tail
all white. Cottontails, which have smaller ears and feet,
do not turn white in winter. Commonest signs are tracks,
longer and much broader than a Cottontail's (diagram,
p. 278).

HABITAT: Mixed woodlands, conifers, more or less wooded
swamps, and brushy areas; in w. mts. to over 10,000 ft.
elevation. Introduced on some Is.—for example 1902–03
on Anticosti in Gulf of St. Lawrence; 1935–36 on Raspberry, Afognak, and Kodiak in Alaska. Introduced in
Newfd. in 1864. Restocked in some mainland areas.

REPRODUCTION: This Hare first breeds when about a year
old. No lining is added to the 'form' (depression) in
which the young are born. Gestation requires 36–40,
usually 37, days. Several litters are produced in the
warmer months, the female again being bred while nurs-

ing. Litter size: 1–10, usually 3–4. Young at birth have eyes open, are furred, about 4¼ in. long, and weigh 2–3½ oz. For a day or so they stay in or near the form, but they can make short hops and so soon explore the vicinity. In less than 2 weeks they eat some green vegetation, but nursing may continue for a month. At least a third of them probably survive less than a year; a few may live 4–5 years; some captives have lived 8 or more.

HABITS: The fleet, silent Varying Hare, which leaves a multitude of conspicuous tracks in the winter forest, spends most of its day in its form. It does not go down holes as Cottontails do. A number gather together occasionally, perhaps to play. Young have a gurgling sound. Adults usually are silent, but have a bleating scream; they thump with their hind feet to signal danger. Summer food: grasses, buds, twigs, and leaves; in winter: twigs and needles of conifers, bark and buds of many hardwood shrubs and trees. Dew is utilized for moisture in summer and snow is eaten in winter. Home range is usually under 1,000 ft. in greatest length, and the Hare knows its terrain well. A few individuals may go a mile from where born, but most never do. The population fluctuates most in N. and E., perhaps being more stable in W. Peaks occur at 9- to 10-year intervals, when, in some areas in Canada, hundreds of Hares reportedly have been noted in a small area. Very few are found at the lowest stage. One factor in the sharp decline that follows the gradual build-up is 'shock disease,' in which there is some degeneration of the liver. The Lynx is so dependent on this Hare as food that its population trends are geared to the Hare's.

ECONOMIC STATUS: The Varying Hare provides excellent sport and table meat. Indians and whites eat many in N.; the former make warm blankets from strips of pelts. This Hare girdles trees, sometimes doing serious damage in conifer plantations. In the N. it springs many traps set for commercially valuable furbearers. Tularemia is discussed on p. 282.

Arctic Hare
(Tundra Hare)
Lepus (part)
Plate 34

Large, with medium-length ears; tail all white at any season. Winter fur, worn about Aug.–June, is of long hair that is white (clear to base), except edges of ears are blackish. Summer coat is like that of winter in Greenland, Ellesmere I., and n. Baffin I.; upperparts are grayish-brown and underparts white elsewhere e. of Mackenzie River, and upperparts are brownish w. of Mackenzie River. Currently it is called *L. arcticus* everywhere e. of the Mackenzie and *L. othus* in Alaska. L. 19–28 in., t. 1½–2, wt. 6–12 lb. Young have grayish upperparts. The smaller Varying Hare has top side of tail dark in summer coat, and fur of white winter coat is dark at base. Hind track of an adult Arctic Hare is 6–7 in. long.

HABITAT: Wind-swept rocky slopes and upland tundra, less often on lowlands. Occasionally ventures into sparsely wooded areas at s. edge of its range, but usually avoids even scrub willows.

REPRODUCTION: Litter size is 4–8; young are born in late June and in July.

HABITS: Arctic Hares are usually found in groups and they are quite unwary at times. Slopes blown free of snow are preferred for winter feeding places, for there various dwarf arctic plants can be gotten easily. The larger upper front teeth that are a characteristic of the Arctic Hare in Greenland are said to be especially useful for breaking through hard-packed snow to obtain food. Hopping on the hind legs without touching the front feet to the ground has been reported a number of times. There are seasonal movements of the population, at least in some areas, and over a period of years numbers fluctuate greatly everywhere.

ECONOMIC STATUS: The Arctic Hare is eaten by humans and other mammals. Eskimos make robes of braided strips of its tender pelt.

Range maps on page 287

Jack Rabbits
Lepus (part)
Plates 34–35

Size large, with long ears and legs. They are Hares, not Rabbits; the distinction is discussed on pp. 277–278. They seek safety by running, not hiding. Females are larger than males. Probably all have 2 or more litters annually. Young are quite like summer adults in pattern. The trim, long-eared Jacks should not be confused with other Hares or Rabbits. The introduced Common Hare of Europe is called 'Jack Rabbit' in N.Y., Ont., and adjacent areas. Long and rather narrow tracks are typical of the Jacks.
HABITAT: Open country mainly.

JACK RABBIT (*Lepus*) **species: *White-tailed** (*L. townsendii*): in all seasons has black-tipped ears; in summer, upperparts grayish-brown, tail all white or with small dusky or buffy stripe on top side, and underparts white; in winter, all white (except ear-tips) in n. part of range and, in s. part, like summer but paler and grayer. L. 21–25 in., t. 3–3¾, ear from notch 5–6, wt. 5–10 lb. Plains and open mt. slopes, in some areas to above timber line at over 12,000 ft. elevation. The smaller Varying Hare is a forest mammal; the Black-tailed Jack has top of tail black. Litter size: 3–6, usually 4–5.
    *Black-tailed (*L. californicus*): top side of tail and tip of ears blackish; upperparts grayish or sandy, with blackish cast that is more pronounced in winter. L. 19–24, t. 3½–4, ear from notch 6–7, wt. 4–7½ lb. Mainly open arid terrain. In comparison, the White-tailed Jack

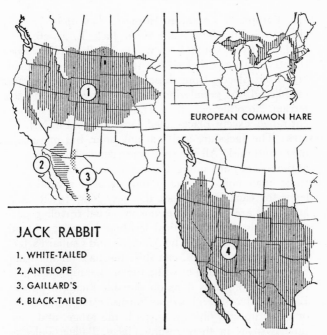

EUROPEAN COMMON HARE

JACK RABBIT

1. WHITE-TAILED
2. ANTELOPE
3. GAILLARD'S
4. BLACK-TAILED

has tail all white or with little dark on top; the Antelope
Jack has no black on ears and more white on sides; the
Snowshoe Hare has no black in tail. Gestation requires
43 days (range of 41–47); litters contain 1–6, usually
3–4, young. Some liberated in E.: Ky. and N.J. (1952?).

Gaillard's (*L. gaillardi*) : very large ears with no black
on them; middle of back buffy; sides and underparts
white; top side of tail blackish. L. 21–22, t. 3–3½, ear
from notch 5–7, wt. 3½–5 lb. Grassy plains from sw.
N. Mex. southward. Our only other white-sided and
black-tailed Jack—if the 2 are distinct species—is the
following.

*Antelope (*L. alleni*) : as preceding, but ears longer
and middle of back paler. L. 21–24, t. 2½, ear from
notch 7–8¼, wt. 4–6 lb. A desert dweller. Litter size:
1–5, usually 2.

288　Pikas, Hares, and Rabbits

NOTE: **European Common Hare** (*L. europæus*): very closely resembles our Black-tailed Jack. L. 21–26, t. 3–3½, ear from notch 6–7, wt. to 12 lb. Prefers open country. In the period 1888–1911 liberations were made at various places; from those introductions that became established, the population has spread over considerable terrain. No other very large Hare occurs within its present range, except Black-tailed Jack liberated in N.J.

HABITS: The Jacks are active at any hour, but more so at dawn and dusk. All the species are somewhat gregarious at times. They are among the most conspicuous of smaller game mammals. A Jack usually makes several short leaps for each longer one; the very long 15- to 20-ft. leaps that are recorded are not the usual traveling pace. At intervals a nearly vertical 'spy hop' is made, evidently to watch any pursuer. The Antelope and Gaillard's Jack, by use of skin muscles, can shift the hair on the rump, exposing a large area of white fur on one hip like a great puff of cotton. It is done on the side facing a pursuer. Each Jack has several beds or 'forms,' often under bushes or other upright objects, on its home range, and much time is spent in these resting places. Badger holes are sometimes used for shelter. The White-tailed Jack makes burrows in snow. Preferred food of Jacks is grasses and herbs, but they eat parts of many woody plants also. Much cactus is eaten in the drier months in the arid SW. Populations fluctuate greatly, with peak numbers occurring about every 7 years. One Jack per 5–10 acres is a high population; individual home ranges ordinarily are larger than that.

ECONOMIC STATUS: Jacks compete with livestock for range plants; they also eat grains and other cultivated crops. When they increase to 'plague' numbers, crops have been destroyed in a night. Thousands of them have been captured in a single drive. They are hunted extensively. Tularemia is discussed on p. 282.

EVEN-TOED HOOFED MAMMALS
Order Artiodactyla

PECCARIES Family Tayassuidae

Collared Peccary
(Javelina, Musk Hog)
Pecari angulatus
Plate 35

Pig-like, with coarse coat and almost no tail. Color, in all seasons, tends toward blackish in Tex. and more grayish, with blackish streak down back, in N. Mex. and Ariz.; there is a lighter collar from shoulder to shoulder. L. 30–37 in., t. ½–1½, ht. at shoulder 20–22, wt. 40–65 lb. Young are reddish, with blackish back stripe. The Peccary somewhat resembles a half-grown domestic pig gone wild, but its coarser coat at once distinguishes it. Peccaries leave rounded hoof tracks (diagram, p. 298); each hind foot has a single dewclaw, quite high up on the *inside,* which might register if tracks are in mud. Other signs are trails, wallows, and a disagreeable musky odor.

HABITAT: Mainly brush country in Tex. and areas of scrub

289

growth on foothills and lower mts. in N. Mex. and Ariz.;
to about 6,000 ft. elevation.

REPRODUCTION: Young are born in a cave, hollow log, den
dug by some other mammal than a Peccary, or in a
thicket. Gestation requires 112–116 days; twins may be
usual, but 5 and 6 fetuses are recorded. In a few hours
the young can run; in a day or so they accompany their
mother, who joins other Peccaries.

HABITS: The gregarious Peccary is more active in the cooler
hours and at night. It goes in bands of 3–25 or more
and travels at a fast running gait when frightened. Limestone caves are occupied, especially as winter quarters,
in some areas. When alarmed, it erects its back hair
and a musky-smelling secretion comes from the gland
on the rump; this odor can be detected for several hundred feet. Young whine; adults grunt, give subdued
yaps, and bark. The Peccary grubs up herbs, roots, and
a variety of animal life. Surface food includes fruits, nuts,
berries, bird eggs, and sluggish animals. Favored items
are pads and fruits of prickly pear and roots, beans, and
pods of mesquite. It needs water, and its well-used trails
and wallows are conspicuous about ponds and water
holes.

ECONOMIC STATUS: As a game mammal, the Peccary is an
elusive target and hard to kill. The flesh is usually good
eating, but the rump gland must be avoided. At various
times in the past, flesh, hides, and bristles were sold. The
hide makes fine leather. The Peccary formerly occurred
well n. in Ark. but now has a much smaller range in U.S.

NOTE: Family Suidae. **European Wild Boar** (*Sus scrofa*):
introduced; full-blooded stock is long-legged and rangy
as compared with various strains of domestic swine with
which it freely interbreeds. Adults vary from pale gray
to blackish in general tone; young have dark brown
ground color with light rusty or sandy longitudinal
stripes that disappear in about 6 months. Occurs in
greatest numbers in Tenn., but also in N.C., on the
Corbin Preserve in N.H., and on Santa Cruz I. off s.

Calif. Range (not mapped) nowhere overlaps that of the native Peccary.

DEER Family Cervidae

Elk
(Wapiti)
Cervus canadensis
Plate 37

A large Deer, with maned neck and pale rump patch and tail. Bulls have unpalmated branching antlers, shed annually. L. 7½–9½ ft., t. 5–8 in., ht. at shoulder 4½–5 ft., wt. of bulls 575–750 and cows 450–600 lb. Cows are about ¼ smaller than bulls. The short summer coat (May–Aug.) is tawny, with slight mane and darker head and limbs. In longer winter coat the body is grayish-tawny, mane longer and darker, and head and limbs dark. There is much variation as well as fading. Antlers are shorter and stouter in Pacific humid forest population. The small, pale, arid plains Elk, occurring in the wild in Kern and Inyo Co., Calif., have been named *C. nannodes*. Elk calves are tawny, with many diffuse light spots and yellowish-brown rump. With or without antlers, pale rump and tail are diagnostic of Elk; the Mule Deer has blackish in the tail, which in most cases is surrounded by a whitish rump area.

Tracks of adult Elk (diagram, p. 298) may be difficult to tell from those of young cattle, which are somewhat stouter and more squarish. Elk tracks are larger and more blunt than Deer tracks and smaller and less pointed than Moose. Where Elk traverse slopes regularly, they leave conspicuous, more or less parallel trails. In winter, Elk droppings are many globular pellets about 1 in. long, with somewhat flattened ends (Moose pellets are more cylindrical and longer); in summer these are pressed out of shape and form a mass more or less like miniature cattle dung. Other signs include browsed shrubbery and young trees up to nearly ½-in. diameter, bark eaten from aspen trunks, broken low tree branches, wallows, and bugling (mainly fall).

HABITAT: Mainly a highland dweller, having local seasonal movements. Such diverse habitats are occupied as the Rockies, Pacific coastal rain forests, humid lowlands, and hot arid plains. Elk have been released in unenclosed areas and in parks in many states, some Canadian provinces, and on Afognak I., Alaska—some of these places being outside the known former range. Introduced in New Zealand.

REPRODUCTION: Cows usually are bred first when about 28 months old; yearling bulls are physically capable of breeding, but may not, even the following year. Young bulls try to steal cows from older ones. The latter collect harems of as many cows as they can herd together and maintain by intimidating or fighting rivals. Rutting lasts early Sept.–late Oct., when bugling is most pronounced. Gestation requires 249–262 days, and 1 calf (occasionally 2) is born annually. Most calving occurs May 15–June 15. At birth a calf weighs 30–40 lb. and is about 38 in. long; it moves about very little for several days, but in 6–7 days can run rapidly. Its spotted coat is usually shed by early fall. Some vegetation is eaten from about 2 weeks on, but suckling may continue into winter. Apparently calves associate with their mothers into winter, perhaps often much longer, but this is hard to determine in bands of cows and offspring. Full size is attained in about 4 years. Probably few wild Elk survive 10 years, but some have lived 22, and captives 25.

HABITS: The Elk has keen hearing and sight; it is alert and curious. It is essentially a herd animal the year round. Cows are alone or in scattered twos and threes at calving time, but as summer advances they join in larger bands or even herds of several hundred cows, calves, and younger bulls. Older bulls then are by themselves or in small groups. In rutting season the bands break up as the older bulls obtain harems, while younger bulls are out-casts. Both sexes and all age groups are more inter-mingled in winter. Antlers are shed in late winter or early spring. Calves have a very high-pitched squeal or bleat; older Elk have a coarse explosive bark of alarm. A vibrant and resonant bugling, which reaches greatest development in mature rutting bulls, is given by both sexes and at any season, although mainly by bulls in fall.

Elk travel during the rut, but true migration comes later, when snowfall evidently is the chief cause of many moving to lower elevations. They prefer to graze on slopes and to eat grass at any season. They are, however, the least specialized feeders of our Deer and graze or browse on many plants, shrubs, and trees. On cattle range, 3 Elk roughly approximate 1 cow in food consump-tion; as a rule of thumb also, on reasonably good winter range, one might figure 12 acres per Elk as adequate. Fluctuations and population irruptions occur. Winter losses, largely of Elk in their first year, are due mainly to disease following malnutrition.

ECONOMIC STATUS: Elk yield excellent meat, and hunting is usually not difficult. Their aesthetic appeal to the non-shooter is great. The population has exceeded the carry-ing capacity of winter range in many areas, thus causing an 'Elk problem.' Winter feeding of hay, which keeps numbers of Elk concentrated on poor range, has ag-gravated the situation at times. They compete for food directly with other wildlife and with domestic livestock, Deer in particular suffering in this competition. Gen-erally speaking, Elk have been on the decline on shrink-ing range for decades, owing to hunting and to human occupation of the land, but this has been offset partly by local increases and numerous transplantings.

Mule Deer
(includes Black-tailed Deer)
Odocoileus hemionus
Plate 40

Antlers (only on bucks normally) curve forward and inward, with erect tines—the
largest pair of which typically
is forked; ears very large;
belly white, also usually a
white patch on throat. Both
the yellowish- or brownish-red summer and grayish-
brown winter coats are very variable in color. L. 4¾–6½
ft., t. 4½–9 in., ht. at shoulder 3–3½ ft., wt. 100–300
lb. or more. Bucks are larger than does.

The widespread 'Mule Deer' type has a *large whitish
rump patch* and rounded white tail with *black on tip*
that, in some cases, continues as a narrow blackish or
brownish stripe along its top side; general body color is
much more pale and drab in dry sw. areas than elsewhere. Intergrading with it is the 'Blacktail' type of the
NW. (formerly called *O. columbianus*), which has relatively little whitish on rump and color of back merges
into that of the *blackish or brownish upper tail surface*
tail is white below. The latter averages smaller, with
smaller ears and often darker coat, than the former. The
spotted fawns of both types have notably large ears. See
comparative remarks on identification and signs under
White-tailed Deer (p. 296) and track diagrams (p. 298).

HABITAT: Forests and brushy areas, including mts., uplands,
and rocky terrain; very humid to dry climates; less inclined to wade in water than the Whitetail. Local transplantings have been made in some areas. Blacktails were
introduced 1924 and 1930 on Long and 1934 on Kodiak
I., Alaska.

REPRODUCTION: So far as known, the general pattern is
quite like that of the Whitetail (which see), with these

main differences. Rutting bucks may have single does, but many commonly gather harems of 3–4. Breeding occurs later than with the Whitetail, hence most fawns (twins are common) are born late June–early July. Fawns at birth weigh 5–7 lb.

HABITS: The Mule Deer is characterized by a jumping gait and more gregariousness than the White-tailed Deer. Bucks, for example, often associate in small groups in spring. The buck, at least, has a *ba-a-a* note and uses his voice at times. Many Mule Deer spend the summer in the aspen and pine country at considerable mt. elevations. After the rut there is a leisurely movement down to winter range in sheltered valleys, where this Deer is essentially a herd animal. The return to higher elevations is usually completed by late June, some bucks preceding the does, which are heavy with young. The airline distance between individual summer and winter ranges in some instances may exceed 50 mi., and the circuitous annual round trip may be over 300. Grasses are much eaten in spring; at other seasons low woody plants and mosses are browsed considerably more than is characteristic of the Whitetail, and over larger areas.

ECONOMIC STATUS: A 1948 census indicated that there were over 2,190,000 Mule Deer (including 489,000 Blacktails) in the U.S.; to this should be added a sizable Canadian and small Alaskan population. The legal hunting kill in the U.S. that year was over 325,000. This Deer is often a pest on agricultural land. When overprotected, it multiplies beyond the carrying capacity of the winter range, depletes the available food, and suffers die-offs similar to those described for White-tailed Deer. In Calif., in 1924–25, many thousands died in a hoof-and-mouth-disease epidemic; over 22,000 more were slaughtered in an attempt to control this outbreak. The Mule Deer fares badly when in competition with Elk for food, which fact must be reckoned with in planning for a sustained population of both mammals.

White-tailed Deer
(Virginia Deer)
Odocoileus virginianus
Plate 40

Antlers (only on bucks normally) curve forward and
inward, typically with erect
unbranched tines; the wide-
flaring tail is colored like the back above (or may have
black in it) and has white edges and undersurface. The
summer coat is reddish or tawny (brighter than the
Mule Deer's); the winter coat is grayish-brown. L. 4½–
6¼ ft., t. 7–11 in., ht. at shoulder 2⅓–3¾ ft., wt. 50–
300 lb. Bucks are larger than does. Fawns have white
spots on their reddish coats for about 3½ months. This
Deer is large and bright-colored in n. part of its range,
but much smaller and paler in arid SW.; smallest, and
with smallest antlers, are the Deer on a few keys (islands)
off s. Fla. The White-tailed and Mule Deer hybridize in
some areas in NW., hybrids showing a mixture of characteristics of both species.

Tracks made by the cloven hoofs of our Deer (diagrams, p. 298) are pointed, not rounded as in sheep, nor
short and blunt as in pigs. In walking gait, hind feet are
placed nearly in tracks of front feet. The Whitetail makes
10- to 22-ft. bounds, placing hind feet ahead of front and
with dewclaws registering. Walking tracks are very like
the Mule Deer's. The latter, however, tends to make stiff-
legged bounds, leaving bunched imprints. Tracks, collections of dung pellets about ½ in. diameter by ¾ in.,
long worn trails, woody plants cropped off leaving ragged
ends, and matted-down vegetation at bedding places are
common Deer signs. The white underside of the raised
tail is seen and a whistling snort heard when a startled
Whitetail bounds away.

HABITAT: Mixed or deciduous woodland with an understory,
also forest edges, usually not far from water; dense stands

of mature conifers (except in winter) and very extensive open areas are generally avoided. Occurs commonly on farmland, in back yards and even suburbs. Often transplanted within the normal range and introduced elsewhere at home (as in the Blue Mts., Wash.) and abroad.

REPRODUCTION: Some does are bred at age 7 months, but most not until a year later. Rutting bucks roam, searching for does, and fight other bucks viciously. A buck may breed a single doe, or there may be a limited polygamy (several does bred). Peak of breeding activity occurs in Nov. in N., last half of Dec. in s. Tex., in Jan. in parts of the arid SW., and (?) no set breeding season in Fla. keys. Gestation usually requires about 196 days, thus the peak of fawning comes about 6½ months after that of breeding. Usually there is 1 fawn in the first litter, 2 are common thereafter, and 3 are not uncommon; 4 may be very rare.

At birth a fawn weighs 3–5 lb., has a beautiful spotted coat, and is capable of walking, but it travels very little for some time. The doe leaves her fawns in shrubbery, where they lie still until she comes to nurse them. In a few days they nibble some vegetation, but are not weaned for 4–6 weeks or longer. Young bucks often leave their mother in a few months, but does stay with her longer— even well into their second year—depending somewhat on when they are first bred. Life span seldom exceeds 10 years in the wild, but tame or captive does have lived up to 20, and one had fawns at age 16.

HABITS: The secretive, alert, and graceful White-tailed Deer has remarkably keen hearing and sense of smell; it depends on these more than on sight. A doe with fawns usually remains within a small area having food and water. The fawns have a dry bleating call, seldom uttered; adults snort and blow. While growing antlers, bucks lead an easygoing, unsocial life. The antlers (number of points is not a good criterion of age) are shed after the breeding season, and the Deer then are more gregarious, often associating in groups with a doe as leader. Most

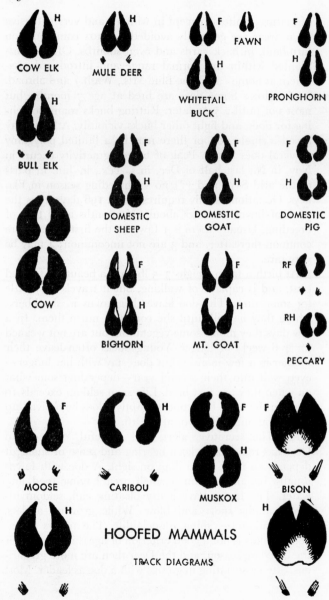

COW ELK

MULE DEER

FAWN

WHITETAIL BUCK

PRONGHORN

BULL ELK

DOMESTIC SHEEP

DOMESTIC GOAT

DOMESTIC PIG

COW

BIGHORN

MT. GOAT

PECCARY

MOOSE

CARIBOU

MUSKOX

BISON

HOOFED MAMMALS

TRACK DIAGRAMS

gregarious are those in the arid SW.; there the groups move up and down mts. seasonally, spending the colder months lower down, in thickets, bottomlands, and on warm slopes. In winter, in areas of heavy snowfall, the Deer live in a restricted area called a 'yard,' where cedar, balsam, or other browse is available. Groups break up before the fawning season.

The White-tailed Deer is a very selective feeder, keeping on the move and eating an aquatic or succulent plant here, mushrooms or nuts there, and twigs, leaves, or lichens elsewhere. Thus it has a great variety of foods. In winter it is mainly a browser on woody twigs, conifer branches, and tree lichens. Good habitat easily supports a Deer per 20 acres, but much higher densities are known. If mortality rate is low, the population increases rapidly and, by eating selectively, the available nutritious food is practically eliminated. Adults, standing on hind legs, can reach higher for food than young Deer. The young thus get poorer food on overutilized range. Undernourished ones get bronchial or other diseases, and a die-off results. Some large areas are in a chronic state of being overbrowsed and overgrazed, and die-offs are known to have occurred at intervals for over a century. Many Deer die in winter, with stomachs more or less full of food having little nutritive value, rather than move to some nearby area having adequate sustaining food.

ECONOMIC STATUS: A 1948 census indicated that there were then over 5,000,000 White-tailed Deer in the U.S.; to this should be added the sizable Canadian population. The legal U.S. hunting kill that year was over 450,000. After near extermination in some areas, this Deer, with legal protection and with reduction of predators, has increased in parts of its range to the point where it has depleted its natural food and has become a nuisance to crops. It is folly to shoot bucks only, since the remaining ones breed many does and keep the population too high to be well nourished. The Whitetail has not increased in some w. portions of its range because of competition with other mammals and alteration of habitat by man. It has extended its range northward in recent decades. Its aesthetic value is great but hard to evaluate.

Moose
Alces alces
Plate 37

Our largest Deer; high at the shoulders, with overhanging muzzle, and a 'bell' of skin and hair hanging from the throat. Antlers (only on bulls) are typically broad and palmate; they are shed annually. Body is brownish or blackish; legs are lighter. There is much fading or bleaching. L. 8–10 ft., t. 2–3 in., ht. at shoulder 5½–7½ ft.; wt. of mature bulls 900–1400 lb. or even to 1,800 in Alaska and Yukon Terr., cows 600–800 lb. Calves are plain, dull reddish-brown, lighter in tone than adults.

This huge and rather ungainly mammal can hardly be mistaken for any other species; at any season, and whether antlered or otherwise, Elk have a pale rump and Caribou a whitish neck. Moose signs are large tracks with dewclaws showing (diagram, p. 298), spaced in 3- to 5-ft. strides (bull's tracks tend to point outward, cow's straight ahead), wallows in moist places, heavily browsed twigs, shredded bark on trees or saplings where antlers were rubbed, and bark eaten from trunks of aspens (poplars). Dung pellets are much larger than those of Elk, and usually a quart or much more is deposited at one time.

HABITAT: Over most of its range, occurs among willows at any season; also in forested uplands and along watercourses during warmer months. Introduced in Newfd. and on Anticosti I. (not established on latter?).

REPRODUCTION: Cows first breed when 2 or 3 years old; bulls

3 years old or even older are kept away from cows by older bulls. A bull's mating behavior sometimes includes making a wallow and urinating there, then both sexes roll in it. They both call in the rutting season in autumn, when bulls travel widely and may fight for a cow. A bull may stay with a cow and her calf up to 6–10 days, then he seeks another cow. Gestation requires 8 months, and calves are born mid-May to early June. The first litter contains a single calf, twins are common thereafter, and triplets may occur rarely. A calf at birth weighs 20–25 lb., has a hair coat, eyes are open, and it can walk in a few hours. Rough wts. in lb. for a bull are: yearling 400–600, 2-year-old 700, and 3-year-old 900; cow: yearling 400, 2-year-old 600, and at maturity 600–800. The cow defends her calves, which suckle until winter or even until near time of the next birth. Then yearlings are driven away. A cow not pregnant allows the calves to remain longer. A Moose is in its prime at 6–10 years, and maximum age attainable is probably 18–22 years.

HABITS: The Moose has poor vision but acute smell and hearing. It is a strong swimmer. Although slightly gregarious, not shunning company, individuals act independently. The bull's mooing call ends with an upward inflection or throaty gulp; the cow's is longer and not as loud—more like that of a domestic cow. She grunts to her calves. In late spring cows go to secluded calving places and bulls to higher ground to feed. After the young are born, cows and calves go to uplands also. They return to lower ground as winter begins. Seasonal movements thus are usually local. Willow leaves and twigs are a year-round mainstay; other preferred foods are leaves and twigs of maples, mountain ash, birch, aspen, and balsam. In summer the Moose kneels to eat low ground vegetation and wades for aquatic plants. Poplar bark is often eaten. One Moose per square mile in good habitat is a fairly high population level. Numbers fluctuate over long time spans for reasons not clearly known. It can winter successfully in areas where the snow is too deep for Elk. The Moose is subject to many accidents, some Wolf predation, and Bears kill calves.

ECONOMIC STATUS: Especially in some w. parks, Moose are a tourist attraction of much importance. The meat is a staple item in some n. areas, and the hide has many uses. The largest trophy heads are obtained in Alaska, Yukon Terr., and Brit. Columbia. When overprotected, the Moose is its own worst enemy, for it practically eliminates willow, balsam, and other nourishing foods from its habitat. Although its range has been reduced in E., it appears to be occupying some new terrain in W. and N., and the population continues to hold up quite well in many wilderness areas.

Caribou
(includes Reindeer)
Rangifer
Plate 39

Large and rather stoutish Deer, with large feet; antlers (both sexes grow them annually) typically have slender beams that curve backward and upward, then are not invariably palmated; also, palmated or slender brow tines project forward over the face; facial profile of adults usually straight or convex—'Roman nose'; underside of neck maned; muzzle large and squarish. Except on some Arctic islands (where all of coat is pale), end of muzzle, the neck, and a stripe along the lower sides are usually much lighter than rest of upperparts; area above hoofs also is very light. There is much wear and bleaching. Does are smaller than bucks, with smaller antlers.

   1.—*Barren Ground (*R. arcticus*): northern; antlers have lower portion of main beam nearly round in cross section; color varies from entirely white, including antler′

velvet, or with grayish area on back (Ellesmere I. and vicinity) to grayish-brown (Greenland) to very variable but generally brownish (Newfd. to Alaska) ; running and loping gait. L. 5¼–6½ ft., t. 3–5 in., ht. at shoulder 3¼–3½ ft., wt. of bucks 150–400 lb., does 140–275. **2.—— *Woodland** (*R. caribou*)*:* more southerly; larger than the preceding; usually with proportionately smaller ant- lers having beams that are more oval in cross section; many have brownish-black dark areas in new coat; more bounding gait. L. 5½–8 ft., t. 4–6 in., ht. at shoulder 3½–4 ft., wt. of bucks 150–700 lb., does 150–350. Fawns of both species are brownish—except in far N., where adults are white or nearly so, fawns are pale grayish- brown. Yearlings are darker than adults.

Caribou hoofs are wide and rounded, with hollow center and sharp outer edges; the spreading hoofs and dewclaws give a large supporting surface for travel on snow and soft ground. Compare with Muskox track (diagrams, p. 298). In any gait of Caribou or Reindeer, a tendon slips over a bone in the foot, producing a clicking noise that can be heard perhaps 50 yds.

NOTE: ***Reindeer.** Compared with our Barren Ground Cari- bou in Alaska, the semi-domesticated strain of this mam- mal from the Old World (where there are wild ones also) is usually smaller, shorter-legged, darker, and many adults have a dished-in (concave) facial profile. To help the native economy, in 1891–1902, 1,280 Reindeer were in- troduced from Siberia into Alaskan tundra areas; the population may have exceeded a half million in the early 1930's, but had declined, because of range depletion, lack of skilled herders, and other causes, to about 25,200 in 1950. The Canadian Government purchased about 2,400 in Alaska in 1929; these were driven e. and, 6 years later, a sizable number arrived on e. bank of the Mackenzie River, NW. Terr.; about 8,000 were reported there, under care of herders, in 1950. Gestation period is similar to that of our Barren Ground Caribou, but the rut comes earlier in Reindeer, hence fawning is earlier. Alarmed

Reindeer bunch together, as sheep do, more than do wild Caribou. Herding them is a year-round, open-range 'activity. They breed with our native Caribou, this being one of several reasons why the two cannot be maintained in the same area. A few Reindeer existed for a while in Labrador, also on Anticosti I.; those introduced in Iceland never were tended by herders.

HABITAT: The Barren Ground species (includes Reindeer) prefers well-vegetated tundra in summer; part of the mainland population moves into open coniferous woodland in winter. The Woodland Caribou inhabits coniferous forests and open places such as muskegs, also mt. areas to above timber line. Restocked in Minn., but not again established.

REPRODUCTION: Barren Ground Caribou. There is a limited polygamy with about 5–10 does per buck. Yearling does are sexually mature; many have a fawn in their second year. Bucks first breed when 2 or 3 years old. The rut occurs Sept.–Oct., gestation requires about 240 days, and fawns are born in early summer. The fawn (twins are rare) at birth weighs 10–15 lb., has eyes open, a complete hair coat, and can follow the doe in a few hours. She defends it for several weeks; it begins foraging when about a month old, its first coat is shed about Aug., and it may suckle until spring. Yearlings of both sexes have spike antlers their first autumn. By the time the next fawn is born yearlings are more or less segregated in groups but later may return to the does. Two-year-old bucks have antlers quite like those of mature does; in their third year antlers are of the adult form. Full growth is attained in 4–5 years. Reindeer does cease having fawns when about 12 years old and may live some time longer, but probably wild Caribou seldom live more than a decade. The Woodland Caribou probably has a reproductive pattern quite like that of the Barren Ground species.

HABITS: Caribou are spirited animals that exhibit a mixture of curiosity and shyness. They have relatively poor eyesight, good hearing, and very keen smell. They are the most amphibious of our Deer, all age classes taking to water readily. Gregarious, they occur in groups and even, in N., in herds of thousands. Adults snort in alarm and have a medley of grunting noises; rutting bucks utter a belching roar; fawns bawl.

Although the Woodland Caribou may have only local seasonal movements in some areas, some Barren Ground Caribou may spend the summer and winter at points 800 mi. apart. Seasonal movements of the bulk of the population of the latter, between Hudson Bay and Alaska, are as follows: In Apr.–June herds move n. from forested areas; calves are born on the tundra; in late July–early Aug. there is a southerly movement which loses its impetus when herds are near the s. limits of the tundra; in Sept. they move away from the forest, and rutting occurs on the tundra in Oct.–early Nov.; after the rut they migrate to wintering areas in the forest, usually arriving in Dec. Some remain on the tundra all year. Barren Ground Caribou are restless nomads, eating very selectively, browsing willows, birches, heaths, and grazing grasses and ground lichens in summer, and browsing twigs, also tree and ground lichens in winter. The Woodland species is less nomadic and even more of a browser. Barren Ground Caribou tend to use the same summering and wintering areas for a period of years, then change to distant places; this is perhaps related to availability of preferred food.

ECONOMIC STATUS: In large areas in N., habitation by humans at times would be impossible without Caribou as food for man and dogs; the hides are used for winter clothing and summer tents. Improvident hunting methods have resulted in much unnecessary wastage of Caribou, which has contributed to the decline in their numbers. A 1950 estimate gave only 160,000 Caribou in all of Alaska, and a 1951 report gave 670,000 from n. Ontario w. to the Mackenzie River and n. to include a few Arctic islands. Figures are not at hand for Newfd., n. Ungava, or other parts of the range (numbers are not large), nor for the remaining Woodland Caribou population in Canada. Its estimated population in U.S. in 1950 was: Ida., 20; Mont., 15; Wash., 10. Forest fires, shooting, and human occupation of the land have caused the latter to become rare or absent in much of its range. In both species, warble flies damage hides and deplete the animal's energy. Nose flies are a common pest. In N., tapeworm eggs in droppings of dogs, Wolves, and Foxes are ingested by Caribou, in which the larval stage of the worm is passed; the carnivores are reinfected when eating Caribou viscera. Introduced Reindeer, to help the economy of certain Alaskan natives, have proved to be far from an unqualified success.

PRONGHORN   Family Antilocapridae

Pronghorn
(Antelope)
Antilocapra americana
Plate 36

Upperparts are a warm tan (rather grayish in winter); large white rump patch with erectile hair shows at a distance; underparts and two bands across underside of neck white. L. 47–56 in., t. 3½–4, ht. at shoulder 35–41, wt. of mature bucks 100–140 lb. and does 80–105. The small erect horns (in both sexes) are backward-curving at the tips and consist of permanent bony cores covered with a sheath that is shed annually. The sheath, in bucks at least, has one forward prong. Bucks shed this thick sheath in late fall, and does and young later. The new sheath grows both up and down from the core tip and is complete in mature bucks by July. Sex of adults can be distinguished at a distance, for a buck has black face and patch on side of neck, horns are longer than ears, and he runs with nose pointed somewhat downward; a doe lacks most or all of the mask and patch, seldom has horns greater than ear length, and holds her nose more nearly horizontal when running.

This unique N. Am. mammal—only species in its family and not a true Antelope—is hardly to be confused with any other. Front hoofs are slightly longer than hind, and all are pointed; see diagram (p. 298) and compare with domestic sheep. Sight of the Pronghorn is commonest indication of its presence.

HABITAT: Open prairies; sagebrush areas on rolling plains, deserts, and tableland. Badly eroded places, also areas of tall sage, are usually avoided. Prefers to be near water; active day and night. There have been local transplantings within the former range.

REPRODUCTION: Does breed first when about 15–16 months old, bucks perhaps first at 2 years. Mature bucks become restless in late summer, strike odd poses, erect their hair, and make sudden sidewise jumps. They fight among themselves and drive does into harems of up to 15 individuals, which may dwindle later. The actual mating season lasts only about 2 weeks, and bucks maintain their harems as do Elk. Gestation requires 230–240 days. The kids are born late May in N. and late Feb.–early Mar. in S. When time of having young nears, does seek the semi-solitude of rolling country with low vegetation.

After the first litter (usually one kid), does commonly have twins, weighing 4–5 lb. each at birth and having a beautiful, wavy, rather grayish coat. At 4 days of age the kids can outrun a man. They nibble vegetation in 3 weeks and acquire a coat like that of adults before 3 months. At an early age young begin flashing their rump patches when startled or excited. Does with yearlings and small young are together at all seasons, except kidding time. Both sexes evidently breed to the end of their lives, which is usually 5–7 and perhaps rarely 8–10 years.

HABITS: The Pronghorn is very curious and watches any strange object in its environment. The eyes are as big as a horse's and they can see small objects several miles away. Either sex, when disturbed, erects the long white hairs of the rosette-like rump patch as a signal. The Pronghorn can attain a speed of 60 m.p.h. on hard ground, going in 12- to 20-ft. leaps. Fifty m.p.h. is common and 20–30 an easy gait. Fast runs of 3–4 mi. are common, then exhaustion occurs rapidly. A doe ½ mi. from her kids can reach them in 45 seconds, traveling at 40 m.p.h. The wt. is carried on the front feet when running; Pronghorns use the front feet also for digging food buried under snow and to scratch depressions for deposit of droppings. They swim well.

Pronghorns occur in small scattered bands in summer, but sometimes several hundred are together in winter. There is strong group leadership in the bands. Mature bucks occasionally are solitary. Kids have a high-pitched quavering note which the doe can hear at 500 yds.; adults have an explosive snort or blow, and I also have heard a doe, when away from her kids, repeatedly give a sort of bleat. Pronghorns shift from one area to another several times a year, or change elevation, for water or food. Usually does with kids stay at lower elevations. When snows force Pronghorns down to valley floors which subsequently become snowed under, they move to ridges where wind exposes vegetation. Browse plants are sustaining food, followed by weeds and a few grasses. Sagebrush is a favorite at all seasons. The daily feeding range may be up to about 3 sq. mi., with occasional trips away from it to water.

ECONOMIC STATUS: The Pronghorn has a high aesthetic appeal; also, a buck makes a fine hunting trophy. A mature buck may yield only about 30 lb. of meat, and the hide is valueless for leather. Because the Pronghorn is easily shot and has a low reproductive rate, it can stand only limited hunting pressure. Pronghorns do not damage range, as do foraging sheep and cattle, except that rarely they over-graze early-spring grasses locally. Winter concentrations locally overutilize desert vegetation. Occasionally they cōmpete with cattle for water, or trample hay, or eat farm crops. The Pronghorn is an open-range mammal and does poorly when forced off this range or kept from water by fences. Pronghorns now occur in much less area than they did a century ago, but a good population exists.

CATTLE, SHEEP, AND GOATS Family Bovidae

Bison
(Buffalo)
Bison bison
Plate 36

Very large Wild Cattle, with hump at shoulders, short neck, large head, horns on both sexes, tufted tail, and long hair on head and front quarters. Bulls are brown, lighter on shoulders, and darker on head, legs, and tail. L. 10–11½ ft., t. 2, ht. at shoulder 5½–6, wt. to about 2,000 lb. Cows are smaller, more evenly colored, less bearded, have less massive hump, and horns are more curved and slender. L. 7–8 ft., t. 1½, ht. 5, wt. to about 950 lb. Winter coat of adults is more yellowish-brown than the darker summer coat. There is much wear and fading. This large, dark, humped mammal is unmistakable in appearance.

Tracks (diagram, p. 298), rather like those of domestic cattle, are about 5½ in. long, and the hoofs are often widely spread. Its wallows in dry or wet places, tracks and worn trails, also rubbing places, such as tree trunks, telegraph poles, and boulders, are Bison signs.

HABITAT: Prairies and open woodland, formerly perhaps

to over 10,000 ft. elevation in a few U.S. localities; occurs in heavily wooded as well as open areas in Wood Buffalo Park, nw. Canada. Introduced in 1928 e. of Fairbanks, Alaska, and established there.

REPRODUCTION: A few cows are bred at 2 years of age, but most not until 3. Bison breed at any season in close confinement, otherwise in July–Aug. Bulls fight for possession of cows. Most calves are born in May, after a 9-month gestation period, and the cow is secretive and solitary when having her calf (twins rarely). The hump is hardly noticeable on the newborn calf, which has eyes open and a reddish-yellow coat that is paler on belly and legs. In 2–3 days the cow and calf join a band or family unit. Both parents, or even the herd collectively, defend calves, which may nurse for nearly a year if plentiful food enables cows to give milk. By fall the hump, especially in bull calves, is much in evidence. Calves then assume a rich brown coat and have small horns. Growth continues 6 or more years, the horns become longer and heavier, and the hump—especially in bulls—grows enormously. Life span is usually about 15 years, but captives have lived over 22.

HABITS: The Bison has keen hearing and smell but not exceptional eyesight. It feeds mostly in morning and evening, with a siesta at noon, but at times is active even at night. Although it is gregarious, formerly existing in immense herds, units of a mature bull, one or more cows and their offspring (for 2 or 3 years) are maintained. Old bulls often are solitary, or several occupy an area where each seems to get some companionship from others nearby. Bison lie down, roll, and kick furiously, getting a dust or water bath and ridding themselves of bothersome flies. These wallowing places, either dry or partly filled with rain water, may be used for many years. Voice is a bellow, varying widely with age and emotional state of the animal. Seasonal travels, whether on the plains or lower elevations in mts., are related to getting adequate food. A herd may stay in a limited area for a long time, or move often and for considerable distances. Grass and some herbs make up the diet. Water is necessary, but Bison can go longer than domestic cattle without it. At the present time there is no serious predation on mature Bison, except killing by man of surpluses in herds.

ECONOMIC STATUS: In colonial times there were many millions of Bison (estimates vary), occurring from near the Atlantic seaboard into Mexico, beyond the plains into the mts., and to Great Slave Lake and slightly beyond in nw. Canada. Killing for meat and hides and wanton slaughter were main factors in reducing the population in U.S. to only 541 Bison in 1889. About 1900, in Canada, there were only a few Plains Bison and perhaps about 250 of the darker Wood Bison. In 1951, including zoo captives, there were perhaps 8,875 in the U.S., perhaps 13,900 in Canada (about 12,000 of these in Wood Buffalo Park in n. Alberta and NW. Terr.), and 200 in Alaska. The Bison appears to be safe from extermination, but one should hope that herds can be maintained permanently under primitive conditions rather than in any state of partial domestication. Visitors to parks should beware of Bison, for they can be very dangerous to a person afoot or even on horseback. Bison have been crossed with domestic cattle ('cattalo') and yaks ('yakalo'), but the hybrids usually are sterile or have low fertility.

Muskox
Ovibos moschatus
Plate 39

A small, stocky Ox, with slight hump at shoulders, short legs and neck, horns (on both sexes) nearly joined at base and curving sharply downward and then upward at the tips, very short tail, and very long hair that conceals the body form and sometimes trails on the ground. Color is deep brown or blackish, with paler patch behind the shoulders, whitish nose (in Greenland much whitish hair on face is typical), and lower part of legs whitish. Bulls: l. 5–6 ft., t. 4 in., ht. at shoulder 4–5½ ft., wt. 500–700 lb.; cows considerably smaller. Cows have more slender horns and sometimes more light area on face. Calves have short wool, a variable (often greater than adults) amount of white on face, and white legs.

The cloven hoofs, front as large as hind, leave rather squarish tracks (diagram, p. 298); dewclaws, when they register, appear behind the hoofs. Caribou and Reindeer have more spreading tracks with more lateral dewclaws. Where Muskoxen occur, one finds rather spherical dung pellets of about ⅗ in. diameter (sometimes adhering in a lump), also mats of shed wool and hair on vegetation, rocks, and ground.

HABITAT: Slightly- to well-vegetated Arctic and Subarctic terrain. In 1935–36 a total of 31 of the light-faced Greenland animals were released on Nunivak I., Alaska (indicated by arrow on range map), where they had increased to 65 by 1949.

REPRODUCTION: Cows do not breed until 3–5 years old (reports vary), then only every other year unless the calf is lost the season it is born. Breeding occurs in July–Aug. when, to obtain harems, bulls fight by charging and meeting head-on. After a gestation period of about 9 months a single calf (twins are rare) is born Apr.–June; it is about 20 in. long, 18 high, and weighs 16–25 lb. It huddles in its mother's long hair 'skirt' for warmth and protection, nibbles vegetation when a few weeks old, continues nursing for 3 months or longer, and probably associates closely with the mother for a much longer period. Both sexes defend the calves.

At some stage in their development young bulls are driven out by the herd master; they then go through a period of trying to gain admission to a herd by fighting. Fatal combats are not rare. Young bulls often unite in pairs for company. Bulls past prime are ousted from

herds and thereafter lead solitary lives. Muskoxen probably grow for 5–6 years, and some individuals may survive up to 20 years in the wild.

HABITS: ·Muskoxen are gregarious, the groups containing
several to over 100 individuals (at least formerly). An
alarmed group forms a circle with calves more or less
inside; the others face outward and charge if approached
too closely. Both sexes snort and stamp their feet. Excited
bulls bellow and give a sort of challenge by rubbing the
gland below each eye on the inside of the forelegs. This
gland, which gives off a musky odor, especially pronounced in spring, also is rubbed against brush and other
'signposts.'

Summer is usually spent on well-vegetated lowland
areas; Muskoxen are more scattered in winter when they
move to wind-swept ridges, hills, or mts. where vegetation is exposed or less buried under snow. At times they
paw away the snow to feed. They eat about the same
quantity of vegetation daily as Caribou (largely of different kinds) and may be even more selective feeders. Sedges
and grasses are eaten in quantity, also willows, aspens,
birches, and many heaths; they are grazers and browsers
in summer and primarily the latter in winter. They can
stand exposure to cold better than Caribou, and are less
inclined to seek shelter. The heavy coat is protection
against cold and insects, the latter being a nuisance
mainly to the ear, nose, and eye region.

ECONOMIC STATUS: The circle defense formation is usually
adequate against Wolves but has rendered shooting of
entire herds an easy matter. Formerly, all adults in some
groups were sometimes shot in order to obtain calves for
zoos. In the Canadian Arctic and on the mainland Muskoxen have legal protection, enforced by the Mounted
Police. There has been agitation for full protection in
Greenland. Range of the Muskox has decreased, but this
mammal still occurs in most areas where formerly it was
numerous; the total population is not many thousand. A
danger to Muskoxen would be local shortages of Caribou

and other food, forcing people in those areas to shoot Muskoxen for survival. Reindeer, having depleted the forage on Nunivak I., Alaska, compete for food directly, especially in winter, with the introduced Muskoxen. There are no Wolves on Nunivak.

Sheep
(Bighorn, White Sheep, etc.)
Ovis
Plate 38

Wild Sheep, with massive permanent horns that curl a full circle or more on old rams; smaller, erect, slightly backward-curving horns on ewes, and mere spikes on younger Sheep. Ewes are smaller and weigh much less than rams of corresponding age after their first year. **1.— *Bighorn** (*O. canadensis*): rather stout form; large whitish rump patch; coat varies from dark brown over most of range to pale buffy in arid SW., with much individual variation in color and seasonal wear and bleaching. Rams: l. 4⅔–6 ft., ht. at shoulder 3–3⅔, t. 3¾–5 in., wt. to 320 lb. Ewes: l. 4⅙–5⅙ ft., ht. 2½–3, t. 3½–5 in., wt. to 160 lb. Size of this Sheep is progressively larger going northward. Young lambs have fairly long, woolly, pale brown hair, but by first fall color and pattern are very like adult. **2.—*Dall's** (*O. dalli*): more slender form than preceding; coat white (often stained yellowish or brownish) in Alaska and upper Yukon Terr.; from cent. Yukon Terr. to n. Brit. Columbia the bands of Sheep contain light and darker individuals ('Fannin's Sheep'), averaging progressively darker southward; s. of Stikine and Laird rivers in n. Brit. Columbia most Sheep are dark brown, almost black, with white rump, underparts; and face; and neck grizzled ('Stone's Sheep').

Thin-horned; horns more slender and generally with more outward-flaring tips than in Bighorn Sheep. Rams: l. 4⅔–6½ ft., ht. at shoulder 2¾–3⅓, t. 3½–4 in., wt. to 200 lb. Ewes: l. to 4½ ft., ht. 2½–3, t. 3–3½ in., wt. to 125 lb. Size of this Sheep is progressively smaller going northward. Newborn lambs always have much lighter coat (usually some shade just off white) than adults— except, of course, where adults and young both are white. By fall, lambs have adult pattern and color.

Sheep form and horn shape render field identification relatively easy. Sheep usually occur in bands. Ewes and partly grown rams are often hard to tell apart. The cloven hoofs leave tracks (diagram, p. 298) having *outer* side of each toe slightly incurved, as with domestic sheep, unlike the more roundish outer profile of Mountain Goat tracks. Dung pellets, under ½ in. long, are somewhat pointed at one end and flattened at the other. Tracks, droppings, Sheep odors, bedding places, and trails left where Sheep regularly travel are signs of occurrence.

HABITAT: Both species. Relatively dry mt. and upland areas, usually near rugged terrain for escape from pursuit; often at lower elevations in winter, but usually within a mile of rough terrain. Some water is essential. Even small tracts of dense forest are avoided. There have been local transplantings of Bighorn Sheep.

REPRODUCTION: Probably, in both species, ewes are first bred at about 2½ years of age and rams begin breeding at 3½. In late fall and early winter, rams fight for ewes by striking with the hoofs or meeting in head-on collision. Some rams are killed. In the Bighorn Sheep, gestation requires about 180 days or perhaps a little longer. Both the Bighorn and Dall's Sheep have one lamb, occasionally twins. Lambs are born Mar.–early Apr. in sw. U.S. and May–early June or later in Alaska. A ewe guards her lamb, which travels little if any for about a week, and then it follows her. In both species, families of ewes, lambs, and yearlings join company, and one ewe or more stands guard for the band. In 2 weeks a lamb can run as fast as its mother for a short distance; in a month it is eating considerable herbage. Some lambs continue to nurse until early winter. Young associate closely with the mother for perhaps 2 years.

The horns have growth rings, showing amount added yearly, but some of the early increments may be lost from frayed or broken tips. A Bighorn ram up to 2 years has horns essentially like the ewe's; horns of a 5-year-old ram have reached the bottom of the downward swing. After 8–10 years, the amount added yearly is slight and often it is impossible to detect the annual rings. Growth appears to persist longer in the thin-horned Dall's Sheep ram. Horns of Bighorn ewes grow rapidly for 3–4 years, slightly the next year or two, and hardly at all thereafter. In both species of Sheep, body growth slows down at 5–6 years of age and probably ceases at 8–10. Maximum attainable age may be limited by life span of teeth, which are worn out or some lost maybe at about 15–17 years. Most Sheep in the wild do not survive more than 7–8 years, but a captive Bighorn ram lived to age 20.

HABITS: Both species. These sure-footed climbers have remarkable eyesight and good senses of smell and hearing. Rams are in groups by themselves in summer, taking no part in the life of the bands of ewes and younger Sheep. Ewes and lambs bleat rather like domestic sheep; adults snort at danger; angered rams grunt, snort, and grind their teeth. Many Sheep spend the year in an area of under a mile in radius, others move in winter to lower elevations where food is obtainable more readily, and still others cross wide valleys in going from a summer to a winter range and back. A ewe is the leader. Both species swim readily. Home range at any season includes feeding areas and bedding places, the latter preferably under protection of an overhanging rock and commanding a good view of all approaches from below. In arid SW., Bighorns are largely browsers and often are concentrated near available water. Elsewhere, both species are mainly grazers on grasses, but also eat sedges, heaths, willows, buds of various trees, and other items. Sheep in N. maintain good numbers unless a succession of winters of heavy snowfall makes foraging difficult and forces the then weakened animals to move to areas where predators can capture them more readily. Many so taken, however, already are undernourished and further weakened by disease.

ECONOMIC STATUS: Wild sheep of both species make excellent trophies, which must be earned by strenuous climbing and good marksmanship. The stiff-haired pelts have little value. Because of overshooting, competition with domestic sheep for food, and disease, the Bighorn Sheep has been eliminated from parts of its former range and reduced on other areas. Dall's Sheep also has been subjected to excessive human predation in some areas.

Mountain Goat
Oreamnos americanus
Plate 38

Goat-like form; humped shoulders; whitish or slightly yellowish-tinged coat; bearded chin; small, slender, slightly backward-curving black horns worn permanently by both sexes. L. 5–5¾ ft., ht. at shoulder 3–3½, t. 6–6½ in., wt. 125–300 lb. Nannies are about ⅙ smaller than billies. No marked seasonal or age variation in color; nannies and young have smaller horns. Goat-like form and long shaggy coat render sight identification easy.

The cloven hoofs leave tracks generally showing toes well spread. See p. 315 for comparison with Sheep tracks. Where Goats occur, one finds tracks (diagram, p. 298), bedding and resting places in dusty spots or even on snowbanks, scattered mats of shed hair and wool, piles of rather Deer-like dung pellets (shorter and stouter than

Sheep droppings), and well-used salt and other mineral licks.

HABITAT: Slopes and cliffs, usually above tree line, but occurs lower down at times—even to tidewater in some localities. In 1923, introduced from near Juneau to Baranof I., Alaska, and established there; and 1952 (?) on Kodiak I. Accidentally introduced about 1924 and established in Black Hills, S.Dak. Also, there have been some local transplantings within the former range.

REPRODUCTION: Nannies probably are bred first when about 2½ years old. In Nov., billies fight for mates, and thrusts of their sharp horns sometimes inflict fatal injuries. Billies are seasonally monogamous or perhaps have more than one mate (but this is unproved). Gestation is reported variably as 147 and 178 days; perhaps many nannies breed only every other year. Birth of the single kid, or twins quite commonly, takes place late Apr.–June. The newborn Goat has a woolly coat, weighs about 7 lb., and stands about 13 in. high. After a few days of isolation with her young, mother and offspring join a band of nannies and young Goats. A captive lived nearly 10 years; it is probable that some survive 10–12 years in the wild.

HABITS: The Mountain Goat—actually a Goat-like Antelope closely related to the Chamois—with its stiff-legged and deliberate gait, is undaunted by great heights and nearly sheer cliffs. Although its climbing feats are well known, much of its life among the crags, especially its winter activities, are as yet unrecorded. The Goat is calm and self-possessed; it takes a good look before heading for the roughest ground. It is perhaps the only horned mammal that regularly sits on its haunches—which it may do when curious and watching some object. Adults grunt, although they usually are silent; young kids have a plaintive, squeaky bleat. Mature billies usually have about 9-in. horns, and both sexes have a large gland at the rear base of each horn. Billies in the rutting season (perhaps both sexes then and at other times) slash brush; musk from the glands marks these 'signposts.'

Goats are mainly browsers on woody plants, but graze to some extent on alpine grasses, sedges, and other flora. In winter they live on the sparse forage exposed where snow is blown from the soil and niches in the rocks. The summer range of a band may encompass only a few mt. slopes and bedding places. Some billies are solitary then and travel greater distances; others associate with females and young. Goats know their home range well. After the fall rut, groups containing adults of both sexes associate until spring. There are shifts in feeding areas with the changing seasons. Goats come into forest at any season to visit mineral licks or sometimes to cross to another foraging place. Rock slides and snow avalanches kill some Goats. The Golden Eagle is accused of capturing kids, but many of those that it is known to have eaten may have been injured or dead when found.

ECONOMIC STATUS: The most difficult part of a Goat hunt is the climb; a billy usually is not wary. The head is a rather insignificant trophy, and a hunter seldom wants another. Meat from an old Goat can hardly be called good eating. Its habitat preference and relatively low trophy value have saved the Goat from more than appreciable human exploitation.

SLOTHS AND ARMADILLOS
Order Xenarthra

ARMADILLOS Family Dasypodidae

Nine-banded Armadillo
Dasypus novemcinctus
Plate 35

A stoutish brown mammal of about House Cat size; 9-banded shell; head and long tail also encased, but ears and underparts naked; tail appears segmented; claws large. L. 28–32 in., t. 14–15, ht. at shoulder 6–9, wt. 9–17 lb. The shell covering distinguishes it. Signs of its presence are den holes of 7–8 in. in diameter, fairly well-defined trails with scattered marble-sized droppings containing insect remains, and rooted furrows or cone-shaped holes dug in the earth. This mammal often is seen at dusk or on highways at night. It is seldom abroad in bright daylight.

HABITAT: Dense shady cover such as brush, woodland, cactus, and chaparral, also limestone formations. Partial to pine forests in e. part of range. Has been extending its range in U.S. for many decades. Introduced and increasing its range in Fla.

REPRODUCTION: Many females probably are bred first when about a year old. The nest, of vegetation, may be in a natural hole in limestone or one dug in dirt. A dug tunnel has a meandering course, not far below the surface, extending horizontally for up to 25 ft., and with one or more enlarged cavities along its course or at branch ends. Copulation occurs in July–Aug., with the armored female on her back. After several weeks the fertilized egg divides, and these cells again divide, the result being identical quadruplets—all the same sex. The embryos do not develop much until Nov.; then most development occurs in a period of about 120 days (probably it varies considerably), and the annual litter is born Feb.–Apr. Young at birth have eyes open and soft armor which soon hardens; they can move about in a few hours. They nurse for about 2 months and, before being weaned, come out of the nest and hunt insects with their mother. The male is said to take an interest in the family. The bony plates in the skin are not fully formed until adult size is reached. They are not shed. Probably most Armadillos live less than 4 years.

HABITS: This mammal is active mainly at dusk and after dark, but females with young are more or less active by day also. The Armadillo swims well, gulping air to inflate itself if in water very long; it can walk on the bottom for short distances. It can be approached quite easily, being more sensitive to vibrations in the ground than to visual cues. It is gregarious; many occur in a small area and sometimes several use one tunnel system. A soft grunt is uttered while digging. Food: mainly invertebrates, including scorpions, fire ants, roaches, tarantulas, and many destructive insects. Proven instances of its eating wild bird or hen eggs are not common. An individual may have several refuge dens scattered over several acres. This species of Armadillo does not curl up in a ball for protection, but instead runs to a thicket or down a hole. The armor protects the animal when it invades thorny thickets. Dogs have learned to pursue it, flip it over, and attack the unarmored underparts. Many are killed by autos on highways.

ECONOMIC STATUS: The pork-like meat of this 'poor man's hog' is very good eating. The armored hide is made into baskets and other novelties. The holes it digs provide shelter for Opossums, Skunks, and Rabbits, but sometimes the Armadillo undermines buildings or digs holes in dikes or levees. Its rooting actions in gardens damage crops. Food habits are neutral or beneficial from man's viewpoint. Since about 1870 or 1880, the Armadillo has increased its range a great deal in U.S., in spite of predation by humans and dogs and the death of many in freezing weather. It is easily tamed but should not be confined in a cage.

DUGONGS AND MANATEES
Order Sirenia

MANATEES Family Trichechidae

Manatee
(Sea Cow)
Trichechus manatus
Page 324

A large aquatic mammal; rounded body; small head; squarish snout with thick, centrally divided, overhanging upper lip; small eyes; no external ears; forelimbs modified into flippers; body ending in a broad, horizontally flattened, rounded fluke. Stout bristles covering part of the muzzle assist in working food into the small mouth; bristle-like short hairs occur singly at about ½-in. intervals over the rest of the body. Adults: l. 8–12 ft.; a 15¼-ft. male is recorded. A 7½-ft. male weighed 432 lb.; the 15-footer perhaps weighed 1,300 lb. No sex differences in size or color are known. Absence of hind limbs and presence of a spatula-shaped tail distinguish the Manatee. A series of upboilings, receding from the observer, at the surface of turbid water is the commonest sign of its presence. Usually a few together, or else a single individual, are seen.

323

HABITAT: Shallow sheltered marine bays; up sluggish rivers to points well inland; most often in turbid water.

REPRODUCTION: A Manatee under 8 ft. long probably is sexually immature. Breeding may begin at 3 or 4 years of age. Gestation requires at least 152 days (not accurately known), and the single calf is born under water, apparently in any season. At birth it is about 3 ft. long, weighs perhaps 40 lb., and is pinkish; otherwise it is quite like an adult in appearance. A captive cow and calf were observed to link flippers, in effect go arm in arm, as they swam about in a pool. The calf is believed to remain with the cow for about 2 years, since groups, apparently composed of young of 2 different ages with a cow, are not uncommon.

HABITS: The aquatic Manatee evidently is active at any hour. It tends to go in small herds of family-group size, although single ones are seen. It can swim submerged for a long distance and often rests on the bottom in shallow water, surfacing for air a number of times per hour. Voice, if any, is unrecorded. There is a short northward movement of Manatees along the Atlantic coast of Fla. and Gulf coast of Tex. during the warm season. A variety of aquatic vegetation, also plants hanging from the shore, are worked into the mouth by the prehensile upper lip.

Man is the only known predator on adults, but possibly sharks or crocodiles are a minor hazard to young.

ECONOMIC STATUS: The flesh is excellent eating and the oil without equal for cooking. The Manatee is said to eat water hyacinth in such quantity as to allow better navigation on portions of small rivers. Formerly the Manatee was far more plentiful, but hunting has reduced its numbers. A night or two of freezing weather apparently results in pneumonia, and several severe freezes are known to have killed Manatees. Some are shot illegally for food, some are killed wantonly for so-called sport, and boat propellers may injure a few fatally. Good enforcement of existing protective laws would adequately conserve this interesting mammal. Captives in aquaria or pools become quite tame.

WHALES, DOLPHINS, AND PORPOISES
Order Cetacea

Aquatic mammals with horizontal tail flukes. Warm breath, expelled just before or when they break the water's surface, condenses in colder air to form the spout. If they blow just before emerging, surface water is carried up by force of the expelled air. Height of the spout is easy to overestimate. Most cetaceans cannot generally be identified while in the water, except through long experience, and some not even then. In many species, color cannot be depended on to any great degree as an identifying character because of individual variation; also, in many species, it changes rapidly after death. Cetaceans are illustrated in color in *Nat. Geog. Mag.*, vol. 67, no. 1 (Jan. 1940). Many of the smaller species especially are rare, and specimens found stranded should be reported to a museum. Diagram in front of book (bottom of p. 8) shows how length of a cetacean is measured. Ranges are given in words, not mapped, in the following pages, wherein the vast subject of cetology is treated briefly. Cetaceans are arranged here in five families of Toothed and three of Whalebone Whales; the latter eat small swimming invertebrate animals mainly, and the 'whalebone,' properly called baleen, serves as a straining device whereby the whale retains its food.

BOTTLE-NOSED OR BEAKED WHALES Family Ziphiidae

At least one pair of teeth in lower jaw, but in young of both sexes and females at any age they are embedded in tissues of gums, giving a toothless appearance; blowhole single; 2 deep furrows on throat that join anteriorly; center of hind margin of tail flukes not notched.

Beaked Whales
Mesoplodon
Page 337

Tapering head and a beak; back fin well behind middle of body; upperparts dark, shading to light below. These Whales are difficult to distinguish on the basis of external characters. Some are very rare. The lower jaw of any *Mesoplodon* found stranded should be forwarded to a museum for identification. ***Sowerby's** (*M. bidens*): l. to 16 ft.; a tooth in each half of lower jaw about ⅓ length of jaw from front end. Atlantic s. to Mass. **Blainville's** (*M. densirostris*): l. to about 12 ft.; lower jawbone abruptly quadruples in height about ⅓ way back and has large triangular tooth on top front of thickened part. N. Atlantic (Mass. and N.J.), Antarctic, and S. Pacific. **Gervais'** (*M. europæus*): l. to 22 ft.; lower jaw has tiny tooth about ⅕ length of jaw back from front end. N. Atlantic. **True's** (*M. mirus*): l. to 17 ft.; a laterally compressed tooth at tip of each half of lower jaw projecting obliquely forward. Atlantic, n. to Nova Scotia. **Stejneger's** (*M. stejnegeri*): l. about 16 ft.; each half of tapering lower jaw has a very large tooth about ⅖ distance back from tip. None of these is fished regularly, although several species occasionally are taken—probably Sowerby's in the N. Atlantic most often. Perhaps more were taken in the 19th century when related Bottle-nosed Whales were fished.

Cuvier's Beaked Whale
Ziphius cavirostris
Page 337

Also called Goose-beaked Whale. L. 18–28 ft.; short-beaked; lower jaw projects beyond upper; 'forehead' prominent but receding; back fin well behind middle of body and with raised ridge extending along back behind it; single pair of rounded or conical teeth at tip of the lower jaw; upperparts bluish-black and underparts light (but pattern sometimes reversed), and head light. All seas, except possibly polar. Rather rare.

Giant Bottle-nosed Whale
Berardius bairdii

Also called Baird's Beaked Whale. L. 35–42 ft.; prominent 'forehead,' about at right angles to conspicuous beak; 2 large teeth in each half of lower jaw near front end, the foremost pair longest; externally very similar to *Hyperoodon*. Bering Sea and N. Pacific, s. to Calif. Has been fished by Russians and Japanese in their waters.

Flat-headed Bottle-nosed Whale
Hyperoodon ampullatus
Page 337

Males: l. to 30 ft.; females: to about 24; sharp snout and very prominent 'forehead' which in male bulges much more with age; small back fin well behind middle of body; upperparts dark gray to black and underparts somewhat lighter gray to white. Old individuals are lighter than younger ones. Old male has whitish 'forehead' and back fin. Arctic and Atlantic. Food: squids.

Goes in schools, usually 4–12 individuals. Migratory. Quite often stranded. Formerly fished extensively in Arctic seas.

SPERM WHALES Family Physeteridae

Functional teeth restricted to lower jaw; single blowhole on left side near front end of head; spermaceti organ (a reservoir of translucent oil) lies above bones of forepart of head.

Sperm Whale
Physeter catodon
Page 333

Also called Cachalot. Males: l. 42–60 ft.; females: to about 40; massive head comprises about ⅓ of total length; no back fin—instead a slight hump on lower back and series of ridges behind it; general body color very dark; lower jaw appears disproportionately small and has 18–28 teeth in each half. Distinguished at sea by low spout diagonally forward, long low back with slight hump, and nearly perpendicular dive with tail flukes in air. Widely distributed in both hemispheres and wanders to high latitudes. Migratory. Harems of a few males and many females with young occur in tropical waters all year; bachelor males occur in colder waters of both hemispheres in summer. Food: large squids almost exclusively. Newborn calf is 12–14 ft. long. Main Sperm-whaling grounds at present: Subantarctic waters, w. coast of S. Am., coasts of Japan, Bonin Is., the Azores, and S. Africa. Oil of blubber and bone is largely a wax; oil of the head, wax with much spermaceti. Meat is eaten by the Japanese. Melville's Moby Dick was an albino Sperm Whale.

Pigmy Sperm Whale
Kogia breviceps
Page 335

L. 9–13 ft.; head comprises about ⅙ total length; small curved back fin about midway along body; upperparts blackish and underparts light; 9–14 teeth in each half of narrow lower jaw and very rarely one in each half of upper. Warm seas. Solitary. Occasionally is stranded. Rare. Feeds on squids, and these leave scars on its skin. Young are said to be proportionately larger than those of any other cetacean; a 2-day-old calf was over 5 ft. long and weighed 181 lb.

WHITE WHALE AND NARWHAL   Family Monodontidae

Family character is an internal one: first two neck vertebrae joined together. Blowhole single. No back fin.

White Whale
Delphinapterus leucas
Page 337

Also called Beluga and White Porpoise. Males: l. to 18 ft.; females: to about 12; color white after 4–5 years old; small young are dark gray, later they are mottled, then yellowish, before becoming white; 8–10 teeth in each half of both jaws. Circumpolar, in Arctic seas; also in Pacific regularly to s. Alaska and rarely to Wash., and in Atlantic regularly to Nova Scotia and rarely to Mass. An inshore Whale, having seasonal migrations. A school may contain a few to scores of individuals. Often ascends rivers. Food: fish, squids, and crustaceans. 'Porpoise leather,' formerly an item of considerable importance in commerce, is tanned White Whale hide. Economically important fisheries for this Whale are in Greenland, Hudson Bay, Gulf of St. Lawrence, and in Old World. It also is important in economy of the Eskimo.

Narwhal
Monodon monoceros
Page 337

Body l. to 16 ft.; no back fin, instead a low ridge extends for about 3 ft. along mid-part of back; male has 'unicorn' tusk—a greatly elongated, spirally twisted canine tooth—up to about 9 ft. long; adults (both sexes) have a single pair of teeth in upper jaw which are embedded and not visible in females, but in males the right tooth normally is hidden and the left becomes the tusk. Occasionally a second tusk is somewhat elongated in the male or left tooth of female is enlarged in some measure. Adults vary from gray to near white, with underparts lighter, and may be mottled; young are plain gray and can be confused with young White Whales. High Arctic seas. Schools of Narwhals, also of White Whales, or the two together, occasionally crowd into patches of open water in ice fields. Eskimos sometimes kill many at such places.

TYPICAL DOLPHINS   Family Delphinidae

Usually with functional teeth in upper and lower jaws; most species have a back fin near middle of back; single blowhole well back from end of snout; center of rear border of tail flukes notched, at least in species known from Am. waters. In general, 'Dolphin' is applied to beaked species and 'Porpoise' to small beakless ones. There is also a marine fish called Dolphin, and a Dolphin called Blackfish. The Killer is called a 'Whale'; 'Grampus' has been applied to several cetaceans.

Rough-toothed Dolphin
Steno rostratus

L. to 8 ft.; well-developed back fin; beak 4–6 in. long, compressed laterally, and not marked off from 'forehead' by a groove; upperparts blackish or lead-colored; beak and underparts whitish, the latter with slaty spots; teeth have roughened or furrowed crowns, and there are 20–27 in each half of both jaws. Oceans except polar. Rare. Habits unknown.

Long-snouted Dolphins
Stenella

L. to about 8 ft.; well-developed back fin; beak elongated, narrow, and set off from 'forehead' by a groove. **Spotted** (*S. plagiodon*): upperparts grayish-black with many white spots; underparts pale gray; 34–37 small smooth teeth in each half of both jaws. Calf is gray. Atlantic, from N.C. southward, and Gulf of Mexico. Habits unknown. Another species (*S. euphrosyne*): has no common name: back and tips of both jaws black; belly white; a narrow dark stripe along sides from eye to vent; 45 teeth in each half of both jaws. Atlantic and Pacific. Rare. Has stranded in Wash. and Ore.

Common Dolphin
Delphinus delphis
Page 335

L. 6½–8½ ft.; prominent recurved back fin; beak about 6 in. long, set off from low 'forehead' by a groove; upper-

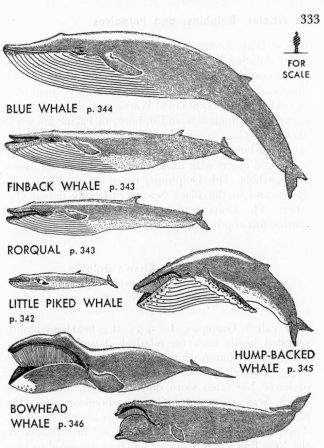

FOR SCALE

BLUE WHALE p. 344

FINBACK WHALE p. 343

RORQUAL p. 343

LITTLE PIKED WHALE
p. 342

HUMP-BACKED WHALE p. 345

BOWHEAD WHALE p. 346

NORTH ATLANTIC RIGHT WHALE
p. 346

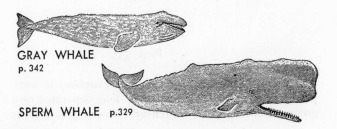

GRAY WHALE
p. 342

SPERM WHALE p. 329

part of beak, foreflippers, and tail flukes black; on sides are undulating bands of gray, yellow, and white that appear to overlap behind flippers; 2 narrow white lines on 'forehead' where it joins the beak; 20–25 very small teeth in each half of both jaws. Warm and temperate seas, occurring on high seas and inshore; in Pacific known as *D. bairdii*. Goes in schools; accompanies ships and plays about the bow. Makes graceful curving leaps clear of the water and enters with hardly a splash. Food: fish, swallowed whole. This Dolphin is fished extensively around Japan and in the Black Sea; occasionally netted elsewhere. The Dolphin of art and folklore. A species of marine fish also is named Dolphin.

Risso's Dolphin
Gramphidelphis griseus
Page 335

Also called Grampus. L. 9–13 ft.; beakless, bluntly rounded head; back fin relatively large and narrow; males mainly bluish-white with dark brown patches; females brownish; 7 teeth or less in front end of each half of lower jaw often worn down to gums, and none in upper. Seas except polar. Goes in schools or singly. The name 'Grampus' has been applied to several cetaceans. The present species is called 'Grampus' or 'Cowfish' on the New Eng. coast, where a few have stranded or been captured and utilized for watch oil.

Bottle-nosed Dolphins
Tursiops
Page 335

Also called Bottle-nosed or Common Porpoises in some places. L. 9–12 ft.; beak about 3 in. long, separated by a groove from rounded 'forehead'; lower jaw slightly

DALL'S PORPOISE
p. 341

ATLANTIC COMMON
PORPOISE
p. 341

0   1   2
FEET

COMMON DOLPHIN
p. 332

NORTH ATLANTIC
WHITE-SIDED DOLPHIN
p. 336

ATLANTIC BOTTLE-NOSED
DOLPHIN   p. 336

RISSO'S DOLPHIN
p. 334

RIGHT WHALE
DOLPHIN   p. 340

PIGMY SPERM WHALE   p. 330

longer than upper; dark gray upperparts and lighter underparts; 20–26 teeth in each half of both jaws. Seas except polar. This description fits the ***Atlantic** (*T. truncatus*), which is common Me.–Tex.; the **Pacific** (*T. gillii*), which occurs in N. Pacific s. into Mexican waters, has darker back and white on upper lip. Migratory, mainly in inshore waters. Schools may contain scores to hundreds of individuals. These Dolphins often leap well clear of the surface, then plunge in headfirst or fall on side or back. Food: fish. Commonest Dolphin along Atlantic Coast. Formerly fished at Cape Hatteras, N.C., and Cape May, N.J. Average yield per individual: 2 gals. blubber oil, ½ pint of jaw, and a pint of head oil. The Atlantic species thrives and becomes tame in enclosures, as at Marineland, Fla., and elsewhere. As to common names, it should be borne in mind that there are also Bottle-nosed Whales.

White-sided and White-beaked Dolphins
Lagenorhynchus
Page 335

Also called Striped Dolphins. L. to 10 ft.; short beak set off from low sloping 'forehead' by a cross groove; moderately high back fin with concave hind edge; pointed foreflippers; tail stock ridged above and below. ***North Atlantic White-sided** (*L. acutus*): l. to over 9 ft.; back and foreflippers bluish-black and belly white, sharply contrasted; in the dark area of upper sides there is a light area extending back along sides from below back fin; ridges on tail stock highly developed; 30–34 teeth in each half of both jaws. N. Atlantic s. to Cape Cod. **North Pacific White-sided** (*L. obliquidens*): l. to 9 ft.; in general similar to the North Atlantic; longitudinal bands in shades of dark and light along sides; 34 pairs of teeth in each half of upper and 30 in each half of lower jaw.

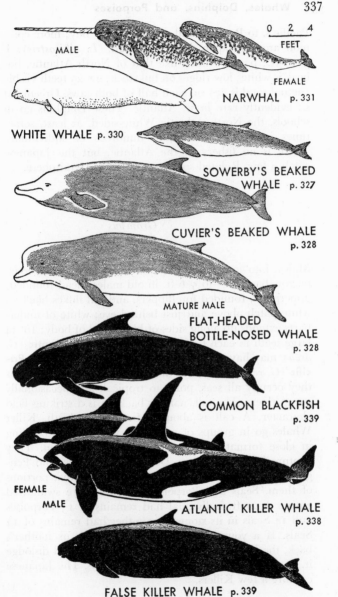

MALE

FEMALE

0   2   4
FEET

NARWHAL p. 331

WHITE WHALE p. 330

SOWERBY'S BEAKED
WHALE p. 327

CUVIER'S BEAKED WHALE
p. 328

MATURE MALE

FLAT-HEADED
BOTTLE-NOSED WHALE
p. 328

COMMON BLACKFISH
p. 339

FEMALE
MALE

ATLANTIC KILLER WHALE
p. 338

FALSE KILLER WHALE p. 339

Pacific s. to Puget Sound and Monterey Bay; more common around Japan. **White-beaked** (*L. albirostris*): l. 9–10 ft.; pattern much like that of North Atlantic, but beak is white; low ridges on tail stock; 22–25 teeth visible (actual total is 27) on each half of both jaws. Greenland s.; evidently rare in w. Atlantic. These Dolphins go in schools, the North Atlantic White-sided, at least, sometimes in groups containing hundreds of individuals. There is no fishery in the Atlantic, but the Japanese catch a few. Related species occur in S. Hemisphere.

Killer Whales
Grampus
Page 337

Males: l. to 30 ft.; most females: not over 15; long, erect, narrow back fin—to 5–6 ft. in old males; head rounded; upperparts, rounded foreflippers, and tail flukes black; a white patch above and just behind eye; white of underparts extends up along sides of hind third of body; 10–14 large teeth in each half of both jaws. The ***Atlantic** (*G. orca*) may have a more recurved back fin than the **Pacific** (*G. rectipinna*), but differences are slight. Together they occupy all seas, polar to tropical, and occasionally go up rivers. The tall, narrow back fin is a striking field character. A calf is about 7 ft. long at birth. Killer Whales go in groups of 2–3 to 40 individuals, traveling in close formation, rising and diving in unison. They capture Seals, Sea Lions, Dolphins, Porpoises, and Penguins—and even kill very large Whales and eat portions of them. Seals and Porpoises sometimes are swallowed entire. A 21-ft. individual had remains of 13 Porpoises and 14 Seals in its stomach; another had remains of 14 Seals. If a young Walrus seeks refuge on its mother's back, the Killer is said to strike the mother and dislodge it. It also bumps ice floes to dislodge Seals. The Japanese capture a few Killers.

False Killer Whale
Pseudorca crassidens
Page 337

L. 12–18 ft.; uniformly black, sometimes with light markings; rather flattened head and bluntly rounded snout;
low rounded back fin just forward of middle of body;
narrow tapering flippers; 8–12 strong teeth in each half
of both jaws. All seas except possibly polar. Wandering
schools containing up to hundreds of individuals occasionally have stranded in various parts of the world.
Food: squids and fish. This species is hunted commercially only around Japan.

Blackfish
Globicephala
Page 337

Also called Pilot Whales, Caa'ing Whales, etc. L. to 28
ft.; back fin (largest in males) low, with long base, and
situated forward of middle of body; long narrow foreflippers; color black, or with small amount of white.
*Common (*G. melaena*): l. to 28 ft.; foreflippers about
⅕ total length of body; 10 teeth in each half of both
jaws; black, except light stripe on belly that expands into
a heart-shaped patch on throat. Atlantic waters. **Pacific**
(*G. scammonii*): smaller than the preceding; entirely
black; 8–12 teeth in each half of both jaws. Pacific
waters. **Short-finned** (*G. macrorhyncha*): females to 15
and males to 20 ft.; foreflippers average about ⅙ total
length of body; 7–9 pairs of functional teeth in each half
of both jaws; difficult to distinguish from Common
Blackfish. Atlantic n. to N.J. The migratory herds move
with cohesion and precision, following a leader. They
probably feed mainly at night on squids. Economically,
perhaps they are the most important small cetaceans.
Sometimes they beach themselves to escape from Killer

Whales. They strand in herds or are driven ashore by man in Greenland, off the Gulf of St. Lawrence, in Newfd., on Cape Cod, and in Faeroe, Orkney, and Shetland Is. They are hunted at sea by the Japanese. Average oil yield per individual: 40-50 gals. from blubber and about 2 from head and jaw.

Right Whale Dolphin
Lissodelphis borealis
Page 335

Also called Finless Dolphin. L. to 8 ft.; like the Right Whale, it has no back fin; tapering slender form; small beak merges with low 'forehead'; upperparts and foreflippers black; white of underparts extends up to base of foreflippers but narrows posteriorly; 44 teeth in each side of upper and 47 in each side of lower jaw. Bering Sea and N. Pacific s. to Calif. Wanders in small schools. Some are taken by the Japanese.

TRUE PORPOISES   Family Phocœnidae

Beakless; size small; blowhole single. The names 'Porpoise' and 'Dolphin' are discussed on page 331.

Common Porpoises
Phocœna (part)
Page 335

Called Harbor Porpoise, Puffer, Puffing Pig, etc. L. 4-6 ft.; back fin triangular; back and foreflippers blackish; sides of body shade into white underparts; unique among small cetaceans in having spade-like crowns on the teeth,

of which there are 23–27 in each half of both jaws. The
*Atlantic (*P. phocæna*) occurs from Greenland to N.J.,
and the **Pacific** (*P. vomerina*) from Bering Sea s. into
Mexican waters. They are very similar. A few to over
a hundred travel together in inshore waters and river
mouths. The puffing or sighing sound that they make
when blowing has given rise to various common names.
A newborn calf measures 30–34 in. long. Food: fish,
squids, and occasionally swimming crustaceans. They are
hunted commercially in Greenland and Japan. The oil
is valuable and the flesh good eating. An adult weighs
100–120 lb. It should be noted that the Bottle-nosed
Dolphin is called 'Common Porpoise' in some localities.

Dall's Porpoise
Phocæna dalli
Page 335

L. 5–6 ft.; color black, shading to gray on triangular back
fin and on tail flukes, with sharply defined white area
on belly that extends more than halfway up sides behind foreflippers; tail stock with fin-like ridge above and
below; teeth small, 27 in each half of lower and 23 in
each half of upper jaw, nearly concealed in pits in gums.
Pacific waters, mainly inshore; Alaska s. rarely into Calif.
Usually in small groups. Plays about bows of ships. The
striking pattern renders identification easy. It is commonly seen from shipboard along the Inside Passage to
Alaska.

GRAY WHALE Family Eschrichtiidae

Flexible horny plates of 'whalebone,' properly called
baleen, hang in rows from each side of upper jaw; blowhole double; throat with a few furrows; no back fin.

Gray Whale
Eschrichtius glaucus
Page 333

Also called California Gray Whale. L. to about 50 ft.
(adults av. 42); a slight hump, but no back fin; color
mottled gray over-all, varying in individuals from light
gray to nearly black; spout vertical, rising 10–11 ft.;
sides of lower lips not arched; 2–3 furrows on each side
of throat, about 5–6 ft. long; whalebone thick, heavy,
pale yellowish toward front end of mouth, gray toward
back, and longest blades 14–18 in. Mainly in Arctic
Ocean in summer; migrates in inshore waters—on Am.
side of Pacific—to Calif. and Mexico, where present
Nov.–May. Food: small swimming invertebrates. Quite
often comes into very shallow water. Where common,
likes to gather in groups. Calves are born in winter. Now
increasing under protection, after being depleted on both
sides of the N. Pacific by American and Japanese whalers.

FINBACK WHALES   Family Balœnopteridae

Flexible horny plates of 'whalebone,' properly called
baleen, hang in rows from each side of upper jaw; blowhole double; throat with many furrows; back fin present.

Little Piked Whale
Balœnoptera acutorostrata
Page 333

Also called Least Rorqual. L. to 33 ft. (av. 25); small
back fin fairly erect, with curved tip, and well back on
body; upperparts bluish- or brownish-gray or grayish-
black and underparts white; a wide white band across

outer side of foreflippers—a conspicuous distinguishing feature; vertical spout very faint, rarely visible; 50–70 furrows on throat (smallest whale having them); snout triangular in shape when viewed from above; whalebone white or yellowish-white, l. to 8 in. All oceans. Migratory. Goes in small groups or singly. Hunted commercially around Japan and Norway; meat is main product because blubber is thin.

Rorqual
Balænoptera borealis
Page 333

Also called Sei or Pollock Whale. L. 40–60 ft.; back fin has deeply concave hind margin and is larger and farther forward than in Finback and Blue Whale; back bluish-black and sides gray; a white area from chin back along undersurface; underside of tail flukes never white; vertical spout, rising 10–14 ft.; many furrows on throat; whalebone mainly black, with notably fine frayed white inner edges, and 10–25 in. long. Atlantic and Pacific in n. latitudes. Migratory. Food: mainly small swimming invertebrates. Calves are 15–16 ft. long at birth; they are weaned after at least five months when 26–30 ft. long. Oil yield of this Whale is small; some are captured for meat by Norwegians and Japanese. Color of whalebone distinguishes this species from the Finback.

Finback Whale
Balænoptera physalus
Page 333

L. to 75 ft. in N. Am. waters and to 87 in Antarctic (av. 60); back fin triangular, usually with concave hind border, situated well back toward tail and with a ridge behind it; upperparts and outer side of foreflippers

grayish or brownish (turning black in dead Whale);
right side of head lighter than left; underparts, including
inner side of foreflippers and underside of tail flukes,
white; vertical spout, rising to 20 ft.; many throat furrows that extend well back on stomach; whalebone yellowish, whitish, or slate color, except in right front where
white, and with whitish or yellowish fringe; longest
blades 20–36 in. All seas. Occurs in groups of 2–3, or
even hundreds where food is plentiful, and there are
seasonal population movements. Calves are 21–22 ft. long
at birth and are nursed at least 6 months. A very fast
Whale. Over a quarter million Finbacks were taken
1900–40, even though oil yield is relatively low. Color of
whalebone distinguishes this Whale from near relatives.

Blue Whale
Balœnoptera musculus
Page 333

Also called Sulphur-bottom. L. to 85 ft. in N. Am. waters
and to 100 in Antarctic (largest known animal); small
back fin far back on body; bluish-gray above, paler and
somewhat mottled on sides and underparts (yellowish
film on underparts of some individuals gave rise to name
'Sulphur-bottom'); inner surface and tips of foreflipper
white; columnar spout, rising to 20 ft.; tail flukes generally thrown out of water when starting deeper dives;
U-shaped snout, as viewed from above; 80–100 throat
furrows extend well back on stomach; bluish rear whalebone blades 23–40 in. long. In all seas, occurring singly
or in small groups. Migrates to warmer water to breed.
Gestation requires about a year. Newborn calf (twins
occasionally) is 23–26 ft. long; it is nursed for about 7
months and weaned at av. length of 52 ft. Can breed in
2 years when 74–77 ft. long. Food: mainly tiny swimming shrimp-like animals called Euphausians. Has become commercially extinct (too scarce to be pursued with

profit) in N. Hemisphere, and numbers in Antarctic are dwindling. An average-sized one yields 100–120 barrels of oil. An 89-footer weighed over 119 tons. Shape of snout and size of this Whale are identifying characters.

Hump-backed Whale
Megaptera novæangliae
Page 333

L. to 50 ft. (adults av. 45); back fin low, thick at base, and situated behind middle of body; thickset body; very long flippers—nearly ⅓ as long as the whale—with scalloped lower edge; upperparts black; throat, breast, most of foreflippers, and underside of tail flukes white or nearly so; spout balloon-shaped, rising 8 ft.; tail flukes generally thrown out of water when making deeper dives; rows of knobs on snout and lower jaw; 14–20 furrows spaced 5–8 in. apart on throat and extending well back on belly; whalebone grayish-black, longest blades 22–24 in. In all seas, occurring mainly not far from shore. Migrates to warmer waters to breed and to colder for feeding. Newborn calf is 15–16 ft. long and weighs about 1½ tons; it is nursed for about a year. The Humpback is noted for its playful antics at the water's surface. Food: small swimming invertebrates and some small fishes. Not common in N. Atlantic or around Japan; fairly common in NE. Pacific; common in Antarctic. Extremely long foreflippers identify it.

WHALEBONE OR BALEEN WHALES Family Balænidæ

Flexible horny plates of 'whalebone,' properly called baleen, hang in rows from each side of upper jaw; blowhole double; throat smooth (no furrows); no back fin.

Bowhead Whale
Balæna mysticetus
Page 333

Also called Greenland or Arctic Right Whale. L. to 60 ft.; no back fin; body very stout; ponderous head comprises more than a third of total length; usually blackish, except end of lower jaw whitish, and some have white spots on stomach; lower jaw *bowed* upward—not arched high as in *Eubalæna;* whalebone black, longest 10–14 ft.; throat smooth. Spout V-shaped, broad at top, rising 12–14 ft.; tail flukes generally thrown out of water in making deeper dives. Calves are bluish-gray. Arctic seas. Not migratory. Once the commonest Whale within most of its range, it has become rare because of overexploitation by whalers. Protected by international law and increasing slowly.

Right Whales
Eubalæna
Page 333

L. to over 60 ft.; no back fin; body very stout; very large head comprises ⅕–¼ total length; color blackish, but some individuals have patches of white on undersurface; profile of lower jaw forms an evenly upward-curved arch; whalebone blackish, longest blades 6–9 ft.; throat smooth; a broad cushion near muzzle called the 'bonnet.' The V-shaped spout rises to 15 ft.; tail flukes generally are thrown out of water in making deeper dives. ***North Atlantic** (*E. glacialis*)*:* l. to 59 ft. N. Atlantic s. to S.C. **North Pacific** (*E. sieboldii*)*:* somewhat larger than preceding. N. Pacific s. to Calif. These are slow-moving deep-water Whales that rarely have stranded. Because of their high yield of oil and whalebone, their numbers were depleted by whalers. Under protection of international law they are increasing slowly.

INDEX

Numbers in Bold-face type refer to drawings and color plates
The small maps at heads of sections are not indexed

347